CHARLES DARWIN

CHARLES DARWIN

AND THE THEORY OF EVOLUTION

By

HENSHAW WARD

Author of *Evolution of John Doe*
The Circus of the Intellect

The New Home Library

NEW YORK

THE NEW HOME LIBRARY EDITION PUBLISHED NOVEMBER, 1943
BY ARRANGEMENT WITH THE BOBBS-MERRILL COMPANY

CHARLES DARWIN AND THE THEORY OF EVOLUTION was formerly
published as CHARLES DARWIN THE MAN AND HIS WARFARE

THE NEW HOME LIBRARY, 14 West Forty-ninth Street
New York, N. Y.

CL

PRINTED IN THE UNITED STATES OF AMERICA

TO

MAJOR LEONARD DARWIN

AS THE ONLY WAY OF THANKING HIM

FOR HIS KINDNESS IN HELPING ME

CONTENTS

CONTENTS—*Continued*

APPENDIX

CHARLES DARWIN

CHAPTER I

WHY DR. GRANT LIKED YOUNG DARWIN

"DR. GRANT one day, when we were walking together, burst forth in high admiration of Lamarck and his views on evolution. I listened in silent astonishment." So Charles Darwin reports an episode in Edinburgh while he was studying medicine there. The greatest puzzle that ever science grappled with was Dr. Grant's subject—*what is a species?* He favored the brilliant new theory of Lamarck, but young Darwin was so astonished at this judgment that, for fear of seeming disrespectful, he remained silent. It is doubtful whether any famous man ever reported so ironical a story about his youth, or indicated in so few words the result of a lifetime's potent labor. For it was to be his fate to make Lamarck's theory credible and thus revolutionize the ways of human thought.

It is easy to see why he remained silent, even though he thought the Lamarckian views preposterous; for he was only sixteen years old, had been trained for seven years in a famous school to be respectful to his betters, had no fondness for controversy, and was ignorant of all science. Whereas Dr. Grant was an adept in science, thirty-two years old, who had heard Lamarck lecture at Paris, had attended many Continental universities, and had during the past five years studied marine life on the coasts of Scotland and Ireland; he had lectured at the

1

University of Edinburgh, and was now publishing monographs to prove that sponges are animals. He was giving to the world new ideas about animal life, quite sound
ideas, which, as the biologists later admitted, "marked a
notable advance in knowledge." What was more important, in this comradeship with a boy, was that "he had
much enthusiasm beneath his outer crust." Small wonder that the sixteen-year-old Darwin kept silent.

Why the boy should have been astonished is harder to
guess. Perhaps his family pride was involved, because
he had reason to think that his grandfather's idea had
been stolen by Lamarck. More likely he had been used to
hearing that the Lamarckian view of evolution was bad
form scientifically—nothing but a French fancy. The
reasons for young Darwin's astonishment will be unfolded in due time. Just now it is more important to
know why the "dry and formal" Dr. Grant has chosen
to be walking with a medical freshman and expatiating
to him about a matter of biological philosophy. There
was a very good reason. It is the key to Darwin's life
and to the influence of Darwin's work.

Charles Robert Darwin, who never used his middle
name, was born in the ancient town of Shrewsbury on the
very same day that Abraham Lincoln was born—February 12, 1809. He was the fifth of the six children of
Dr. Robert Waring Darwin, whose skill as a physician
had made him well-to-do and highly respected. Dr. Darwin was six feet and two inches in height, and weighed
nearly three hundred and fifty pounds. He was a rapid
and copious talker. He kept his household orderly and
punctual, and had an uncanny instinct for diagnosing
what was going on in people's minds and bodies. He was
a very affectionate man who inspired the devotion of his
children. "When Charles said that his father thought or
did so and so," (his cousin Emma Wedgwood testified)

"we all knew that there could be no further question in the matter; what his father did or thought was for him absolutely true, right, and wise." Emma never felt quite at ease in the Doctor's presence, but she confessed that he was extremely kind to her and that she was fond of him. Even when she once remarked sharply in a letter that "one gets rather fatigued by the Dr.'s talk, especially the two whole hours just before dinner," she admitted in the next sentence that "the Dr. has been as pleasant as possible, and I never saw him enjoy anything so much as Susan's account of all her gaieties." (It appears that Susan, Charles's sister, six years older than he, had been brought home from a ball in the chariot of the very tipsy young Sir Watkin, and that "it was rather a tight squeeze," and that Susan had to sit at the bottom of the chariot.) So Dr. Darwin could hardly have been a kill-joy even for an Emma who was used to a very gay life at home. Charles never ceased to honor and love him. In a letter to a friend, telling of the father's death, Charles wrote: "No one who did not know him would believe that a man above eighty-three years old could have retained so tender and affectionate a disposition, with all his sagacity unclouded to the last." The boy who felt such skeptical astonishment toward an accomplished zoologist had a reverence for his father that was called "boundless and most touching."

Charles had hardly any recollection of his mother, for she died when he was only eight years old. She was Susannah Wedgwood, a daughter of the Josiah Wedgwood who is credited with being "the most successful and original potter the world has even seen, whose skill influenced the whole subsequent course of pottery manufacture." She is described as having "a remarkably sweet and happy face, a gentle and sympathetic nature."

The motherless family lived in a large, homey, well-lighted brick house, surrounded by pleasant trees and well-planted shrubbery, on the steep bank of the Severn River, just west of the town. At this point in its course the Severn, a swift stream fifty yards wide, is describing a loop, circling round a knob of land which is three-fourths of a mile in diameter, and returning so nearly upon itself as to leave the neck of the knob only three hundred yards in width. The river, forming thus a moat around a rocky hill, created a natural fortress where the ancient Britons withstood the Romans, and which the later English kings used as an important post on the Welsh marches. The town of Shrewsbury is within this loop of the Severn; its streets mount steeply from the river to the summit of the hill; its suburbs are reached by four bridges; the bridge on the northwest leads to Frank-well, where Dr. Darwin's house still stands and is still called "The Mount."

At the age of nine Charles was sent to the Shrewsbury School, then more than two hundred and fifty years old and housed in a building two hundred years old. He was a boarder, but was free to run home during intervals between roll-calls. Often he lingered so long at home that he had to run to be on time for a locking-up. "From being a fleet runner," he says in his autobiography, "I was generally successful in being on time; but when in doubt I prayed earnestly to God to help me, and I well remember that I attributed my success to the prayers, and marveled how generally I was aided." In his run to the school he went three hundred yards east to the Welsh Bridge, crossed this into the town, panted up the hill six hundred yards, and then raced three hundred yards down-hill toward the old Castle that guarded the neck of the peninsula. A hundred yards short of this he turned into the school yard and scuttled up the path beside which he now sits in bronze—a severe figure of a man with a long beard meditating upon his boyish hurry.

For seven years at this school he continued to recite Latin and Greek, Latin and Greek, Latin and Greek. The standard of scholarship was kept as high as that of any school in England by the headmaster, the Rev. Samuel Butler, a canon of Lichfield Cathedral, who had been headmaster for twenty years. When he was an undergraduate at Cambridge he had won two medals for composing Greek odes, and would have won a third if he had not been in competition with the poet Coleridge. Yet in spite of these and other classical honors by which he had been distinguished, the boys of the school were still tittering at him when Charles Darwin entered in 1818; for his edition of *Æschylus* had been severely criticized by the *Edinburgh Review*. Another reason for gibing at the headmaster was that the only subject he would tolerate in the curriculum except classics and a bit of history was geography. Geography was thus favored because Mr. Butler had written the textbook and liked the royalties— so, at any rate, the merciless boys believed.

"Nothing could have been worse for the development of my mind," Darwin testified late in life, "than Dr. Butler's school. The school as a means of education to me was simply a blank." Yet he worked conscientiously, not using a crib. "The sole pleasure I ever received from such studies was from some of the odes of Horace, which I admired greatly." He was rated by all the masters as rather below the average in mental power.

Charles was yearning for something besides memory work. He took private lessons in geometry because he had "a keen pleasure in understanding any complex subject." He worked eagerly with his older brother at chemistry experiments in a tool-house at home, reading several books, and learning how to make "all the gases."

Such an occupation seemed ridiculous to his school mates, who nicknamed him "Gas"; and it seemed positively immoral to Mr. Butler, who reprimanded him for wasting his time, calling him, in the presence of the whole school, a *poco curante*. "As I did not understand what he meant," says Darwin, "it seemed to me a fearful reproach."

The epithet has been a boomerang in the Butler family. Charles Darwin, to be sure, was one who cared little about quantities in machine-made verses; but the headmaster has written himself down for posterity as one who cared not at all for the mysteries of the universe in which he lived. He was blind and deaf and unfeeling in the midst of the marvels which all sensitive minds of the period were puzzling about. And this curse of the blindness of a good intellect was transmitted to his grandson, Samuel Butler, author of *Erewhon,* who has written a book of captivating scholarship, *Evolution Old and New,* to reprimand Charles Darwin once more for being something much worse than a poco curante. Any one who has an inkling of the Darwinian theory can only read the book with silent astonishment. Perhaps the Darwin statue in front of the Shrewsbury School is meditating upon the sense of values that runs in the Butler family.

Charles had a passion for collecting during his years of schooling. At the age of ten he observed that some moths and a tiger beetle on the Welsh coast were different from any kinds seen about his native town, and he was doubtless itching to capture them. But, after consulting with his sister, he decided that it was not right to kill insects for the mere pleasure of possessing their corpses. Another equally moral resolution was that not more than one egg should ever be taken from a nest for his collection. So fascinating did he find the observing of the habits of birds that he wondered why every gentleman did not become an ornithologist. His fondness for specimens extended to minerals, which he enjoyed decorating with learned names; and he had a desire to know something about every pebble in front of the hall door.

At this early period of boyhood he was somewhat of a sportsman, though his tenderness of heart was a handicap. For example, after he had learned how to kill angleworms painlessly, he quit spitting them alive on his fishhook, resigning himself with magnanimity to poorer catches of fish. The same tenderness of heart caused him lifelong remorse for once beating a puppy "simply [as he self-accusingly thought] from enjoying the sense of power." In old age he still remembered with contrition the exact spot where he committed this atrocious deed when he was eight years old. However, he got some consolation from the fact that the beating was not severe enough to make the puppy howl, and from the knowledge that all the rest of his life he was an adept at stealing the affections of dogs.

Of course his pure chivalry toward animals was corrupted later in his youth by the ignoble customs of the society about him. He learned to rejoice in killing insects. He acquired a passion for killing birds. "I do not believe that anyone could have shown more zeal for the most holy cause than I did for shooting birds. How well I remember killing my first snipe, and my excitement was so great that I had much difficulty in reloading my gun from the trembling of my hands."

Indeed the love of sportsmanship so grew upon him and so occupied his time that even the affectionate father was moved to angry despair. "You care for nothing but shooting, dogs, and rat-catching," he declared to his son, "and you will be a disgrace to yourself and all your family." Darwin's gentle resentment at the scolding is as follows: "But my father, who was the kindest man I ever knew and whose memory I love with all my heart, must have been angry and somewhat unjust when he used such words." Probably he was no more than "somewhat" unfair. There must have been some justice in the combined judgment of father and headmaster that Charles cared little or nothing for what seemed to his elders the serious concerns of life.

Perhaps they judged that even his reading was frivolous. It is true that he read the two thick volumes of his grandfather's *Zoonomia; or the Laws of Organic Life,* a book written to furnish physicians with a general perspective of biology and with concrete advice for their practice. But perhaps Charles read it out of mere curiosity or family pride. He was too fond of mere time-wasting with poetry like Thomson's *Seasons* or the recently published works of Byron and Scott. He confesses that he "used to sit for hours reading the historical plays of Shakespeare, generally in an old window in the thick walls of the school." Surely it might be only idle pleasure which would lead a Shrewsbury boy to read, in the Shrewsbury School, about Falstaff fighting a long hour by the Shrewsbury clock. Even when he read *The Wonders of the World* he did not seem to be caring for the information he might amass from it. No. He liked to doubt the truth of its statements and to dream of traveling in far countries where he might see for himself what the wonders were and by what laws they operated. How could a father and a headmaster know that he was not a poco curante?

But the father took heart in the summer of 1825, for the boy agreed to go to Edinburgh to study medicine and prepare himself to uphold in the third generation the professional reputation of his family. He showed some real zest for the profession. During the vacation he gravely "attended" some poor people, keeping a record of their symptoms, consulting with his father about them, and gravely compounding the prescriptions that his father recommended. So well did he deport himself that Dr. Darwin predicted that his son would be a successful practitioner. And Dr. Darwin was seldom in error when he judged people's capacities. The son never knew a reason for the father's faith, but presumably it was this: Dr. Darwin's own success was due to "a sharpness of observation that enabled him to predict the course of an illness," and this quick, shrewd faculty of observation was possessed by Charles. It was the chief element in his scientific career.

So there was high hope at The Mount when, in October, 1825, Charles took coach for the three-hundred-mile ride to Edinburgh, where his grandfather, Erasmus Darwin, had become an M. D. seventy years before. The grandfather, also, had had the sharpness of observation in a high degree; he "intuitively recognized disposition or character and ever read the thoughts of those with whom he came into contact with extraordinary acuteness." And the grandfather was a daring speculator about the nature of life, and how an organism is generated from its parents, and what the ancestry of all life has been. Such speculations as the Lamarckian views on evolution were no novelty in the brain of this boy who was to enjoy a week of stage-coaching to the capital of Scotland.

But it is doubtful whether biology and philosophy occupied his thoughts as the coach rattled northward from Shrewsbury. More likely he was thinking of a certain Emma Wedgwood, whose home was thirty miles to the northeast. History contains no record of how young Darwin felt about her in October of 1825, and speculations about a sweetheart should not be allowed to intrude into the severe account of a scientific war about species. But she was to play a very important part in the war, and well deserves, just as a matter of scientific history, more space than the two following paragraphs.

She was a very good-looking, healthy, original, and much loved girl, the youngest of the eight children of the younger Josiah Wedgwood, who continued his famous father's business of making pottery. Her father and Charles Darwin's mother were brother and sister. The house in which she lived was a large stone structure more than two hundred years old, situated near the border of a small lake, a "mere." The estate had therefore been named Maer, by adopting a supposedly Saxon spelling. The mere had been extended and beautified by a landscape gardener; there were fish in it and a rowboat on it; in winter it furnished a skating-place for the children. On the slope between it and the house was a lavish series of flower beds. The house was a focus of social doings for the relatives and friends in the whole countryside—the Tolletts, the Caldwells, several families of Wedgwoods, and the Darwins. Emma's mother wrote to a sister in October, 1824: "These young things have kept me in such a whirl of noise, and ins and outs, that I have not found any leisure. I may say to you under the rose that a little calm will be agreeable. . . . We are just now very flirtish, very noisy, very merry, and very foolish. . . . Last night they performed some scenes in the 'Merry Wives of Windsor.' . . . Master Shallow, Emma, very good." Emma's diary record of this period (two weeks after she had been confirmed) was as follows: "1st Oct., Revels; 2nd, Revels; 4th, Revels; 5th, Acted some of Merry Wives; 6th, Oct., quiet evening."

Emma was likely to be very good at whatever she undertook. At school in London, the year before, she had been one of the show performers on the piano. When she returned to Maer she composed "four delightful little stories written in simple words, and had them printed for use with her Sunday-school class." She was a clever hair-dresser for her older sisters when they were preparing for a ball. She made good use of a nine-month tour in Europe, "enlarging her sympathy and outlook." From this tour she had returned on the first of October, so that Charles Darwin had a chance to welcome her home and to say good-by before setting out for Edinburgh. He always liked to go to Maer. It was a flirtish place.

But there is no record of what girl he was thinking about as he sat in the coach with his brother Erasmus, five years his senior, bound for Edinburgh, rolling along between hills that were covered with autumn brown.

He dutifully wrote home on the Sunday after his arrival:

My dear Father,

As I suppose Erasmus has given all the particulars of the journey, I will say no more about it, except that altogether it has cost me seven pounds. We got into our lodgings yesterday evening, which are very comfortable and near the College. . . . The terms are £1-6 s for two very nice and *light* bedrooms and a sitting-room; by the the way, light bedrooms are very scarce articles in Edinburgh, since most of them are little holes in which there is neither air nor light. We called on Dr. Hanley the first morning, whom I think we never should have found, had it not been for a good-natured Dr. of Divinity who took us into his library and showed us a map, and gave us directions how to find him. . . . I should think Dr. Butler or any other fat English Divine would take two utter strangers into his library and show them the way! . . . Bridge Street is the most extraordinary thing I ever saw, and when we first looked over the sides, we could hardly believe our eyes, when instead of a fine river, we saw a stream of people. We spend all our mornings in promenading about the town, which we know pretty well, and in the evenings we go to the play to hear Miss Stephens, which is quite delightful . . . On Monday we are going to Der F (I do not know how to spell the rest of the word). . . . We just have been to Church and heard a sermon of only 20 minutes. I expected, from Sir Walter Scott's account, a soul-cutting discourse of 2 hours and a half.

I remain yr affectionate son,

C. Darwin

Three months later he described to his sister his impressions of the medical school:

Many thanks for your very entertaining letter, which was a great relief after hearing a long stupid lecture from Duncan on Materia Medica. . . . Dr. Duncan is so very learned that his wisdom has left no room for his sense, and he lectures on the Materia Medica, which can not be translated into any word expressive enough of its stupidity.* . . . Dr. Hope begins at ten o'clock, and I like both him and his lectures very much. . . . I dislike Monro and his lectures so much, that I can not speak with decency about them. . . .

I will be a good boy and tell something about Johnson again (not but what I am very much surprised that Papa should so forget himself as to call me, a Collegian in the University of Edinburgh, a boy). . . . You mentioned in your letter that Emma was staying with you: if she is not gone, ask her to tell Jos that I have not succeeded in getting any titanium, but that I will try again. [Here the editor deletes some words.] I want to know how old I shall be next birthday—I believe seventeen, and if so, I shall be forced to go abroad for one year, since it is necessary that I shall have completed my 21st year before I take my degree.

It was unkind of the editor to suppress the rest of the message to Emma. From the scandalous remarks about

---

* "A whole, cold, breakfastless hour on the properties of rhubarb."
Letter to Hooker, 1847.

lectures it is easy to guess that Charles Darwin is once more on the way to being called a poco curante. He seems not to care properly for scholarship. What he liked was to indulge his craving for collecting and observing. He found his way to Newhaven, a little port north of Edinburgh, and made friends of some fishermen, who took him trawling for oysters (whatever "trawl" meant at that time in those waters). He collected marine specimens. A much deeper impulse was at work in him—to see the how and why of sea-life. "Drs. Grant and Coldstream," he records, "attended much to marine zoology, and I often accompanied the former to collect animals in the tidal pools." When he inquired of Dr. Grant about certain little vesicles that floated in the water, the zoologist replied that they were seeds of the brown rockweed which was abundant everywhere about. That was standard knowledge. Any ordinary boy who had learned and remembered it would have deserved credit.

But Charles Darwin behaved most peculiarly in regard to this knowledge: he insisted on seeing, for himself, *what came out of the vesicles.* The more I ponder that boyish skepticism, the more amazing it seems. For the desire was so strange: to see, with his own eyes, what actually happened. That is the rarest impulse of the intellect. The human mind almost always prefers two other ways of solving problems—either to ask an authority or to use pure reason. If we ever encounter a mind that instinctively desires *to see for itself,* we know that we are in the presence of a superior being.

What came out of the vesicles was not rockweed at all. It was the young of a bright-green worm, a kind of leech. Charles discovered that another sort of floating vesicle had the power of locomotion and was a young animal hunting a place to start a colony of "sea-mats." He read a paper on the animals before the Plinian Society, a student organization. When Dr. Grant later wrote a monograph on them (the genus *Flustra*) he credited the boy with the discovery.

So it is easy to understand why Dr. Grant enjoyed walking with young Darwin. What shall we suppose he felt about the boy's astonishment at the Lamarckian views? He doubtless assumed that any one so sharp-eyed for details was lacking in power to apprehend more profound issues. A man who is intellectual and enthusiastic usually does pass that sort of judgment on the Darwin type of mind.

CHAPTER II

WHY YOUNG DARWIN WAS ASTONISHED AT DR. GRANT

IF I were reading about Darwin's career, I should want an early chapter to give me a background of his life —the guesses about evolution which were in the air when he was a youth. So I have made such a chapter and inserted it here. But I suspect that many of my readers will be happier if they omit it for the present. It should never be read by any one until he feels curiosity about the subject. You might try a few paragraphs, and then skip the rest if you begin to fidget at the theories. There is no narrative in Chapter II; the story continues in Chapter III.

Suppose that Charles Darwin had been seven years older, that he had come to Edinburgh as a sixteen-year-old boy in 1818, and that he had taken a walk with a famous professor of mathematics at the University, John Playfair. It is possible that Playfair would have burst forth in high admiration of Spence and his views on perpetual motion. If he had done so, it is certain that Charles Darwin would have listened in silent astonishment. This imaginary case will make it easy to see why he was astonished at Dr. Grant's enthusiasm about perpetual change among the species of plants and animals.

Spence was a shoemaker who lived at Linlithgow, eighteen miles northwest of Edinburgh. He had an active mind. His mind became engaged with the ancient and fascinating puzzle of creating a mechanism that could run itself, with no supply of force from outside. At length he constructed an apparatus, operated by magnets, which he claimed was a proof that a machine can generate its own energy. Most physicists of the period were entirely skeptical about perpetual motion, were not even interested in this latest of a long line of attempts to prove the theory, and felt perfectly certain that Mr. Spence's contraption was a fraud. But Playfair, who had been thirty years a professor of mathematics and had made authoritative textbooks on physics, inspected the shoemaker's machine and announced that it was a solution of the problem of perpetual motion. Perhaps there was some philosophical Scot in 1818 who had faith in squaring the circle. Perhaps there was another who admired the doctrine of the transmutation of base metals into gold. And if young Darwin had walked with them, and if they had burst forth in admiration of the theories, he would have listened in silent astonishment. Not that he had read the evidence. He knew nothing about mathematics or physics. He simply knew that those fanciful theories were regarded with skepticism by the learned world. Dr. Darwin was a skeptic about medical superstitions. He had taught his sons the folly of seeking for a philosopher's stone or a miraculous widow's cruse of energy. So his sons would have been astounded to hear from any savant an argument in favor of those doctrines.

In 1825 the Lamarckian view of evolution seemed a similar sort of folly to Dr. Darwin and his sons. The transmutation of species—whether of metals or of animals—was just a philosopher's dream. Conventional skeptics of that day might not presume to deny that transmutation or perpetual motion was possible; for physics had not yet made a complete demonstration of the conservation of energy, nor had chemistry actually disproved the existence of a simple "prima materia." It was an ignorant world in 1825. But the evidence was so strongly negative that few practical scientists had any faith in those speculations which persuaded Professor Playfair and Dr. Grant. The speculations were, intellectually, bad form.

The fate of those two theories—perpetual motion and alchemy—illustrate what Darwin's labor was all about. And without such illustration we are likely to misconceive his life. Consider perpetual motion. The theory that a machine might forever generate its own power is too ancient to be traced to its source. It was a natural assumption for a primitive mind to make, and it was a proper and rational theory through the seventeenth century. Nobody is to be blamed for working with it seriously in the eighteenth century, because it could not be disproved. Nor does any one deserve any credit for holding the theory; it had long been common property. Credit belongs only to men like Joule, who investigated the *facts* of heat and energy in mechanism. When facts enough had been investigated, it appeared that perpetual motion is inconceivable. Hence all the clever intellects that once believed it are now disregarded, and any intellect that still persists in hoping for a revival of the theory is called mad.

Consider alchemy. It was less esteemed in 1825 than perpetual motion, but had not been absolutely disproved. It had been the common property of the intellectual world for fifteen centuries; hence no one deserved any credit for expounding it, or any blame for believing in it. Credit was due only to investigators of the facts of chemical reaction and the nature of matter. The historian of science does not celebrate Paracelsus for brooding upon possibilities, but extols a Mme. Curie for *observing the fact* that one radioactive element actually does change into another. We do not praise Arabian thinkers for arguing that there is one simple basis of all metals; we praise J. J. Thomson for discovering facts which indicate that the one simple basis of all metals is electricity. In one sense he has merely proved the truth of the alchemists' theory. Yet the theory was only an idle dream; it was nonsense to Thomson and Rutherford; it did not direct their researches. Their fame was not earned by espousing a doctrine, but by discovering something about natural law in the universe.

The theory of evolution is a parallel case. It was as old as Aristotle. No one deserved credit for upholding it by a logical dissertation. The Lamarcks and Grants could have theorized till doomsday without contributing a jot to the intellectual advancement of the human race. The only man worth eulogizing would be one who could discover some facts—some evidence that the transmutation of species was as false as perpetual motion or as true as the new kind of electronic alchemy.

The notion of the transmutation of species was mere biological alchemy in 1825. It looked probable as a matter of logic, because any classifier of animals knew how the array of varied organisms formed a kind of ascending series, from animalcules to clams and on up through insects and reptiles to birds and monkeys. All along the extent of this series there were resemblances of structure that could hardly be thought accidental. To any naturalist, familiar with the endless similarities and overlappings in this gamut of animal forms, there was inevitably suggested an order of development. The animal kingdom looked as if it might have grown by a progressive development from simpler forms to more complex or "higher" forms. An ignorant man, who knew only a few dozen species of animals, would never have conceived such an idea of development. An unimaginative man could not have visualized a whole "scale of nature" in which the thousands of kinds of organisms formed steps in a continuous stairway from sea-anemone to elephant. But if a naturalist had wide knowledge and strong imagination, he could not fail to see the scale of nature. Once he had seen it, he never could escape the haunting queries about it.

Aristotle caught this view of life twenty-two centuries before Dr. Grant felt his high admiration for a certain theory about it. Aristotle reasoned that there is a constant tendency of life to advance to higher forms, up a scale of increasing complexity, each step in which was a definite and peculiar form—a "species." Three centuries later, in Rome, Lucretius imagined that all nature has been a steady process of development by natural law, and that man has evolved from an early beast-like form. So this theory was sponsored by great names and was a proper speculation in philosophy. The literature of the eighteenth century was dotted with ideas of evolution of some sort. Thus, for one example, Boswell used to enjoy spurring Dr. Johnson by an allusion to Lord Monboddo's theory of the descent of man from a brutish ancestry. Johnson responded with sarcasm. "Mankind would soon degenerate into brutes," he asserted when arguing for the advantages of social inequality; "they would become Monboddo's men; their tails would grow." When he wrote to Boswell about the failure of the Scotch to produce Erse manuscripts, he used Monboddo as a sarcastic illustration: "If there are men with tails, catch an *homo caudatus*." Shreds of evolution theories were so numerous in Europe that it would be mere pedantry to offer an account of them as a background for understanding Darwin's lifework. Of what use could it be to balance the opinions as to whether de Maillet did or did not set forth an evolution theory? Why would it be worth while to debate whether Bonnet's mystic words mean or do not mean what they seem or do not seem to say? Can any modern mind feel an interest in the sort of evolution that Leibnitz and Kant philosophized about or Goethe intuited? The St. Hilaires, father and son, were admirable naturalists, whose opinions would be worth recording here—if they were known. But the father was so hesitant that the son had to interpret him; and modern commentators can not agree as to whether the interpretation is right or as to the meaning of the son's expression of his own views on evolution. Such exegetic ambiguities would be proper only in a history of guessing. We are told that Treviranus was not ambiguous, that in 1805 he spoke out loud and clear for a belief in progressive development; yet there are different opinions as to whether his speaking was of any moment.

I set down those names of some early evolutionists in order to show that their combined theories—however valuable in the history of speculation—have only a slight and antiquarian interest in the history of science. If Darwin had proved by the method of science that all evolution theories were as baseless as the perpetual motion idea, the early evolutionists would be shrouded in complete oblivion. They proved nothing. They did not even point out the road to any proof. They were of no help to Darwin and had no part in the building of a scientific hypothesis of evolution.

That way of stating the case, which may appear unjust and unphilosophical, is the most essential truth for any one who wishes to understand the meaning of Charles Darwin's life. At the age of sixteen Darwin was completely out of sympathy with Dr. Grant's enthusiasm for Lamarckian philosophy. And through all the rest of his days he was not to take any interest in speculations about the nature of species. He always continued to feel astonished at what he called the "nonsense" of such speculation. He always preferred to examine some objects—like the seeds and eggs in the water at Newhaven —and to ask the world, as he asked Dr. Grant, "What do you make of these facts that I observe?" The business of his life was to show the futility of mere logic. He took his sling of observation in his hand and advanced against the great Goliath of Speculation, who championed the whole host of Philistine logic—the "views" of biologists, the beliefs of theologians, the conclusions of philosophy, the mysticism of natural philosophy, the faith in the power of pure reason to arrive at knowledge. This entire army of reasoners was animated by the assumption that a human mind, if it contemplated portentously, could give forth wisdom. They considered that acute Speculation was the greatest warrior among them. So they sent him forth against young Darwin. And this Goliath cursed Darwin by his gods of intellectual processes. And Darwin smote him in his forehead, that the stone sunk into his forehead. And of course this Goliath isn't dead yet, and probably will never die. But he has been less vigorous since the encounter.

Be patient with my little parable and my dogmatic way of setting up Darwin as an opponent of theorizers. I am aware of the exceptions and explanations that could be made and that will be made in the course of this book. I shall later describe Darwin as the man who was forever theorizing, who could not even begin an investigation without a preliminary hypothesis to attack or defend. And I shall tell of Darwin's concern about priority in developing a theory of evolution. But such facts are quite secondary and partial. Here, at the outset, I want to display the chief meaning of Darwin's career: that the result of his fifty years of observing nature was to teach the world not to rely on Speculation.

I am the more anxious to do this because every book about Darwin or his theory implies the contrary. A fair sample of the misapprehension of Darwin's work is the following innocent-looking statement from a recent essay: "Goethe to some extent anticipated Darwin as to the possibilities of metamorphosis in the natural world." The inference is that Darwin somehow deserves less credit if a poet perceived certain evolutionary possibilities before Darwin investigated them. But the poet had not anticipated Darwin's work. Darwin had no poetical power to "perceive" a beautiful theory, full-formed, all in bulk. His business was to find out whether such a venerable theory was true. The two men were in different fields of mentality. No divination of poetry or philosophy can anticipate the knowledge that comes from dissecting barnacles and observing fossil armadillos and studying the methods of pigeon-breeders—and then unlocking all the dissimilar mysteries with one key.

Darwin's precursors are not being robbed of any glory. If it is a merit to have originated an evolution theory, then the precursors deserve all the glory. Darwin was not even in competition with them. He found their theory set forth in speculative books. It was his starting-point. If we are to follow his career with any interest, we must be clear as to where it began. A philosophizing world has generally assumed that Darwin, by long and deep thought, arrived at a theory as at a goal— where he found Goethe and Lucretius awaiting him, resting on their laurels. No, Darwin set out from this heap of easily-won laurels. He pressed toward an entirely different goal, which no one reached ahead of him, where his fame is now commemorated by a thousand tablets and ten thousand hosannahs from scientific admirers. The narrative of his victory begins with an evolution theory for which the diviners and anticipators deserve all the credit.

At the risk of seeming to delay too long before pro-

ceeding with the account of Darwin's youth I will give
one further illustration of how the whole meaning of his
life has been distorted by a philosophizing world. Prof.
John W. Judd, in his *The Coming of Evolution*, relates
that he once fell in talk with Matthew Arnold, who exclaimed, "I cannot understand why you scientific people make such a fuss about Darwin. Why, it's all in
Lucretius." When Judd argued that Lucretius had
guessed what Darwin proved, Arnold retorted, "Ah! that
only shows how much greater Lucretius really was—for
he divined a truth which Darwin spent a life of labor in
groping for." Arnold's judgment was axiomatic in the
learned world of fifty years ago; the intellect that divined
was glorified. The judgment is still accepted, as matter of course, by a large proportion of the literary and
critical world. Does it seem valid to you? To modern
science it seems topsy-turvy. In this life of Darwin you
are to see why science regards Matthew Arnold as an
arch-Philistine. Then you will be free to pitch your tent
with the army of your choice.

In 1825 Dr. Grant stood with the forces of the diviners. He highly admired the ingenious intuitions of
Lamarck. Whereas young Darwin could only regard it
as he did the vesicles floating in sea-water. "What is
actually inside of them?" he asked. Speculation about
them was only to be regarded with polite silence. He
would have sympathized completely with Dr. Johnson's
summary of the Monboddo theory: "Knowledge of all
kinds is good. Conjecture—such as whether men ever
went on all four—is very idle."

The Monboddos and Lucretiuses fascinate the Arnold
type of mind because their conjectures have proved true.
In just the same way prophets fascinate most of us, because we are impressed by any true prophecy. The Darwins alone inquire about all the host of prophecies that

When we consider the boundless fertility given to every species, the innumerable progeny that result, the sudden and prodigious multiplying of some animals, we are astonished that they do not overrun nature. . . . It is really frightful to see these thick clouds of famished insects coming, which seem to threaten the whole world. . . . And have we not seen those torrents of the human race pour suddenly from their caves? . . .

These great events, however, are merely trifling changes in the usual course of animated nature. The course is, in general, always steady, always the same; its movement, always regulated, rotates upon two unshakable pivots—one, the boundless fertility given to every species; the other, the numberless obstructions which reduce the product of this fertility by a fixed rate, and leave, in the whole course of time, only about the same quantity of individuals in every species. (Tome VI, page 247.)

Even a modern scientist would admit that the embryo of an evolution theory is in another passage of Buffon:

So we see why there are such large reptiles, such big insects, such small quadrupeds, and such unemotional men in the new world. This is due to the nature of the land, the kind of climate, to the degree of heat and humidity, to situation, to the height of mountains, the amount of stagnant or running water, the extent of forests, and especially to the dry state of nature there. [After descanting upon the remains of the mammoth found in many parts of the world.] How many other smaller animals must have perished without leaving us any evidence or token of their existence! How many other species, after their nature had been altered—that is to say, improved or degraded by the great changes of earth and waters, by the neglect or fostering of nature, by the long-continued influence of a climate that had become adverse or favorable—are no longer the same as they once were? And yet quadrupeds are, after man, the creatures whose nature is most permanent and whose shape is most constant: that of birds and fishes varies

more; that of insects still more; and if we come down as
far as to plants (which we can not exclude from animated
nature), we shall be surprised at the quickness with
which species vary, and at the ease with which they alter
their nature by taking on new shapes. (Tome IX, pages
106 and 126.)

Reasons for believing in the descent of man were sum-
marized clearly by Buffon; any reader who is curious will
find them in the Appendix of this book. Also he will
find there an account of how Goliath shook his spear at
Buffon, and of how Buffon kissed the ground in token of
surrender to the Philistines. It was probably this fear
of Goliath that made Buffon deny his own theory and
leave a puzzled world to guess whether or not there was
any meaning in his now-you-see-it-and-now-you-don't discussion of species. He says that they alter their natures;
also he says that their natures can not be altered. There
is no one section of his work in which evolution is discussed to some definite conclusion. The comments on
evolution are side-remarks, a few pages at a time, in the
course of seven thousand pages. Scholars who now investigate the fifteen large tomes, striving to discover
some consistent message, reach opposite conclusions as to
Buffon's meaning. Even a Matthew Arnold could not
reasonably claim that Darwin's effectiveness had been
anticipated by Buffon's bits of mystifying self-contra-
dictions.

Yet there was a powerful fertility in those ideas of
Buffon's. They stimulated the adventurous mind of
Erasmus Darwin when, in 1756, he began to practise
medicine; they flourished in Dr. Darwin's treatise on
medicine. In this treatise there is frequent reference to
"the ingenious Mr. Buffon." Also there is frequent reference to "Dr. Robert W. Darwin of Shrewsbury"—
for Erasmus enjoyed giving prominence to his success-

ful son, and included a chapter written by him. Charles had read the treatise during his poco curante days at Shrewsbury. So Buffon was not a mere dead name to him, but was associated with pride in the fame of a grandfather and with admiration for a father. The extracts from the noted Frenchman's work are not mere antiquities in an account of Charles Darwin's youth. They formed part of the background of his family pride—all the more so because his grandfather had by no means been a disciple or imitator.

Erasmus Darwin was one of the most interesting characters in England during the last half of the eighteenth century. In 1757 he settled at Lichfield—just two years after Lichfield's most famous son completed his *Dictionary of the English Language*. Dr. Johnson, when he visited in Lichfield during the next quarter of a century, occasionally met Dr. Darwin, but there was no friendship between them. "They seemed to dislike each other cordially," wrote Charles Darwin in a sketch of his grandfather, "and to have felt that if they had met they would have quarreled like two dogs." Dr. Darwin once scribbled a stanza about Johnson's edition of Shakespeare:

From Lichfield famed two giant critics come,
Tremble, ye poets! hear them! "Fe, Fo Fum!"
By Seward's arm the mangled Beaumont bled,
And Johnson grinds poor Shakespeare's bones for
    bread.

Dr. Darwin was tall and heavy; he stammered; he was witty; in an age of heavy drinking he was a teetotaler. Though unorthodox, he wrote an ode against the "dull atheist," and he defined Unitarianism as "a feather-bed to catch a falling Christian." In general he sympathized with liberal or revolutionary thought; he wished for the success of the revolutions in North America and France; he expressed his hatred of slavery by writing:

Fierce SLAVERY stalks and slips the dogs of hell.

He espoused the revolutionary idea that all kinds of plants and animals may have descended from one common ancestor; he had some correspondence with the revolutionary Rousseau; he exchanged letters with the very revolutionary geologist Hutton.

His mind always ran to the novel and ingenious in any line of thought. The friend in whom he most delighted was R. L. Edgeworth, the father of Maria, who was perpetually engaged with such inventive efforts as the making of a telegraph and the educating of his children by improving on Rousseau's methods. Dr. Darwin made a "talking head" which produced some of the consonantal sounds accurately. He observed the wind by means of a vane which operated a dial in his study. He investigated artesian wells and rotary pumps and canal-locks. He did not subscribe to Buffon's theory of the origin of the planets, but conceived that they were shot forth by solar volcanos. He studied the history of the steam engine, and forty-four years before the first load of passengers was hauled on Stephenson's railway he boldly predicted:

Soon shall thy arm, unconquered steam, afar
Drag the slow barge, or drive the rapid car;
Or on wide-waving wings expanded bear
The flying-chariot through the fields of air.

His vivid imagination drove him to the writing of verse as a fit way of showing the wonders of plant life. In the opening canto of his first poem, *The Economy of*

Vegetation, 1781, he invokes the Botanic Goddess, who is to bring in her train Pomona, Ceres, and Flora. Spring comes, with her Zephyrs and Gnomes and Sylphs and Nymphs, and in a speech of three hundred lines summons the spirits of heat. She bids them "assail the Fiend of Frost" through all the northern regions, in another apostrophe of nearly two hundred lines. "The exulting tribes obey"—and so ends Canto I. This mass of rhetorical mythology would be an absurdity to twentieth-century readers. Nor would they concede much poetical merit to Dr. Darwin's way of describing the wonders of nature— for example, the way in which plant-lice procreate without mating for several generations and then procreate by mating:

> Unmarried Aphides prolific prove,
> For nine successions uninform'd of love;
> New sexes next with softer passions spring,
> Breathe the fond vow, and woo with quivering
> wing.

Yet the Doctor's three volumes of poetry were highly esteemed in their day. No less a critic than Horace Walpole testified in 1792, of a passage called "The Triumph of Flora": "It is most beautifully and enchantingly imagined; and the twelve verses that by miracle describe and comprehend the creation of the universe out of chaos, are in my opinion the most sublime passage in any author or in any of the few languages with which I am acquainted." The public liked the botanical poems; so popular was the first volume that the publishers advanced a thousand guineas on the second volume before it was printed—an extraordinary sum for that sort of matter in those times.

The poems deserve a mention in a life of Charles Darwin, not because of their large sale, but because of the copious notes that the Doctor delighted to add to them. Half of every page, on the average, is occupied by fine-print notes, and then the second half of each volume is filled solid with "Additional Notes." These are about all conceivable topics: a dark day in Detroit, Sir Joshua Reynolds' theory of art, opium-eating, the London Plague, divining-rods, sleep, alcohol as the curse of the the Christian world and as the cause of hereditary diseases, the Gulf Stream, meteors, fossil tar, etc., etc.

The notes on botanical subjects prove that the Doctor was a close and expert observer who had a vast lot of dependable information. He was also an enthusiastic gardener: "I had last spring six young trees of the Ischia fig with fruit on them in pots in a stove" [i. e., a green-house]. He was a painstaking anatomist of plants as well as a romantic lover of them.

He loved to let his imagination play with the mysteries of their reproduction. Especially he seems to have been struck by the remarkable statements and speculations of the early evolutionist Bonnet:

Mr. Bonnet saw four generations of successive plants in the bulb of a hyacinth. [Note that Erasmus never flattered himself that he could see any such marvel.]

Mr. Bonnet says the male salamander . . . Who knows but the power of the stamina of certain plants may make some impression on certain germs belonging to the animal kingdom?

I am acquainted with a philosopher, who thinks it not impossible, that the first insects were the anthers or stigmas of flowers; which had by some means loosed themselves from their parent plant; and that many other insects have gradually in long process of time been formed from these; some acquiring wings, others fins, and others claws, from their ceaseless efforts to procure their food, or to secure themselves from injury. He contends that none of these changes are more incomprehensible than the transformation of tadpoles into frogs, and caterpillars into butterflies.

(The curious reader will enjoy comparing that acknowledgment of the source of an idea with what is said about Lamarck in Section 3 of the Appendix of this book.) Imagine how that notion, of stamens as the forefathers of insects, affected the grandson—the skeptical youth of a new world of thought, the boy who would not take the word of an expert about certain vesicles of plants and animals that floated off Newhaven.

These glimpses of poetry and annotation give the impression that Dr. Erasmus Darwin had a somewhat flighty mind. But he was a fellow of the Royal Society and a very hard-headed physician, with a wide reputation for professional skill. A London physician once came to consult him as "the greatest physician in the world," and when Dr. Darwin referred him to the celebrated Dr. Warren, replied, "Alas! I am Dr. Warren. I want you to tell me how much longer I have to live." Dr. Darwin's prognosis was "not many weeks." Dr. Warren died within two weeks. King George III knew of Dr. Darwin, and once said of him, "Why does he not come to London? He shall be my physician if he comes." Dr. Darwin wrote a book of guidance for medical practitioners that was republished in America and translated into German, French, and Italian, *Zoonomia; or the Laws of Life*. The "Introductory Address" to the American edition thus characterizes the book: "Though evidently a work of much labour and study, it appears notwithstanding to be the result of accurate and profound observation, rather than of extensive reading." The estimate is just, for the great bulk of the two volumes consists of direct report and analysis of his experience. The whole book is replete with the keenest observations of an alert and canny mind.

The last of the thirty-nine sections of Volume I (Section 40 is an addendum by Dr. Darwin of Shrewsbury) treats of the greatest mystery of nature, with which Buffon had wrestled at great length, Generation. The section is forty-three pages long. It argues for two conceptions of the way an individual begins his life: (1) that the male furnishes the real seed of the embryo, the female egg being merely a nest for nourishing it; (2) that sex is determined by *the condition of mind* of the male at the moment of fertilization. In support of number two he is not afraid to be quite specific:

For instance: I can conceive, if a turkey-cock should behold a rabbit, or a frog, at the time of procreation, that it might happen, that a forcible or even a pleasurable idea of the form of a quadruped might so occupy his imagination, as to cause a tendency in the nascent filament to resemble such a form by the apposition of a duplicature of limbs.

Such a notion was a sheer absurdity to Dr. Darwin of Shrewsbury, who did not even credit (what is still widely believed among intelligent people) that a violent emotion in the mind of a pregnant woman can produce a corresponding effect in the embryo. Imagine, then, how the notion would cast a ludicrous hue upon other ideas in *Zoonomia*—for instance, upon the idea of an evolution of all living beings from one simple primary form. Dr. Erasmus Darwin set forth that idea in several of the notes to the poems and in several passages of *Zoonomia*. I will cite only four sentences here; some longer quotations are given in Section 2 of the Appendix.

All animals have a similar origin, viz. from a single living filament; and the difference of their forms and qualities has arisen only from the different irritabilities and sensibilities of this original living filament . . .

Hence, as Linnæus has conjectured in respect to the vegetable world, it is not impossible but the great variety of species of animals which now tenant the earth may have had their origin from the mixture of a few natural orders. (Page 367.)

When we revolve in our minds the great similarity of structure which obtains in all the warm-blooded animals, from the mouse and bat, to the elephant and whale, one is led to conclude that they have alike been produced from a similar living filament. In some this filament has acquired hands and fingers; in others toes; in others it has acquired claws or talons.

It is safe to suppose—from Charles Darwin's silent astonishment in 1825 and from what we know of his life during the next twenty years—that this speculation about "a living filament" seemed as groundless to him as the speculation that a male child would be formed if a father's mind happened to be more occupied with his own body than with his wife's. A theory of common descent, by changing species, from a primordial filament, would seem unfounded to a boy who challenged *The Wonders of the World* and who admired an unspeculative father.

Surely a Matthew Arnold could not believe that a Darwinian theory "was all in *Zoonomia*." The theory of Erasmus Darwin gained no credence. It was styled "Darwinising" by Coleridge and (says Krause) "was accepted in England nearly as the antithesis of sober biological investigation."

Arnold could have argued somewhat plausibly, however, that an evolution theory was all sketched in a two-volume book published in the very year Charles Darwin was born. The author was a young "chevalier," J. B. P. A. de M. Lamarck. He was twelve years old when Erasmus Darwin began to practise medicine in the first year of the Seven Years' War (1756). In the fifth year of that war, when he was almost sixteen, he left his native hamlet of Bazentin-le-Petit in northern France, which was in the line of trenches of the World War, midway between Amiens and Cambrai. He was bound for a battle-field a hundred miles away, beyond Antwerp, where an older brother had already been killed. His family was so poor that he had to ride an old and disreputable horse. Though he had had no military training, and was too scrawny even to look like a soldier, he forced his way into a company of grenadiers that was ordered to a hopelessly exposed position. When all the officers and most of the men of his company had been killed, he rallied the handful of survivors and refused to retreat. So remarkable was his valor that he was made an officer as soon as he had been rescued. This brilliant beginning of a military career was spoiled, not long after, by a prank of a comrade, who lifted him by the head in such a way as to injure his neck. So the poor fellow—weakened and in poverty—went to Paris to earn a living as a clerk in a bank.

The fighting quality and the hard luck marked all the rest of his life. He plunged into the battles of science as recklessly as he had forced himself into the army, fighting his way to prominence where veterans would have been afraid to venture. Before long he was challenging the teachings of the most prominent chemists; he developed extraordinary conceptions of mineralogy; he was not afraid of novelties in medicine; and he made himself a master of botany. So original—and so correct and thorough—was his system of classification that Charles Darwin guided himself by it when he went round the world. In 1778, when he was thirty-four years old, he published his *French Flora* in three volumes. This was so useful and brilliant a work that it brought him fame as a scholar and placed him among the world's leading botanists.

It called him to the attention of Buffon, who secured for him an appointment as "Royal Botanist," by the terms of which he was to travel over Europe for two years and familiarize himself with the principal herbariums and museums. With him he took Buffon's son, whom he tutored.

On his return he was made Keeper of the Herbarium of the Royal Garden. All this looks rosy. But his life was pitifully hard. He never could secure a salary or an income sufficient for decent living. During twenty-five years, while he brought prestige to France by vast scientific labors, he could hardly provide fit food and shelter for his family. His largest salary was never more than six hundred dollars a year.

When he was almost fifty years old he was appointed to a chair of zoology at the Royal Garden; and, even at this age, pushed to the front of academic battle as ardently as if he were still sixteen. He braved previous classifiers by announcing that all animals ought to be divided into two great groups—those that have a backbone and those that have not. The zoologists have ever since conceded that this grouping was his invention and that it was a wise one. His field of work in zoology was among the invertebrates—a vast horde of forms, almost unknown and very difficult to assort. Again he was where the fighting was hardest, and again he won distinction. He became the founder of paleontology, and the leading zoologist of his period.

Seven volumes about the invertebrates flowed from his pen; he wrote learnedly on "hydrogeology," on shells, on physiology, on sound and heat, on the moon's influence upon the air, on instincts. Yet his eyesight was failing all the while. The last ten years of his life were spent in blindness. His poverty never decreased. He buried four wives and three children. His ideas were regarded with silent astonishment by young skeptics in 1825. He died in 1829.

Through the century since his death there has been magic in his theory of evolution. His teachings have continued to fascinate philosophical minds; even to-day there are zoologists who pair him with Darwin and believe that his theory of evolution contains a great truth. It may be fairly presented by three short quotations from his two-volume *Philosophie Zoologique,* 1809. In this work—as in the works of Buffon and Erasmus Darwin—the aim is not to present a theory of how life developed. The aim is to show the nature of animal life—what bodily motions are, what consciousness and intelligence are.

The first of the three Parts of the book is a preliminary survey of the classification of animals and of the nature of the "species" into which they are divided. The seventh of the eight chapters of this Part I is entitled: "On the influence of conditions upon the actions and habits of animals, and the influence of these actions and habits upon organisms, as causes which modify their structure and parts." The fifty pages of the chapter, hardly more than a tenth part of the whole work, are the source of Lamarck's fame as an evolutionist. He set forth his idea of development very picturesquely and unmistakably. The figures refer to the pages of Volume I.

245. When snakes had formed the habit of creeping on the ground and hiding under plants, their body, because of ever-repeated efforts to stretch itself out in order to pass through narrow places, acquired a length, out of all proportion to its bulk. Now feet would have been very unserviceable to these animals and therefore useless. . . . So the lack of use of these parts, having been constant in the races of these animals, has caused these same parts to disappear entirely, although they were really in the structural plan of animals of their class. . . . Many insects which, by the natural char-

acter of their order and even of their genus, should have
wings lack them more or less completely, because of lack
of use.

249-251. I am now going to prove that the continual
use of an organ—with the efforts made to derive much
advantage from it in conditions that make demands on it
—strengthens, stretches, and enlarges this organ, or
makes out of it new organs which can perform the functions that have become necessary.

The bird, which need attracts to the water to find
there the prey on which it lives, stretches out its toes,
when it wants to strike the water and move on the surface. The skin which unites these toes at their base
forms, by the ever-repeated stretchings of the toes, a
habit of spreading; thus, in time, the large membranes
that unite the toes of ducks, geese, etc., take such shapes
as we see. The same efforts made to swim—that is, to
push the water in order to get ahead and move in this
liquid—have spread in the same way the membranes between the toes of frogs, sea-turtles, the otter, the
beaver, etc.

Again, we see that the same bird, wishing to fish without wetting its body, must make continual efforts to
lengthen its neck. Now the results of these continual
efforts in this individual and in those of its race must, in
time, have lengthened their neck remarkably; this is, indeed, proved by the long neck of all shore-birds.

260. When the will determines an animal to any
action, the organs that are to execute this action are at
once incited to it by the flow of subtle fluids (the nervous
fluid). . . . The result is that multiplied repetitions of
these acts of organization strengthen, extend, develop,
and even create the organs that are necessary for them.
. . . Now every change acquired in an organ by a habit
of use sufficient to produce it is thereafter preserved by
reproduction [*génération*], if it is common to the individuals that, in the impregnation, came together for the
propagation.

An admirer of Lamarck would say that his theory can
not be fairly judged by these three brief extracts. Espe-

cially he would caution a reader that Lamarck's reasoning about the "will" is not what it might appear to be in the last paragraph. (So I have provided in the Appendix some further quotations.) But, even when allowances have been made for extracts thus snatched from their context, we can see why a Darwin would be astonished at the Lamarckian views. The reason is cogent: *the views were not based on observed facts; they were conjectures.* In the nine hundred pages of the *Philosophie Zoologique* there is no appeal to observations that other men have been able to make. The opening words of Chapter VII are, "We are not concerned here with abstract reasoning, but with the investigation of a positive fact"; and three pages later Lamarck declares, speaking of how needs give rise to inheritable habits, "This is easy to prove, and does not even require any explanation to be understood." That pair of statements fairly represent the argument of the whole chapter. The reader is strongly assured that positive facts are being talked about, but the facts never are explained in such a way that the rest of us can see them. The reader never encounters any concrete example of the "fluids" nor of the inheritance of the habits—never so much as a single shred of evidence that points to possible examples. Lamarck had no interest in observation or examples. He always felt that what he visualized was actual and was already demonstrated. His most ardent admirer—his biographer, A. S. Packard—confesses that Lamarck's chemical views were "formed without reference to experiment;" and most scholars of to-day feel the same way about his zoological views. Their state of mind when they contemplate Packard's eulogy is just that of Charles Darwin when he heard Dr. Grant's admiration.

The charm of Lamarck's way of thinking is a deathless one for the human brain, because it is based on personality, on striving, on the power of the will. Our instinct dreads the impersonal, the reign of fixed, mechanical law to which no purpose or will-power is admitted. All philosophical minds flinch from Darwinism. They respond yearningly to some inner, vital principle of Lamarckism. The reasoning of Lamarck was always absurd to the band of scientists who were destined to rally to Darwin.

It will be interesting to take a peep at the five principal members of the band on the afternoon of a day early in December, 1825.

The oldest, Charles Lyell, is twenty-eight years old. He is a barrister who has been on the western circuit for a few months. The letter that he writes to his sister contains items like these: "Coleridge informed me yesterday. . . . Scrope wants me to pay a visit to Waverley Abbey. He is a gentlemanlike man of fortune, and has just published a very creditable work on volcanos." Lyell always liked men who were gentlemanlike and who had an interest in geology.

Asa Gray is a fifteen-year-old boy who lives at the border of the Adirondacks, on the "Presbyterian side" of the creek, close to the Presbyterian church, which he attends every Sunday. He will enter a rustic medical school next fall and will long for such European advantages as Charles Darwin enjoys.

Joseph Dalton Hooker, though only eight years old, is bravely attending his father's botanical lectures in Glasgow and is having a hard time with Latin grammar, but is "bending all his soul and spirit to the task."

Alfred Russell Wallace will be three years old next month. He is toddling about in the yard of a humble home in the village of Usk, seventy-five miles south of Shrewsbury.

Thomas Henry Huxley is a babe of seven months in

the home of a schoolmaster who teaches in a London suburb, Ealing, which lies six miles west of the Marble Arch. His mother thinks the child looks intellectual. Charles Darwin, aged sixteen and skeptical, would probably have listened to this estimate with silent astonishment.

CHAPTER III

CAMBRIDGE AND THE BEAGLE

CHARLES DARWIN's attempt at a medical education lasted only two years. Most of the lectures were insufferable to him, both because of the subject-matter and of the dry formality of presenting it. The sights and sounds and smells of the clinics always remained horrible memories. Only twice did he venture into the operating theater (this was before the day of anesthetics), and both times had to run away from the unendurable spectacle. "The two cases fairly haunted me for many a long year." To be sure, he made interesting acquaintances during the second year and enjoyed the companionship of young men of scientific tastes. He became a favorite with the curator of the museum, a noted ornithologist. Otherwise Edinburgh furnished him little of the stimulus he craved. Even of the Royal Medical Society he felt that "much rubbish was talked there." Audubon's lectures on birds were interesting, though he "sneered unjustly at Waterton." But Darwin was prejudiced, because he had enjoyed lessons in bird-stuffing given by a negro who had worked with Waterton. Except for this little education in birds, he seems not to have been able to stomach the training he could find at Edinburgh. One professor's lectures on zoology were incredibly dull, and his field lectures denied what any good pair of seventeen-year-old eyes could see was the fact. "The sole effect the lectures produced on me was the determination never as long as I lived to read a book on geology, or in any way to study

42

the science. . . . I was so sickened at Edinburgh that at Cambridge I did not even attend Sedgwick's eloquent and interesting lectures."

During the summer vacation of 1826 he amused himself by a long walking tour in Wales (averaging thirty miles a day), a riding tour, and much shooting at the estates of Maer and Woodhouse. Then there was another dull year at Edinburgh, lighted only by such episodes as seeing Sir Walter Scott preside at a meeting of the Royal Society. It became clear to the discouraged father that this son would never qualify in medicine.

So he made another vehement plea to Charles not to become an idle, sporting country gentleman. "How should you like to be a clergyman?" he asked. Charles rather fancied the idea and read some divinity books to see whether he could subscribe to all of the creed. The result was favorable: "As I did not then in the least doubt the strict and literal truth of every word in the Bible, I soon persuaded myself that our Creed must be fully accepted." So it was decided that he should follow his grandfather to Cambridge and prepare to take orders. In his old age Darwin used to enjoy explaining why he would probably have made a good clergyman: "A society of German psychologists discussed the shape of my head, and one of the speakers declared that I had a bump of reverence developed enough for ten priests."

In spite of the thorough grounding in classics that he had received at the Shrewsbury School, he was not in shape to pass entrance examinations for Cambridge. "I had forgotten almost everything which I had ever learnt, even to some few of the Greek letters." He had to be specially tutored during the closing months of 1827. "One of my autumnal visits to Maer in 1827," he recalled late in life, "was memorable for meeting there Sir J. Mackintosh." Sir James was a philosopher and historian, one of the stream of guests at Maer, who devoted his mornings to writing his *History of the Revolution in England*, in a study that had been specially fitted with tables and shelves for his six-month visit. He enjoyed Charles Darwin: "There is something in that young man that interests me" was his comment. A stronger fondness for Charles was felt by the erratic and crabbed master of Woodhouse. In fact nobody seems to have despaired of the young sportsman at this time except the worried father.

"My visits to Maer were quite delightful, independently of the shooting," Darwin remarked fifty years later. "Life there was perfectly free; the country was very pleasant for walking or riding; and in the evening there was much very agreeable conversation, not so personal as it generally is in large family parties, together with music." A fair addition to the list of attractions would have been "together with Emma." Emma had gone to the Continent in November of 1826 (she had a few piano lessons from Chopin), and in May, 1827, her brother Jos, with Charles and Caroline Darwin, had gone to Paris to meet her and escort her home. This was the only time Charles Darwin ever crossed the English Channel. The travelers had returned late in July, and had inaugurated a series of gaieties that were too much even for such a seasoned hostess as Mrs. Wedgwood. She had Susan and Catherine Darwin as guests for a month, and at the end of their stay wrote to a sister: "The Darwins go on Monday. I like them very much, but I shall not be sorry to have our party lessened."

Charles Darwin enjoyed music, and Emma Wedgwood had been taking piano lessons of a German at Geneva. "He takes great pains about playing with expression," she wrote to her sister, "but I think he plays with so much expression himself that it is as if he was mad." At

Geneva she had stayed with her mother's sister, the wife of Sismondi, the Swiss historian. Sismondi was a gallant courtier to the English girls. "He enters into all their little interests of vanity with greater warmth than I do," Mme. Sismondi explained, "because he does not understand as well as I do how completely without vanity they are. . . . They surpass even my hopes of giving him pleasure; he enjoys every moment at home. . . . He thinks them very pretty, and will tell them so. They do not, however, seem to give him the least credit, and the other day Emma laughed in his face when he said that he would not give one of his own little Emma Wedgwood for ten Emma Pictets. . . . There is a pretty gaiety about Emma, always ready to answer to any liveliness and sometimes to throw it out herself, that will cheer everybody that lives with or approaches her."

The mother made much the same estimate of her daughter: "Emma is going to pay a visit to the Miss Aclands at Clifton. Her manners are in her favor, and she is more popular than any of my girls. Her manners to men are very much to my taste, for they are easy and undesigning without coquetry." Catherine Darwin's opinion of Emma was not so different as it sounds: "You have an unfeigned passion for gaiety and novelty."

It is hard to see what chance Charles Darwin had for recovering the lost Greek letters in the autumn of 1827. He must have had more will-power than the father thought. In January, 1828, he was admitted to Christ's College, where his rooms are pointed out to visitors who enter the first court and gaze at the gray-and-black stone walls and the brilliant flowers. The men of Christ's at that period (seventy or eighty in number) were a well-to-do lot who had a reputation for caring a good deal about the races at Newmarket. In the social doings of this crowd he is described as "one of the most cheerful, the most popular, and the most welcome." He belonged to the Gourmet Club, whose business was supposed to be experimenting with strange meats, such as hawks and owls. He once rode with some companions, "like incarnate devils," to a fire eleven miles away, returning at two in the morning. "From my passion for shooting and hunting, and, when this failed, for riding across country, I got into a sporting set, including some dissipated, low-minded young men. We used often to dine together, and we sometimes drank too much, with jolly singing and playing at cards afterwards." In short, he was quite the normal collegian of that period.

He was not above normal in adapting himself to the curriculum. Though Euclid gave him pleasure, algebra was repugnant to him, and the classics seemed of no more moment now than they had seemed at Shrewsbury. "During the three years which I spent at Cambridge my time was wasted, as far as academical studies were concerned, as completely as at Edinburgh and at school."

Still the intellectuals welcomed his friendship. He was intimate with the senior wrangler, who "inoculated me with a taste for pictures and good engravings." Darwin confesses—for he loved to make fun of himself—that the taste for pictures was not native in him. He also gives a comical description of his lack of a musical ear. He enjoyed music. He often timed his walks so as to happen in to King's College Chapel for the anthem, and at one of these services was so thrilled that he whispered to the friend next him, "How's your backbone?" He hired choir-boys to sing in his rooms. Yet he confessed: "I am so utterly destitute of an ear that I cannot perceive a discord, or keep time and hum a tune correctly." If *God Save the King* was played in faster or slower time, he was puzzled to recognize it.

It is hard to say whether it was music or something

else that lured him away from academic duties in October, 1829, to the Musical Festival at Birmingham. Guess for yourself from his account: "It was the most glorious thing I ever experienced. . . . As for Malibran, she is quite the most charming person I ever saw. . . . A person's heart must have been made of stone not to have lost it to her. I lodged very near to the Wedgwoods, and lived entirely with them, which was very pleasant. It knocked me up most dreadfully, and I will never attempt again to do two things the same day." A hasty and sentimental reader might wonder whether the two "things" were losing his heart to an opera-singer and to Emma in one day; but there is no evidence that his heart was yet lost to either one. In fact he was greatly attracted at this time by Fanny Owen, who could look perfectly charming while she shot one of Charles's guns that kicked her shoulder black and blue. There is no record of any similar admiration for Emma. All we learn is that he saw her whenever the chance offered. The following spring Catherine Darwin wrote to Emma: "I have just heard from Charles to say that he comes home on Monday. . . . I am afraid you will hear as much about the Foxes from him as you did from me." He liked to tell Emma about whatever was interesting him.

Some of the older and accomplished men at Cambridge liked to talk to Charles Darwin about whatever interested them; they felt the same fondness for the boy that had been felt at Edinburgh. The curator of the gallery in the Fitzwilliam Museum liked to discuss the pictures with him. The best-loved professor, Henslow, frequently asked this engaging young Darwin to his house and took walks with him. Darwin reverenced him, delighted in him, and always felt that his influence had been more effective than that of any other man. Henslow encouraged Darwin's zeal for collecting. Darwin always admired the enthusiasm of this amiable scientific saint and felt unable to express how much he owed him. It was through Henslow that he became acquainted with several eminent men who had a taste for natural history— William Whewell, Leonard Jenyns, the younger Ramsay, the philanthropist Dawes. All of them felt "something in this young man that interests me" and liked to have him with them when Henslow conducted them on excursions.

Henslow was so devout a man that he declared he should be grieved if a single word of the thirty-nine articles of the creed was altered. No doubt he rejoiced that so attractive a youth was destined for the church. The talks with Darwin were often on religious topics and must have tended to keep the boy's mind directed toward the ministry. All through the years at Cambridge Darwin looked forward to taking holy orders. In preparation for his final examinations he had to study Paley's *Evidences of Christianity and Natural Theology*. Their reasoning was entirely convincing to him and gave him as much logical pleasure as he felt in geometry theorems.

The interest in such studies was slight compared with the "burning zeal" roused by the volumes of Humboldt's travels. The supreme day of Humboldt's life had been when he reached the top of the twelve-thousand-foot volcano on Teneriffe, in the Canary Islands; and he contrived to convey his exultation in his description. Darwin read it over and over, even committing parts of it to memory and rehearsing them on the excursions with Henslow. To see the peak of Teneriffe became his chief ambition. He burned to see the tropical forests that Humboldt pictured. He sensed the intense pleasure with which Humboldt always looked back upon his months in South American forests. So infectious was Darwin's zest for Humboldt that a college mate retained throughout his life a vivid recollection of "the vehemence with which he rubbed his chin when he got excited on such subjects, and discoursed eloquently of lianas, orchids, etc." In April of 1831 he wrote to a cousin, "At present I talk, think, and dream of a scheme I have almost hatched for going to the Canary Islands. My friends sincerely wish me there, I plague them so with talking about tropical scenery, etc." Suppose some one had predicted to this excitable young day-dreamer that he would one day be advertised on the jacket of a book as the man who "made hell a laughing-stock and heaven a dream." Or suppose it had been prophesied that his name should one day be synonymous with a revolution in human thinking. Poor fellow! He had no design on hell or heaven or thought. He just wanted to see volcanos and lianas and things.

So far was he from any cosmic ambitions that his greatest enthusiasm during his last year at Cambridge was collecting beetles. A person who is ignorant of beetles will never understand how a rational being can feel deep emotions about them; but any one who has had a bit of experience with the way fresh discoveries can always be made in any locality will sympathize with a collector. No other order of animals is so numerous or so diversified in size and markings. Beetles are nature's greatest specializers in habitats and modes of life. By a zoological standard they are the most successful and entertaining sort of animal. Let the sharpest-sighted collector track them for years in any given place—he may always expect to find a new sort that has lived its secret life undetected.

"No pursuit at Cambridge was followed with nearly so much eagerness or gave me so much pleasure as collecting beetles"—and this at "the most joyful period of my life, when I was in excellent health, and almost always in high spirits." Darwin records the "indelible impres-

sion many of the beetles have left on my mind. I can remember the exact appearance of certain posts, old trees,
and banks where I made a good capture. . . . No poet
ever felt more delighted at seeing his first poem published
than I did at seeing, in Stephens' *Illustrations of British
Insects,* the magic words, 'Captured by C. Darwin,
Esq.' " He wrote to a friend in September, 1828, about
finding some beetles unknown at Barmouth, " I think I
shall write and inform some of the crack entomologists."
The youth had again scored in competition with profes-
sionals. He had discovered two sources of supply for
rare species, and employed a man to scrape moss from
old trees and to gather up the rubbed-off bits that were
left in the bottoms of barges which brought reeds from
the fens. "I will give a proof of my zeal," says Darwin
in a passage that no reader of his autobiography ever forgets: "One day, on tearing off some old bark, I saw two
rare beetles, and seized one in each hand; then I saw a
third and new kind, which I could not bear to lose, so that
I popped the one which I held in my right hand into my
mouth. Alas! it ejected some intensely acrid fluid, which
burnt my tongue so that I was forced to spit the beetle
out, which was lost, as was the third one." In February,
1829, he "spent two days in London entirely with Mr.
Hope, and did little else but talk about and look at insects." Two months later he showed his love for beetles
in a more violent manner: "I have caught Mr. Harbour
letting —— have the first pick of the beetles; accordingly
we have made our final adieus, my part in the affecting
scene consisted in telling him he was a d——d rascal, and
signifying I should kick him down the stairs if ever he
appeared in my rooms again." Three months after dealing thus harshly with Mr. Harbour he joined Hope for a
collecting tour through northern Wales.

If so much emphasis on beetles suggests a pettiness

of mind to those who have never known the collector's thrill, they may be better pleased by hearing of the way Darwin's mind reverted during Cambridge days to his early tenderness toward animals, a tenderness which was marked in him for the rest of his life. He resolved to quit shooting as a sport. One day at Woodhouse he found a bird dying a lingering death from a wound of the day before. This sight left such a painful impression on his mind that he had a revulsion of feeling and hoped never again to find his pleasure in "a sport that could inflict such painful suffering."* He was always sensitive, almost morbidly so, about the suffering of animals. "Come along; I can't stand this any longer," he said to a friend when he saw a trained dog in a troupe cower as if in fear of the whip.

In June of 1831 he completed his required terms of residence and laid plans for a trip to the Canaries. There were hopes that his cousin W. D. Fox or Professor Henslow would go with him. But for some reason unknown the scheme fell through.

Instead he went on a long geologizing tramp. He makes two comments on this trip which throw spot-lights on the difference between science in 1831 and science in his old age. The first is an anecdote about Adam Sedgwick, the eloquent and able geologist at Cambridge whose lectures he had failed to attend. The reason he gives for avoiding Sedgwick is that at Edinburgh his stomach had been turned against geology. Yet this distaste did not prevent his being enraptured with Henslow. It is a reasonable guess that he charitably suppressed the actual reason. Witness the affair of the shell in the gravel-pit. Sedgwick had planned a walking tour to observe rocks in

---

*Judge J. M. Herbert's memory must be at fault as to the time of this resolution, for Darwin was ardent about shooting in September of 1831. See page 54.

Wales, and Henslow advised him to take young Darwin along. Accordingly Sedgwick honored the Darwins by spending a night at their house to pick Charles up. A bit of the evening's conversation made a lasting impression on the youth's mind. We may dramatize the talk:

Charles. Sir, a laborer has told me that he found in a gravel-pit a tropical Volute shell.

Professor Sedgwick. That is impossible. There could not be such a shell in this superficial deposit of gravel.

C. But the laborer appears to be a truthful man.

P. S. I am not doubting him. I am judging from my general knowledge that the shell could never have been deposited in the gravel by geological agencies. Some person must have thrown it there.

C. But how wonderful a fact it would be if the shell were actually geological evidence.

P. S. My dear young man, such a fact would be the greatest misfortune. That single evidence would overthrow all we know about the gravel beds of the Midland Counties.

Charles heard this reply in silent astonishment. The mental adjustment of the Rev. Adam Sedgwick was quite beyond his comprehension. *How could any fact be a misfortune?* Sedgwick's remark had thrown a light down the unfathomable abyss between two types of mind: to a Darwin any fact is a welcome treasure; to a Sedgwick a fact may be distressing and abominable. No wonder the revelation of the working of a Sedgwick mind made a strong impression on the young man. Philistines live on beliefs and have no appetite for facts; they may consider facts a calamity. They will rattle spears on shields when an unwelcome fact heaves in sight. They battle for opinion, for preconceptions.

Now it happened that Sedgwick was right. His wide knowledge of facts made it possible for him to pronounce that such a shell could not have been brought to such a place by non-human agencies. Here was a revelation of the nature and power of science which Darwin says he had never realized until that moment. He was quick to see the lesson and admired the master who taught it. If only Sedgwick had said, "Such a discovery is too good to be true," if he had shown a love for startling facts, Darwin's admiration would have been complete. Sedgwick had a *fear* of facts. It is likely that Darwin had sensed this Philistinism at Cambridge and that it was his real reason for avoiding Sedgwick. Certain it is that not many years later he pitied the old man's mode of thinking. The little episode of the Volute shell was a premonition of a great battle between two modes of thought.

The second comment which Darwin makes on the trip shows strikingly how blind we all are—even if we are Darwins—to obvious facts that stand huge before us. "Old Mr. Cotton had pointed out to me, a year or two before I went to Edinburgh, a large erratic boulder called the 'bell-stone'; he told me that there was no rock of the same kind nearer than Cumberland, and he solemnly assured me that the world would come to an end before anyone would be able to explain how this stone came where it now lay. This produced a deep impression on me, and I meditated over this wonderful stone." So now, seven years later, when he was in the company of one of the foremost geologists of England, he saw erratic boulders in Wales: "We spent many hours in Cwm Idwal, examining all the rocks with extreme care; but neither of us saw a trace of the wonderful glacial phenomena all around us; we did not notice the plainly scored rocks, the perched boulders, the moraines." Previous to 1831 a philosophical world had been content to *reason* about rocks, debating Noah's Flood and a paradisal earth and other such logical axioms. Charles Darwin was soon to become one of the small band who thought it more profitable to *observe* rocks and to read the messages plainly written in them.

The two geologists took a course that is familiar to modern tourists who coach in Wales—westward from Llangollen, through Bettws-y-Coed, by the pass of Llanberis, to Bangor. This shows a visitor the wildest portion of Wales and takes him past the northern foot of Snowdon, the highest mountain in England. From a tiny village eight miles northeast of Snowdon, Capel Curig, Darwin set out alone to train himself in the use of map and compass. He tried to keep as straight a line as possible to Barmouth, thirty miles south, on the coast of Merioneth.

He did not suppose that he had made himself a geologist by this and previous trips. "I was far too ignorant to have aided Sedgwick," is his comment on the part of the observation entrusted to him. Nor did he suppose that telling the crack entomologists about a few beetles was proof that he belonged among them. His observations at Newhaven had not made him master of marine zoology or botany. He was very much of an amateur in all departments of science. Indeed he considered that he was doing no more than play with science. "At that time I should have thought myself mad to give up the first days of partridge-shooting for geology or any other science." But it is evident that he was a scientific amateur of a very unusual sort. Instead of caring to absorb some system of knowledge, committing a thousand terms to memory and appearing learned, he wanted to examine queer sights that nature thrust in his way. In each of his approaches to science he had shown a peculiar gift for penetrating to some fact that would be a misfortune to Philistine assumptions. He liked to find his own way through a wilderness. No wonder that scientific veterans respected such a youth.

While he was tramping in Wales a letter came to Henslow asking him to recommend a man who could succeed in a type of scientific work that was then much in vogue. The letter came from George Peacock, a tutor at Cambridge, who was soon to be a Very Reverend and a Professor of Astronomy.

My dear Henslow:

Captain Fitz-Roy is going out to survey the southern coast of Tierra del Fuego, and afterwards to visit many of the South Sea Islands, and to return by the Indian Archipelago. The vessel is fitted out expressly for scientific purposes, combined with the survey; it will furnish, therefore, a rare opportunity for a naturalist, and it would be a great misfortune that it should be lost.

An offer has been made to me to recommend a proper person to go out as naturalist with this expedition; he will be treated with every consideration. . . . If Leonard Jenyns could go what treasures he might bring home with him! In the absence of so accomplished a naturalist, is there any person whom you could strongly recommend? He must be such a person as would do credit to our recommendation.

Henslow promptly wrote to Darwin, explaining the situation and saying:

"I fully expect that you will eagerly catch at the offer which is likely to be made you of a trip to Tierra del Fuego, and home by the East Indies. . . . I have stated that I consider you to be the best qualified person I know of who is likely to undertake such a situation. I state this not on the supposition of your being a *finished* naturalist, but as amply qualified for collecting, observing, and noting, anything worthy to be noted in Natural

History. . . . The voyage is to last two years, and if you take plenty of books with you, anything you please may be done. You will have ample opportunities at command. In short, I suppose there never was a finer chance for a man of zeal and spirit. . . . Don't put on any modest doubts or fears about your disqualifications, for I assure you I think you are the very man they are in search of. So conceive yourself to be tapped on the shoulder by your bum-bailiff and affectionate friend,

J. S. Henslow.

Peacock added his pressure:

I feel the greatest anxiety that you should go. . . . You must lose no time in making known your acceptance to Captain Beaufort, Admiralty Hydrographer.

For the next three days there was an upheaval in the Darwin family. Dr. Darwin strongly objected to having his clerical son set off on a madcap expedition around the world in a little brig, studying seaweeds and consorting with rough young naval officers. Charles had always shown a fondness for gallivanting away from duties. Was it not time that he began to care for his career? "How could any man of common-sense advise you to go? If you can find one such man, I will give my consent."

Charles accordingly wrote to Henslow: "My father, although he does not decidedly refuse me, gives such strong advice against going, that I should not be comfortable if I did not follow it. . . . Even if I was to go, my father disliking would take away all energy, and I should want a good stock of that." He told Peacock that he must decline and asked him to notify Captain Fitz-Roy.

Then, heavy-hearted, he set off to Maer for the opening of the shooting season. Of course, he expatiated on his troubles to the Wedgwood family, not forgetting to

mention his father's challenge about "any man of common-sense." Now Mr. Wedgwood was more than sensible; he was a most careful and dependable judge of
affairs. He weighed each one of the list of Dr. Darwin's objections; he wrote a forceful answer to each;
his verdict was that the voyage would be a good thing
for Charles. The first and principal objection was "disreputable to my character as a clergyman," to which
Mr. Wedgwood rejoined: "I should on the contrary
think the offer honorable to him; and the pursuit of
Natural History, though certainly not professional, is
very suitable to a clergyman." The eighth and last
objection was "that it would be a useless undertaking."
To this the answer was: "Looking upon Charles as a
man of enlarged curiosity, it affords him such an opportunity of seeing men and things as happens to few."
No phrase could show a clearer understanding of what
Charles was—a man of enlarged curiosity. No
phrase could better describe the true purpose of a
scientist—to have enlarged curiosity about the world.
I like to dwell on the significance of those words as it
unrolled in the career of Charles Darwin and in the
history of science.

Charles did not claim to have won the debate with
his father. He knew how reasonable the father's fears
were. "If you say no," he wrote when he enclosed Mr.
Wedgwood's answers to the objections, "I should be
most ungrateful if I did not implicitly yield to your better judgment, and to the kindest indulgence you have
shown me all through my life: and you may rely upon
it I will never mention the subject again. . . . I would
not for one *single moment* hesitate if you thought that
after a short period you should continue uncomfortable."

Dr. Darwin was as good as his word. He gave permission by return mail. On September 2 Charles was

in Cambridge, at the Red Lion Inn, writing a few hurried sentences to be taken by a messenger to Henslow's house: "My father has changed his mind. I trust the place is not given away. I am very much fatigued and am going to bed. How soon shall I come to you in the morning? Send a verbal answer."

Next morning Henslow disclosed how attractive the *Beagle* invitation had seemed even to older men. "I was almost minded to go myself," Henslow confessed, though he was thirteen years older than Darwin and had been a professor for nine years. "And Leonard Jenyns was so near accepting that he packed up his clothes, but he thought he ought not to leave his church." Charles must have enjoyed reporting at home that two well-established clergyman jumped at the offer which an irate father had called "disreputable" for a young chap who had not even entered on divinity studies.

It was a busy day, that fourth of September, 1831. Darwin arranged with a friend named Wood, who was a close friend of Fitz-Roy, to write him and certify that Darwin would be an acceptable comrade for the very close intimacy of the years in cramped quarters on a small vessel. Then bad news came so soon that he had to carry his unmailed letter, which described the progress at Cambridge, and add, in London, that his voyage was all off. Wood had received a letter from Fitz-Roy, "which I must say was *most* straightforward and *gentlemanlike*, but so much against my going that I immediately gave up the scheme; and Henslow did the same, saying that he thought Peacock had acted *very wrong* in misrepresenting things so much."

So rapid were the turns of this flurry that even Charles himself, writing on the day of the happenings, seemed not to be sure just what happened or how. "I scarcely thought of going to town," he says, "but here

I am." For some reason, though he had been rejected, he went to London to see Fitz-Roy. And, just five minutes before he met this most straightforward Captain, the Captain had received a letter which entirely cleared the way for Darwin. It was soon explained that Fitz-Roy had planned to take a friend named Chester, and that therefore no room was left for Darwin; but that Chester declined the invitation. So, with a seaman's promptness, Fitz-Roy again invited Darwin. "He offers me to go share in everything in his cabin if I like to come, and every sort of accommodation that I can have, but they will not be numerous. . . . There is something extremely attractive in his manners and way of coming straight to the point. . . . He thought it his duty to state everything in the worst point of view . . . He says I must live poorly—no wine, and the plainest dinners. The scheme is not certainly so good as Peacock describes. . . . The vessel does not sail till the 10th of October. It will probably be out nearly three years. . . . The round the world is not *certain,* but the chance most excellent. . . . If I do not choose to remain with them, I can at any time get home to England. . . . He asked me at once, 'Shall you bear being told that I want the cabin to myself—when I want to be alone? If we treat each other this way, I hope we shall suit; if not, probably we should wish each other at the devil.' "

On the same day Darwin reported to Henslow:

My dear Sir:

Gloria in excelsis is the most moderate beginning I can think of. . . . Captain Fitz-Roy is everything that is delightful. If I was to praise half so much as I feel inclined, you would say it was absurd, only once seeing him. . . . You can not imagine anything more pleasant, kind, and open than Captain Fitz-Roy's manners were to me. . . . What changes I have had. Till one to-day

I was building castles in the air about hunting foxes in Shropshire, now llamas in South America.

Not till long afterward did Darwin learn that Fitz-Roy had concealed a strong reason for rejecting him. Fitz-Roy had great faith in the "physiognomy" furor of that period, and judged from the shape of Darwin's nose that he would not have enough nerve for the voyage. But his instinct for estimating men seems to have triumphed quickly over the bookish theories. He showed no hesitation about accepting the young naturalist during the interview of Monday, the fifth. He was only four years older than Darwin—a slight, dark, handsome man, who had been an officer for seven years and had been in command of the *Beagle* three years before on an extensive South American voyage. He was an enthusiastic theorizer about missionary work, weather, geology, and facial contours, but a practical and zealous admiralty surveyor, whose resoluteness in handling sailors or sails was well recognized. All the officers who had served under him on the previous voyage were with him for the second, and two-thirds of the crew had volunteered to go again. No wonder that so popular a commander should charm a collegian. Fitz-Roy had a duke and a marquis for grandfathers; no wonder that Darwin thought he was "strikingly like a gentleman." It is not surprising that Wood had solemnly warned the tory Fitz-Roy that Darwin was a whig.

The talk extended into the evening; Darwin was getting advice as to what to take aboard ship. On Tuesday, the sixth, he wrote home to have Nancy make twelve instead of eight shirts, to have Edward send up the carpet-bag, a pair of lightish walking-shoes, the Spanish books, the microscope (which must have cotton stuffed inside), the compass, etc., etc. Then followed days of shopping. Fitz-Roy was a prodigal in providing equipment; he advised the naturalist to spend sixty pounds sterling for a case of pistols—which drew two exclamation marks from the naturalist's pen. Tuesday was "the first really cheerful day I have spent, and it is all owing to the sort of involuntary confidence I place in my *beau ideal* of a captain."

On Thursday all the shops were closed on account of the coronation of William IV, and Darwin paid a guinea for an excellent seat to see the procession. "It was like only what one sees in picture-books of Eastern processions." Two thoughts were occupying his whiggish mind as he watched the gold and glitter of the uniforms: (1) So little enthusiasm for royalty is shown by the crowd that I doubt whether there will be any coronations in England fifty years hence; (2) hang me if I give sixty pounds sterling for pistols. For the first time in his life (and perhaps the last) he found London very pleasant: "The hurry and bustle are all in unison with my feelings." The bustle was partly mental, for "I work at Astronomy, as I suppose it would astound a sailor if one did not know how to find Latitude and Longitude."

He finally spent fifty pounds sterling for the pistols, and flattered himself that he had thereby saved money— especially when he compared his expenditure with Fitz-Roy's outlay of four hundred pounds sterling for firearms. Edward, the servant who was to accompany him, bargained with the Shrewsbury smith to make extra parts for the guns. On Sunday Darwin took passage with Fitz-Roy in a packet for a flying trip to Plymouth, two hundred miles west of London, to see the *Beagle*. Why he should have made so long a journey with so slight a purpose at such a busy time is a mystery.

Darwin reported at home that the *Beagle* was "a three-masted brig," which was doubtless correct observation, but a term unknown to shipbuilders. The tonnage was rated at two hundred and thirty-five, though the Captain considered that his raising of the deck entitled him to claim two hundred and forty-two. Of course, no seaman would condescend to give the dimensions of his craft for the sake of us land-lubbers. The best guess I can make, after consulting specifications of similar craft, is that she was not more than a hundred feet long and thirty wide. She drew thirteen feet aft when normally loaded.

All the equipment is described with loving detail. "She looks most beautiful, even a landsman must admire her," Darwin assured Henslow. "*We* all think her the most perfect vessel ever turned out of a dock-yard. One thing is certain, no vessel has been fitted out so expensively, and with so much care. Everything that can be made so is of mahogany, and nothing can exceed the neatness and beauty of all the accommodations." Fitz-Roy's official inventory informs us that there were lightning-conductors on all masts, the bowsprit, and the flying jib-boom. Upon each quarter hung a whaleboat twenty-five feet long. In addition a stout dinghy was carried astern. Seven brass guns were mounted on deck: one on the forecastle, two before the chestree, and four abaft the mainmast; five of these were six-pounders and two were nine-pounders.

The most precious part of the equipment was a set of twenty-two chronometers, with which the Captain was to compute the longitudes all round the world. No such battery of time-pieces had ever before been brought to bear on the comparison of Greenwich time with other times on the earth's surface—for deducing the longitude. The work with time and soundings was the chief mission of the *Beagle;* collecting of specimens by a naturalist was only a supplementary job.

On Saturday, September 19, Darwin was back in London, exulting in his "grand and fortunate opportunity," but realizing, since he had been aboard the *Beagle*, that "leaving for so very long a time so many people whom I dearly love, is oftentimes a feeling so painful that it requires all my resolution to overcome it." But he has "moments of glorious enthusiasm" and observes: "If I live to see years in after life, how grand must such recollections be!" The original sailing-date had been September 10. This had been postponed, when Darwin first met Fitz-Roy, to October 10. Now, on his return from Plymouth, the date was October 20. Darwin made a trip, via Cambridge, to Shrewsbury to say the hard farewells, returning to London early in October.

On the 17th Darwin, still busy with shopping for supplies, learned that the sailing-date was November 4. He shipped his goods to Plymouth by packet and went himself by coach. "What a glorious day the 4th of November will be to me! My second life will then commence, and it shall be as a birthday for the rest of my life."

On October 24 he went into lodgings in Plymouth, waiting for the birthday. But it was postponed. On November 15 the impatient naturalist wrote to Henslow: "We positively sail the last day of this month." On December 3, however, he was still ashore, writing another good-by to Henslow on a Saturday night: "To-night I am going to sleep on board. On Monday we most certainly sail. If you were to hear the various exclamations of the officers, you would suppose we had scarcely had a week's notice. . . . The number of things to be done is infinite. I look forward even to sea-sickness with something like satisfaction, anything must be better than this state of anxiety. . . . If you will send me a letter on the first Tuesday (when the packet sails) in February, directed to Monte Video, it will give me very great pleasure."

Twice during December the *Beagle* got under way, only to be beaten back into the harbor by a heavy gale. "These two months at Plymouth were the most miserable which I ever spent. I was out of spirits at leaving all my family and friends for so long a time. I was also troubled with palpitation and pain about the heart, and . . . was convinced that I had heart-disease. I did not consult the doctor, as I fully expected to hear the verdict that I was not fit for the voyage, and I was resolved to go at all hazards."

At last the gale died down to a dead calm. "At daylight on the 27th we warped from our sheltered retreat in Barn-pool," says Captain Fitz-Roy. "A light cat's-paw rippled the water, we made all sail, the breeze increased, and at noon our little vessel was outside the breakwater, with a fresh easterly wind."

Darwin was off for Teneriffe, one of seventy-four men crowded into a hundred-foot vessel. There were seven officers, five under-officers, two surgeons, and a purser; a squad of ten marines; thirty-four seamen, six boys, and two servants; an artist and an instrument-maker; a missionary and three Fuegians that Fitz-Roy was returning to their home; Charles Darwin, naturalist.

Every hour there was a favorable wind. At the end of ten days the *Beagle* was sixteen hundred miles southwest of Plymouth.

CHAPTER IV

A Year with Fitz-Roy and Lyell: 1832

"In the Bay of Biscay," Darwin wrote to his father, "there was a long and continuous swell, and the misery I endured from sea-sickness is far beyond what I ever guessed at. . . . Nobody who has only been to sea for twenty-four hours has a right to say that sea-sickness is even uncomfortable. The real misery only begins when you are so exhausted that a little exertion makes a feeling of faintness come on. I found that nothing but lying in my hammock did me any good. . . . On the 4th of January we were not many miles from Madeira. . . . I was much too sick even to get up to see the distant outline. . . . We were becalmed a day between Teneriffe and the Grand Canary, and here I first experienced any enjoyment."

He never could overcome the tendency to sea-sickness. "If there is any sea up," he wrote six months later, "I am either sick or contrive to read some voyage or travels." The Master of the *Beagle*, Mr. Usborne, bears witness: "Mr. Darwin was a dreadful sufferer from sea-sickness, and at times when I have been officer of the watch, and reduced the sails, making the ship more easy, and thus relieving him, I have been pronounced by him to be a 'good officer,' and he would resume his microscopic observations in the poop cabin."

There was something worse than sea-sickness in store for Darwin. Captain Fitz-Roy's orders were to stay four days at the Madeiras or the Canaries to rate his chronometers, but a gale made the anchorage unsafe in the roads at the Madeiras, and the course was laid for the Canaries. On the morning of January 6, only ten days out from Plymouth, the peak of Teneriffe was seen, snow-covered and shining in the tropical sun. "At noon," says Fitz-Roy's account, "we approached the sun-burned town of Santa Cruz. . . . Our anchor had just touched ground, when a boat from the Health Office approached nearly alongside, conveying the British vice-consul and some quarantine officers, who told us that it would be impossible to grant permission for any person to land. [They had heard reports of cholera in England.] We weighed without further loss of time and made sail for the Cape Verde Islands. This was a great disappointment to Mr. Darwin, who had cherished a hope of visiting the Peak. To see it—to anchor and be on the point of landing, yet be obliged to turn away without the slightest prospect of beholding Teneriffe again—was indeed to him a real calamity. During the whole of the 7th the Peak was visible; but on the following day no land was in sight, and we made rapid progress. A very long swell from the northwest"—and so the requiem of a young man's dearest hope was sung.

But sickness abated and disappointment faded. "From Teneriffe to Santiago the voyage was extremely pleasant," Darwin could report at home. "I had a net astern which caught great numbers of curious animals and fully occupied my time in my cabin."

I like to imagine—what is quite probable—that during these cheerful and busy days he spent some hours with Volume I of Lyell's *Principles of Geology,* the most remarkable book ever written on this subject, the book that influenced him more than any other. I can believe that he got as much excitement out of it as out of climbing Teneriffe. For he knew as he read it that his eyes were being taught how to see in South America. His mind was being stirred to marvel about the meanings of what the eyes saw. The world was displayed before him with a new wonder, as something different from what Sedgwick considered it. Throughout the rest of his life he bore witness to the power of Lyell's *Principles of Geology*. He dedicated the *Journal* of the voyage to Lyell, "as an acknowledgment that the chief part of whatever scientific merit this *Journal* and the other works of the author may possess has been derived from studying the well-known and admirable *Principles of Geology*."

The cabin in which he read was not quite high enough to permit his standing up straight. It was called the "drawing cabin" because its principal furniture, nearly filling the floor space, was a table on which a large sheet of paper could be spread out for drawing charts. Darwin called it "next best to the Captain's and remarkably light." He shared it with an officer, their two hammocks being slung over the table. In one sense he shared the Captain's cabin, as originally promised, for he "had the run of it" and ate his meals there; but this end of the chart-room was fitted up as his own home. For his clothes and belongings he had a set of narrow drawers in one corner, reaching from floor to ceiling. The use of even this small amount of space for drawers disturbed the sleeping arrangements, because it did not leave enough width to stretch his hammock. Whenever he wanted to sleep he had to take out the top drawer and fasten the end of the hammock in the space. If he wished to read when the sea was rough, he would remove the drawer and hook up his swinging bed. For stowing his specimens he had a very small cabin under the forecastle.

While he lay there, midway between floor and ceiling,

over the end of a table in a creaking cabin, he turned the leaves of Volume I. Captain Fitz-Roy recorded his observations on the long swell from the northwest and dilated on the excellence of a certain reel for deep-sea soundings. He never suspected that the tall, sea-sick naturalist, stretched below deck to read about fossils, was achieving anything in particular. What prophet in all the world could have foreseen that anything significant was happening under the deck of a hundred-foot brig on the Atlantic Ocean? A seer who could have observed in a magic glass all the intellectual doings of the race in January, 1832, would surely have overlooked Charles Darwin. Tennyson was completing his *Poems* (the volume of 1832), "one of the most astounding revelations of finished genius ever produced by a young man." Wordsworth's fame was mounting now, after the long years of ridicule. Schopenhauer was meditating a translation that should carry the profound gospel of Kant to English readers. Carlyle was trying to market *Sartor Resartus*. John Stuart Mill, long depressed by mistrust of all study of society, was roused to an enthusiasm for humanity in January, 1832, and felt confident that he could reach scientifically reliable results in his moral and social reasonings. The intellectual world was teaming with great poetry and metaphysic and logic.

Who could have fancied that any momentous action of a mental sort was being carried out within the planks of the *Beagle* as she dug her bluff bows into the water at six knots an hour, bound on a surveying voyage? Yet a germ-cell of thought was there fertilized. It was very small, quite unrecognized by the naturalist himself, not to become a sizable embryo for many years. That speck of a vessel pitching in the midst of an ocean bore as part of her cargo a peculiar brain, a mechanism that was destined to set the whole thought of the world throbbing to different issues in new ways.

While I now give a brief description of this Volume I of Lyell's I am not dwelling on mere geology, but am showing the sword of an enemy of Goliath. It was sharp and heavy and wrought with great cunning, so that the deepest wounds it made were hardly perceived until the life-blood had gushed out of the victim. What Lyell was plotting when he wrote his book he revealed to his sister in January, 1829: "Longman has paid down five hundred guineas to Mr. Ure of Dublin for a popular work on Geology just coming out. It is to prove the Hebrew cosmogony, and that we all ought to be burnt in Smithfield. So much the better. I have got a rod for the fanatics, from a quarter where they expect it not. *The Pope instituted lectures on the Mosaic cosmogony to set free astronomy and geology.* . . . It is very encouraging to perceive by my letters how much more every year the subject is taking hold of the public mind." A few other quotations from Lyell's correspondence of this and the next year will show what manner of warrior he was.

Feb., 1829. The new opinions must bring about an amazing overthrow in the systems which we were carefully taught ten years ago.

April, 1829. Conybeare admits three deluges before the Noachian! and Buckland adds God knows how many catastrophes besides, so we have driven them out of the Mosaic record fairly.

Oct., 1829. Sedgwick throws over all the diluvian hypothesis; is vexed he ever lost time about such a complete humbug.

Feb., 1830. It would be good policy to be more courteous. . . . I enjoy the work much, as the excitement is great.

In April, 1830, he is in high spirits because of a friend's assurance that his book would create a sensation. In May he wrote: "I have been so cautious that two friends tell me I shall *only* offend the ultras."

June, 1830 (to Scrope, who was reading proof-sheets and preparing to review the sensational new book). The bishops see the mischief and scandal brought on them by Mosaic systems. . . . If we don't irritate, we shall carry all with us. Don't triumph over them, but compliment the liberality and candor of the present age. . . . If I have said more than some will like, yet I give you my word that full *half* of my history and comments was cut out, and even many facts; because either I, or Stokes, or Broderip, felt that it was anticipating twenty or thirty years the march of honest feeling to declare it undisguisedly. Nor did I dare come down to modern offenders.

These were not the chance remarks of a young man who was conceited or loved a fight. Lyell's primary instinct was caution, and he never relished the "shindies," as he called them, in which Huxley engaged. He did not care for flourishes and battle-cries. His method was to thrust a sword quite through an antagonist, with such a smooth and courteous stroke that the antagonist did not know he had been injured. His purpose was unrelenting and had been early formed. Before he planned his book he had said to a fellow geologist, speaking of an article he had written for the *Quarterly Review:* "Some of my friends think I have carried the strong works of the enemy by storm. . . . If you can send me comments on Buckland, *I will use them delicately.*" Buckland, the Oxford professor of geology, was the arch-enemy; Lyell called him and his supporters "Buckland and Co." His reason for fighting Buckland was the same that made Darwin wonder at Sedgwick: "At this very place, which Buckland has been at, without seeing, or choosing to see, *so unwelcome a fact,* we have discovered a formation which would

furnish an answer to the very difficulty which Sedgwick
when at Kinnordy put to me." The issue with the
Philistines he phrased thus when speaking of the most
famous French geologist, Elie de Beaumont: "I expect
to come into collision with his doctrines, for he seems to
be embarked on the plan of *speculating* on ancient times.
Think of his saying that *the Deluge* may have been
caused by the sudden rise of South America!" Lyell
gathered in France that the Institute considered Buckland "to be trading in humbug." It was against humbug and speculation and fear of facts that Lyell armed
himself. He had no misgivings about the outcome:
"We can without fear measure our strength against
most of those in our own land," he remarked eighteen
months before his first volume was off the press.

He stood his ground against the foe and enjoyed the
battle, but always maintained pleasant relations socially.
He worked delicately. He visited Buckland's "glorious
house" at Oxford, traded butterflies diligently with Mrs.
Buckland, and gratefully acknowledged "the most kind
service" that Buckland did in preparing him for a geological trip in Sicily. He freely admitted, when his best-
loved geological companion, Murchison, weakened in
torrid August days, that Sedgwick would not have
flinched and delayed.

No heat or rain or bad food or dismal lodgings could
temper the fierceness with which Lyell geologized. At
the age of eighteen his imagination was deeply stirred by
a geological textbook; at nineteen he was extracting from
the impenetrable Dr. Arnold information about fossils,
was "considering the geological wonders of Yarmouth,"
and journeyed to see the caves of the volcanic island of
Staffa; at twenty he tramped in the Alps for six weeks;
at twenty-five he was visiting and conferring with the
foremost geologists of France and Holland; at twenty-

six he could see into and all around the humbug which the great Professor Buckland still cherished; at twenty-eight he was a Fellow of the Royal Society; at thirty-one he was investigating southern France, Italy, and Sicily; when he was thirty-two (June, 1830) he read the last proofs of his Volume I and hastened to investigate the Pyrenees before he had seen a bound copy.

Henslow heard of the new book and in 1831 advised Darwin to stow it in his sea-chest. "Read it by all means," he urged, "for it is very interesting, but do not pay any attention to it except in regard to facts, for it is altogether wild as far as theory goes."* While Darwin was reading this wild book on the high seas the second volume was issued in London, and Henslow sent a copy to Montevideo.

The volume that Darwin read was an argument in favor of one simple and astounding theory. "My work," said Lyell when he was preparing it, "will not pretend to give even an abstract of all that is known in geology, but it will endeavor to establish the principle of reasoning in the science." He was concerned with only one principle, which he stated thus: "That no causes whatever have from the earliest time to which we can look back, to the present, ever acted, but those *now* acting; and that they never acted with different degrees of energy from that which they *now* exert." Since Lyell wrote those words a hundred years have passed, and to-day his statement is the basis of the science; yet only geologists visualize the truth of it. Educated people in general still take it for granted that in the good old days of its youth this globe was a fearsomely active place, where volcanic cataclysms rent the frame of things, heaving up mountains with prodigious suddenness, en-

---

*John W. Judd heard this precious anecdote from Darwin's own lips in 1880 and records it on page 72 of *The Coming of Evolution.*

gulfing continents with furious rapidity. If a poll could be taken of all the college graduates in the country who have not read a chapter on geology, I doubt whether one per cent would show any knowledge of Lyell's thesis. Practically all of them would assume, as an axiom, that volcanos and earthquakes *used to* act with very much greater violence than now. Lyell's theory is opposed to the very constitution of the human mind: we always romanticize the past, always feel sure that once upon a time there were giants, acting with gigantic forces unknown in the humdrum present.

In 1832 most geologists still reasoned in the romantic vein. Led by Sedgwick and Buckland, they ridiculed young Lyell at the meetings of the Geological Society. All the cohorts of Philistia considered Lyell rash and unphilosophical—even irreligious. Yet Darwin discovered nothing to offend him—and he believed in the strict and literal truth of every word in the Bible. He found Lyell quoting with approval one of the arguments of the theological Paley. In all the dignity and lucidity and preciseness of Lyell's pages there was nothing to offend a religious sense.

In Volume I there were twenty-six chapters. The chapter that most excited Darwin must have been IX: "Theory of the progressive development of organic life considered." This has a different subject-matter and a different tone from any other; its twenty-three pages stand out in high relief amidst all the rest of the book. Its argument is a most delicate and difficult one, for it touches deep prejudices. All the other chapters argue for unchanging uniformity of natural law. Chapter IX admits that the uniformity of nature was broken by the creation of man, but contends that this one case is no proof of other irregularities in the history of living beings: "In reasoning on the state of the globe imme-

diately before our species was called into existence, we
may assume that all the present causes were in operation, *with the exception of man.*" The main argument
is against the theory—then commonly held by
geologists—that there has been a series of wholesome
and progressive creations of plants and animals. Lyell
began his chapter with a quotation from Sir Humphry
Davy, which outlined this common theory of progressive
development: "In the deepest strata the remains of life
are rare; shells and vegetable remains are found in the
next order; the bones of fishes and reptiles exist in the
following class; the remains of birds in the next order;
those of quadrupeds in a still more recent class." Lyell
admits that the remains of human beings are always extremely recent; he is glad to admit it; for his underlying
purpose is to prove that man is a different sort of creature from all other animals. As for all those other animals, he asserts that there was uniformity among them
throughout the ages, that there was no breach in the regularity and sameness of life during all the geologic eras.
He could find no evidence that the total population of the
earliest geological period was a much different set of plants
and animals from the total population that now surrounds
us. He devotes a pair of vivid and sarcastic pages to
showing the extreme unlikelihood that any remains of a
mammal could have been preserved, or should now happen to be discovered, after the long æons of time since
the most ancient strata of rock were formed; he argues
that this merely negative evidence proves nothing. As
for the next younger strata, the "secondary," he says
that in them have been discovered the fossils of two
species of warm-blooded quadrupeds, and concludes:
"The occurrence of one individual of the higher classes
of mammalia in these ancient strata is as fatal to the
theory of successive development as if several hundreds

had been discovered.'' He gives some illustrations of the worthlessness of the negative evidence from the oldest strata: (1) In the recent Subappenine hills, where twelve hundred species of shells have been found, the remains of mammals are extremely scanty, and even these are disputed; (2) In the London clay there are no mammals, whereas in a system of rocks known to be older than this clay there *are* mammals. ''Nature,'' he ironically comments, ''has made a retrograde movement.'' And he concludes with severity: ''There is no foundation for the popular theory of the successive development of the animal and vegetable world.'' He is fond of calling it a ''popular'' theory, and so damning it as unscientific.

The cautious but confident reasoning must have appealed to Darwin. It not only showed that the Lamarckian views were nonsense, but put a quietus on all speculation about one species developing from another.

I should like to know how he felt about Lyell's special creation of man. It was certainly a comforting doctrine. It taught that man did not have a brutish ancestry, that he was not—as Buffon and Erasmus Darwin and Lamarck thought likely—''a link in a progressive chain.'' The quality that Lyell most prized in men was being ''gentlemanlike''; the adjective recurs in his correspondence with monotonous regularity. He desired, with a strong subconscious emotion which he would have ridiculed as a scientist, that the species to which he belonged should be gentlemanlike. I wonder if Darwin thought of this motive.

I wish we could know whether Darwin followed out in his mind the implication of the whole chapter, which is nowhere put into words and is hinted at in only one line. Lyell is speaking of the introduction of the human race to the earth, and says that it raises no presumption what-

ever "that each former exertion of creative power," etc.
This can only mean that every species was separately
and suddenly *created*. I venture that Darwin pondered
the sentence, wished Lyell had discussed the subject, and
was sorry that he gave no promise of saying anything
about it in Volume II. Two pages are devoted to Buffon's geological ideas, but nothing is said of his notion
of species. Lamarck is not mentioned.

I suspect that Darwin dwelt upon and stored in his
mind another sentence which tantalizingly unveiled the
Lamarckian views and was not again referred to. It
spoke of the changes that can be induced in animals by
domestication: "We can only effect such surprising
alterations by assisting the development of certain instincts, or by availing ourselves of the mysterious law of
their organization, by which individual peculiarities are
transmissible from one generation to another."

We shall never know the details of when and how
Lyell influenced Darwin, but we do know what he testified about his reading on the voyage: "Everything
about which I thought or read was made to bear directly
on what I had seen or was likely to see, and this habit
of mind was continued during the five years of the voyage." There is no harm in fancying that by the 15th of
January Darwin had reached the end of Volume I and
was then called on deck by the news that the Cape Verde
Islands had been sighted. The next day he stretched his
legs in Port Praya and felt that "the scene is one of
great interest—if, indeed, a person fresh from the sea,
and who has just walked, for the first time, in a grove
of cocoa-nut trees, can be a judge of anything but his
own happiness." He was aware that his observation
might be of no scientific value. According to Captain
Fitz-Roy, who had to remain in the town and check his
chronometers, the country is "desolate and hilly, sun-

burned and stony, with but few trees even in the valleys."

The purser made up a party which hired horses and rode to several parts of the island. He reports that "the beauty of the interior country exceeds anything I had seen either in Brazil or in the West Indies." Of course Mr. Darwin was in the party, and later wrote six pages of good description for those who care to know about the flora and fauna and geology of the island of Santiago. "Santiago showed me clearly the wonderful superiority of Lyell's manner of treating geology, compared with that of any other author whose works I had with me or ever afterwards read." In choosing what to record for his *Journal* he had an unfailing eye for the picturesque or striking or comical or human points of interest. Even a cuttlefish is a fellow-being to him: "I was much amused by the various arts to escape detection used by one individual, which seemed fully aware that I was watching it. Remaining for a time motionless, it would then stealthily advance an inch or two, like a cat after a mouse. . . . I was more than once saluted by a jet of water. . . . And it appeared to me that it could certainly take good aim by directing the tube on the under side of its body."

The stay at Santiago was twenty-three days. On February 8 the instruments were taken aboard and sails hoisted.

If you lay a ruler on a map of the world from Plymouth to the eastern tip of South America, the straight southwest line will mark nearly the course of the *Beagle*. From Plymouth to the Canaries is sixteen hundred miles; from the Canaries to the nearest point of South America is nearly three thousand more. From this point (Pernambuco) to Montevideo on the Plata River is twenty-four hundred more miles—a total of seven thousand miles from Plymouth to the scene of the first surveying operations.

The young geologist was excited on the morning of February 16 by the sight of St. Paul's Rocks; for he knew that there was in the oceans of the world only one other example of a small, solitary island, rising abruptly from deep water, which was not formed of lava or coral. I can not expect my readers to sympathize with his excitement about so technical a matter, but will call it to their attention. The subject of solitary little islands is going to be the scene of a very pretty engagement in the war with Goliath—a flank movement on the "God knows how many catastrophes" that were invoked by Buckland and Co. We need only note at present that "the highest point of St. Paul's Rocks is not more than fifty feet above the level of the sea and the entire circumference is under three-quarters of a mile." The *Beagle* hove to while Mr. Darwin tapped a while with his hammer—not only at the rocks, but at the unfrightened birds, the boobies and noddies. Darwin merely says in his *Journal* that he "could" have killed birds with his hammer, but the men who rowed him ashore tell a different story: "One of the men tried to borrow the hammer; 'No, no, you'll break the handle,' answered the naturalist; but hardly had he said so when away went the hammer with all the force of his own right arm." In a private letter Darwin confessed this indictment was a true bill. He afterward said to the Captain that till then he had never believed the stories of men knocking down birds with sticks. He was beginning to learn incredible facts. He gathered a quite incredible substance, some guano that had been transformed by the action of water into material so hard that it would scratch plate glass. "I have shown specimens of this to several geologists," Darwin remarked when he prepared his *Journal* for publication, "and they all thought that they were of volcanic or igneous origin." There is no predicting what such a pair of eyes will see during four years in South America.

The next day the *Beagle* crossed the equator. Custom required that all who were crossing for the first time should, without respect to social position, submit to the proper rites, and Darwin was one of the few novices aboard. A sailor impersonated Neptune; his band seized the naturalist, lathered his face with paint and tar, shaved him with a saw, and tossed him in a sail full of water.

On the 20th Mr. Darwin was allowed to examine the thousand-foot pinnacle of the island of Fernando Noronha, two hundred and twenty-five miles from the coast. With great difficulty some of the chronometers were taken through the high surf, to get a comparison of rates, and the naturalist was permitted to land with them. On the 29th he was ashore, five hundred miles south of Pernambuco. "The day has past delightfully. Delight itself, however, is a weak term to express the feelings of a naturalist who, for the first time, has wandered by himself in a Brazilian forest. The elegance of the grasses, the novelty of the parasitical plants, the beauty of the flowers, the glossy green of the foliage, but above all the general luxuriance of the vegetation, filled me with admiration. A most paradoxical mixture of sound and silence pervades the shady parts of the wood."

He describes the mystery of the two-thousand-mile stretch of granite along the Brazilian coast and finds that "it gives rise to many curious reflections." He tells about a curious flabby fish which has frequently been found, floating alive and distended, in the stomach of a shark, and which has been known to eat its way out through the sides of the monster. "Who would ever have imagined that a little soft fish could have destroyed the great and savage shark?'' Darwin has entered upon a long vista of sights in the struggle for existence that are quite beyond the invention of the human mind.

On March 18 the *Beagle* left Bahia, headed south, to take soundings in the Abrolhos islets, which were reached in ten days. On April 3, when seventy-five miles east of Rio de Janeiro, they passed close by the cove where two British frigates were recovering the treasure from the sunken *Thetis,* on which Fitz-Roy had once been a lieutenant. Sixteen months before, in foggy weather, the *Thetis* had driven right on to a cliff, the ends of her yards striking fire from the rock; her three masts had gone down, strewing the deck with killed and wounded men. Darwin got an object-lesson in the purpose of all the sounding and timing done by the *Beagle.* On April 4, in the harbor of Rio, they found that marines were being landed from the British squadron to quell a mutiny of some Brazilian troops.

Fitz-Roy found that his calculation of the longitude of Rio was four miles apart from the standard set by a French expedition; and the matter was so important that he decided to exceed his instructions by returning to Bahia for a check-up. It was two months before the *Beagle* got back to Rio. On the trip three men died of a fever.

Mr. Darwin, meanwhile, fell in with an Englishman who was going to ride horseback to his estate a hundred and fifty miles north of Rio and invited the naturalist to go along, as one of a party of seven. ''We entered a forest, which in the grandeur of all its parts could not be exceeded'' sets the tone of his narrative of the wonders and oddities revealed to him during the two-week excursion. He tells of the gorgeous butterflies, the miserable food, the marvelously low prices, the vampire bats that distressed the horses, the poisonous juice of a plant that furnishes the staple food of the region, the bells and cannon that announce the arrival of a stranger, the slaves who begin the day's work by singing a hymn. The thought of slavery had always been abhorrent to him. Now he records his emotion when a slave thought Darwin's gesticulation was going to be a blow: "I shall never forget my feelings of surprise, disgust, and shame at seeing a great powerful man afraid even to ward off a blow directed, as he thought, at his face."

During the rest of his sojourn at Rio (ten weeks) he lived in a cottage on the beach of Botafogo, three miles south of the city, where the precipices of the Corcovado rose from the tropical forest behind him, and Sugar Loaf Mountain stood across the bay in front. "It was impossible to wish for anything more delightful. In England any person fond of natural history enjoys in his walks a great advantage; but in these fertile climates, teeming with life, the attractions are so numerous that he is scarcely able to walk at all."

His guide to the forest was an old Portuguese priest. "My companion had shot two large bearded monkeys. These animals have prehensile tails, the extremity of which, even after death, can support the weight of the whole body. One of them thus remained fast to a branch, and it was necessary to cut down a large tree to procure it. Down came tree and monkey with an awful crash. . . . On another occasion the padre gave me a fine specimen of the Yagouaroundi cat." The twelve pages of Darwin's *Journal* which describe this residence at Botafogo tell of the climate and atmosphere, of animalcules, of tree-toads; but most of the space is occupied with the insects that swarmed in such prodigious numbers. He fed raw meat to glow-worms. "I invariably observed that every now and then the extremity of the tail was applied to the mouth, and a drop of fluid exuded on the meat, which was then in the act of being consumed. The tail, notwithstanding so much practice, does not seem to be able to find its way to the mouth.''

A philosophical world had never before been curious about a pulpy tail which is both a sucker and a reservoir for a sort of saliva; perhaps an intellectual world to-day can feel no interest in so lowly a topic. I will not try to elevate it by dwelling on it, but will only suggest the nature of the information that Darwin was gathering from glow-worms. He was not merely intent on a digestive process; he was noticing one more example of the infinite variety of *adaptations* by which animals and plants live; he was learning to become, in imagination, this tail or that tendril; he was learning, more than any one else in the world, to see that life is a set of *adaptations* to an environment.

Every zoologist had always known about click-beetles, which if placed on their backs can spring into the air and land on their feet. Every zoologist had paid tribute to the muscular power of these acrobats—and let it go at that. Darwin actually screwed his eyes down on the click-beetles of Brazil, which flew about by night as fire-flies, and considered the mechanism of their operation. His slight and diffident report is this: ''In the descriptions which I have read, sufficient stress does not appear to have been laid on *the elasticity of the spine.*'' Perhaps the world is no better off because it now knows about the spring in a beetle's back; but the thinking of a whole world may be improved by a brain that sympathetically becomes a beetle and detects how its feats are performed. An action may be the pettiest thing in nature; the explanation of the action may cast beams of knowledge far into higher realms.

Darwin describes a butterfly: "This is the only butterfly which I have ever seen that uses its legs for running. . . . A far more singular fact is the power which this specimen possesses of making a noise. I distinctly heard a clicking noise, similar to that produced by a toothed wheel passing under a spring catch. The noise could be distinguished at about twenty yards' distance; I am certain there is no error in the observation." There is no limit to the knowledge that may come from the work of a man who is certain that he has made *no error in observation.*

Darwin gathered a wealth of knowledge about the struggle for existence among plants and animals, of which he gives a few glimpses. He tells of a swarm of ants that drove all the other insects of a region before them. When he put a stone in the path of one file of ants, he noticed that they did not go around it as they would have done if the stone had been there previously; they conceived that they had been attacked, and "the lion-hearted little warriors scorned the idea of yielding."

He was appalled at the host of species that abounded in Brazil. "The number of minute beetles is exceedingly great. It is sufficient to disturb the composure of an entomologist's mind, to look forward to the future dimensions of a complete catalogue. . . . The variety of species among the jumping spiders appears almost infinite." This note of terror at the rising tide of species gives the key for the perplexity that increased among all classifiers during the next three decades and that threatened to make zoology an unscientific hodge-podge of mystery.

The record in his *Journal* was filled with small matters, probably because he felt more secure in his knowledge of them. But his mind was continually occupied with the great problems of geology. He was diffident about recording his amateur guesses; he was training himself. He expressed his preference thus in a letter to his cousin and closest friend, W. D. Fox: "I think I have already taken several new genera of spiders. But geology carries the day: it is like the pleasure of gambling. Speculating, on first arriving, what the rocks may be, I often mentally cry out 'three to one tertiary against primitive'; but the latter have hitherto won all the bets." He realized that his speculations were gambling then, but he was teaching himself by Lyell's method to read rocks with assurance later.

On the 3d of June the *Beagle* returned, and the Captain found, to his great satisfaction, that his reckoning of the longitude of Rio had been correct. There were a few days of leisure, in which boat-races were held between picked crews from the vessels of the British squadron in the harbor. It is curious that neither the emulous Captain nor the gambling naturalist recorded the showing made by the *Beagle's* crew. "On the 5th of July," says the Captain's narrative, "we sailed from Rio de Janeiro, honoured by a salute, not of guns, but of hearty cheers, from H. M. S. *Warspite*. . . . Though not about to encounter a foe, our lonely vessel was going to undertake a task laborious, and often dangerous, to the zealous execution of which the encouragement of our brother-seamen was no trifling inducement."

Geographical details are tiresome; there is no reason why we need lumber our minds with names and distances of the east coast of South America. But a reader who is to spend the next two years with Darwin will be better pleased if he now looks for a minute at the sketch-map facing page 110 and fixes in his mind two places.

1. Montevideo is the port most often mentioned in the account of the *Beagle's* comings and goings. It lies thirteen hundred miles southwest of Rio on the north

shore of the very broad estuary known as the River
Plata. It is one hundred and fifty miles east of Buenos
Ayres, and seventy-five miles west of the port of Maldonado, where Darwin once spent ten weeks. During the
latter half of 1832 the *Beagle* was surveying and sounding along the seven-hundred-mile stretch of coast south
of Montevideo.

2. Tierra del Fuego lies fifteen hundred miles south
of Montevideo; it is a broken and intricate set of islands
that form the southern end of South America; at its
southeastern tip is the little island that is distinguished
by the name of Cape Horn. East of it, three hundred
miles away, are the Falkland Islands.

The *Beagle* never saw Rio again after being
cheered out of its harbor on July 5, 1832. On the 22d
she was in the Plata estuary, encountering a heavy
thunder storm; and Fitz-Roy told Darwin of how he had
brought the *Beagle* through a fierce gale from the pampas, a "pampero," two and a half years before at this
very point. Spars had been shattered, sails slit to ribbons, and two seamen carried overboard and lost; fourteen English merchantmen lay high and dry upon the
shore next day.

Beating up the Plata took a long while. Part of this
time Darwin occupied with writing a letter to Henslow
about shipping specimens, which Henslow had agreed
to receive and take care of.

I did not send off the specimens from Rio Janeiro, as
I grudged the time it would take to pack them up. They
are now ready to be sent off and most probably go by
this packet. . . . When I left England I was not fully
aware how essential a kindness you offered me when
you undertook to receive my boxes. I do not know what I
should do without such headquarters. . . .The box contains a good many geological specimens; . . . I shall

be very glad of some mineralogical information, especially on any numbers between one and two hundred and fifty-four which include Santiago rocks. By my catalogue I shall know which you may refer to. . . . My collection from the Abrolhos is interesting, as I suspect it nearly contains the whole flowering vegetation—and indeed from extreme sterility the same may almost be said of Santiago. I have sent home four bottles with animals in spirits, I have three more, but would not send them till I had a fourth. . . . I made an enormous collection of spiders at Rio, also a good many small beetles in pill-boxes. . . . The false relation the *Planaria* bear to snails is the most extraordinary thing of the kind I have ever seen. In the same genus (or more truly family) some of the marine species possess an organization so marvelous that I can scarcely credit my eyesight. . . . I hope you will send me your criticisms about my collection; and it will be my endeavor that nothing you say shall be lost on me.

On August 3 the *Beagle* was at anchor off Montevideo. Here the wildness of the elements that Darwin had seen on the Plata was accented by the wild conditions of government on shore. Fitz-Roy was so incensed by the misconduct of a naval officer at Buenos Ayres that he would not keep his anchors down an hour, but hastened back to report the insult to the commander of the frigate *Druid* at Montevideo. The *Druid*, with stern British promptness, at once proceeded to Buenos Ayres, to uphold British dignity. "Scarcely had the *Druid* disappeared beneath the horizon," says Fitz-Roy, "when the chief of the Montevideo police and the captain of the port came on board the *Beagle* to request assistance in preserving order in the town, and in preventing the aggression of some mutinous negro soldiers. . . . I landed fifty well-armed men, and thus held the mutineers in check until more troops were brought in from the neighboring country."

On August 15 Darwin dated and concluded his letter to Henslow:

The box will go by the *Emulous*. . . . Owing to bad weather and continual fighting on shore, we have scarcely ever been able to walk in the country. But today I have been out and returned like Noah's Ark with animals of all sorts.

A week later the *Beagle* sailed south, entering upon "the slow and monotonous occupation of examining the shore" to the south of Montevideo. For some mysterious reason Darwin tells nothing whatever about his movements during this period, though the Captain, in his *Narrative*, several times implies that of course Mr. Darwin will describe the geology or fauna of this or that place.* Mr. Darwin, however, tells nothing except about his collecting near Maldonado nine months later.

The *Beagle* worked along the low, sandy coast below Cape San Antonio, recording the very irregular shoals, to the bold promontory of Cape Corrientes, and beyond this for three hundred miles to the first semblance of a port south of the Plata, Port Belgrano, near the head of the Bahia Blanca.

It was probably during this monotonous period that Darwin and Fitz-Roy quarreled. Darwin had reported to his father that "the Captain continues steadily very kind and does everything in his power to assist me"; Darwin always paid tribute to the energy and skill and kindness of the Captain. But there was a violent dif-

---

*The official report of the voyage of the *Beagle* appeared in four volumes: volumes I, II, and the Supplement to II were by Fitz-Roy; volume III, by Darwin was called *Journal and Remarks*, and was reprinted in Darwin's collected works as *Journal of Researches into the Natural History and Geology of the countries visited during the Voyage of H. M. S. Beagle Round the World*. Readers of the *Journal* should notice that its chapters are arrang'd geographically rather than chronologically—for example, page 204 tells of an earlier time than page 63.

ference of opinion between them, which Darwin explained to Henslow: "I thank my better fortune the Captain has not made me a renegade to Whig principles. I would not be a Tory, if it was merely on account of their cold hearts about that scandal to Christian nations—Slavery. I am very good friends with all the officers." Darwin's whiggish hatred of slavery was the cause of the quarrel. I lift this description of it from the *Autobiography*, not as a piece of scandal, but as the truest proof that Fitz-Roy's character was noble and that Darwin's personality was enjoyed by all the officers.

Fitz-Roy's temper was a most unfortunate one. . . . He was very kind to me, but was a man very difficult to live with on the intimate terms which necessarily followed from our messing by ourselves in the same cabin. We had several quarrels: for instance, early in the voyage, at Bahia, in Brazil, he defended and praised slavery, which I abominated, and told me that he had just visited a great slave-owner, who had called up many of his slaves and asked them whether they were happy, and whether they wished to be free, and all answered "No." I then asked him, perhaps with a sneer, whether he thought that the answer of slaves in the presence of their master was worth anything? This made him excessively angry, and he said that as I doubted his word we could not live any longer together. I thought that I should have been compelled to leave the ship; but as soon as the news spread, which it did quickly, as the captain sent for the first lieutenant to assuage his anger by abusing me, I was deeply gratified by receiving an invitation from all the gun-room officers to mess with them. But after a few hours Fitz-Roy showed his usual magnanimity by sending an officer to me with an apology and a request that I would continue to live with him. His character was in several respects one of the most noble I have ever known.

Fitz-Roy makes several references to the naturalist in this part of his narrative, most of them undated.

Several kinds of fish were caught at our various anchorages and carefully noticed by Mr. Darwin.

September 7. Messrs. Darwin, Rowlett, and Harris set out with me to visit the settlement called Argentina. [This was a seven-hour trip, pushing through mud and reeds.] Mr. Darwin and Harris being also mounted behind two gaucho soldiers, away we went across a flat plain to the settlement [which proved to be a mud-walled fort three hundred yards in diameter, defended by half a dozen small brass cannon and a handful of motley soldiers.] Mr. Darwin was carried off before the rest of the party, to be cross-questioned by an old major, who thought we were very suspicious characters, especially Mr. Darwin, whose objects seemed most mysterious. . . . "Un naturalista" being unluckily explained by Harris as meaning "a man that knows everything," any further attempt to quiet the major's anxiety was useless.

After the return from the expedition to Argentina, Mr. Darwin, and those who could be spared from duties afloat, roamed about the country; and a brisk trade was opened with the soldiers for ostriches and their eggs, for deer, cavies, and armadillos. . . . My friend's attention was soon attracted to some low cliffs near Point Alta, where he found some of those huge fossil bones described in his work; and notwithstanding our smiles at the cargoes of apparent rubbish which he frequently brought on board, he and his servant used their pickaxes in earnest, and brought away what have since proved to be most interesting and valuable remains of extinct animals. . . . I may well say that shoals of fish were caught by our men; and as they were chiefly unknown to naturalists, Mr. Earle made careful drawings, and Mr. Darwin preserved many in spirits. . . . In our rambles over the country near Port Belgrano we everywhere found small pieces of pumice-stone; and till Mr. Darwin examined the Ventana,* supposed they had been thrown thence; he has, however, ascertained that it is not volcanic.

---

*A remarkable mountain fifty miles inland which Darwin climbed a year later. See page 131.

While these excursions were being made in September Fitz-Roy bargained with an Englishman named Harris for the rent of two small schooners to carry on the survey work amidst the dangerous shoals. These were fetched from a little harbor at the mouth of the Rio Negro (one hundred and fifty miles south) to Port Belgrano—"as ugly and ill-built craft as ever I saw, covered with dirt, and soaked with rancid oil." A repair camp was established on shore to renovate these schooners (of fifteen and nine tons burden) and to transform them into "smart little cock-boats." On October 18 the small boats under the command of a lieutenant and a mate from the *Beagle,* began their operations, while the *Beagle* returned to Montevideo for further observations and to get mail. Darwin received Volume II of Lyell's *Principles* on October 26.

We may safely imagine that it got scant attention for several days: there were letters from home to be read and many letters to be written; there were expeditions to be made in the mud ashore during a whole month while the Captain was establishing the exact longitude of Montevideo and Buenos Ayres, charting some shoals, and taking on provisions for the long trip to Tierra del Fuego. Not till November 24 did Darwin complete a letter to Henslow. He is weary of "the enormous brackish river" and is shouting "hurrah for Cape Horn and the Land of Storms!"

By ill luck the French Government has sent one of its collectors to the Rio Negro, where he has been working for the last six months, and is now gone round the Horn. So that I am very selfishly afraid he will get the cream of all the good things before me. As I have nobody to talk to about my luck and ill luck in collecting, I am determined to vent it all upon you. I have been very lucky with fossil bones; I have fragments of at least six

distinct animals. . . . Immediately I saw this I
thought they must belong to an enormous armadillo, living species of which genus are so abundant here. . . .
Care must be taken in this case not to confuse the tal-
lies. They are mingled with marine shells which appear
to me identical with what now exist. But since they were
deposited in their beds several geological changes have
taken place in the country. So much for the dead, and
now for the living: there is a poor specimen of a bird
which to my unornithological eyes appears to be a happy
mixture of a lark, pigeon and snipe. . . . But as for
novelty all this is nothing to a family of pelagic animals
which at first sight appear like *Medusae*, but are really
highly organized. I have examined them repeatedly,
and certainly from their structure it would be impossible to place them in any existing order. . . . All the
specimens will be packed in casks. I think there will be
three (before sending this letter I will specify dates, etc.,
etc.). I am afraid you will groan, or rather the floor of
the lecture-room will, when the casks arrive. Without
you I should be utterly undone. The small cask contains fish: will you open it to see how the spirit has stood
the evaporation of the Tropics. . . . The frequency
with which I think of all the happy hours I have spent at
Shrewsbury and Cambridge is rather ominous—I trust
everything to time and fate and will feel my way as I go
on. . . . I purchased fragments (Nos. 837-38) of some
enormous bones, which I was assured belonged to the
former giants! . . . I have sent to you by the *Duke of
York* packet, commanded by Lieutenant Snell, to Falmouth, two large casks containing fossil bones, a small
cask with fish and a box containing skins, spirit bottle,
etc., and pill-boxes with beetles. Would you be kind
enough to open these latter, as they are apt to become
mouldy.

On November 27 the *Beagle* left Montevideo, not to
return for five months. On December 3 she rejoined the
two little schooners and heard of their success in the difficult and vexatious work. The tide-races and eddies had

been so violent among the off-shore islands that even the
English tars had suffered much from sea-sickness. But
they were full of grit and humor. "The pilot of the
smaller schooner, Mr. Roberts, was one of the largest of
men, and his vessel looked, by comparison, no bigger
than a coffin; but Mr. Wickham allayed my doubts by assuring me that when she got aground Mr. Roberts
stepped overboard and heaved her afloat." Still Wickham admitted that the huge man was sometimes troublesome: "He did harm on one day by going up to lookout and breaking the mast."

Poor humor to record, you may think. So it is. But
consider what these humorists were doing. They were
saying good-by for five months of lonely, hazardous,
dirty work on a dreary coast, out of communication with
the *Beagle*. Sailors had volunteered for this dismal
task; officers joked when they faced it. On December 4
the *Beagle* sailed south. Tierra del Fuego was sighted
on the 15th.

CHAPTER V

LYELL'S "CREATION" AT CAPE HORN

"ON DECEMBER 18," says Fitz-Roy's record, "Mr. Darwin, Mr. Hamond, and others went with me to the natives who had so vociferously greeted our arrival; and deeply indeed was I interested by witnessing the effect caused in their minds by this first meeting with man in such a totally savage state. . . . Disagreeable, indeed painful, as is even the mental contemplation of a savage, and unwilling as we may be to consider ourselves even remotely descended from human beings in such a state, the reflection that Cæsar found the Britons painted and clothed in skins, like these Fuegians, cannot fail to augment an interest excited by . . . their healthy, independent state of existence."

Little did the tory Captain dream, as he watched the meeting, that the name of this refined young whig would one day be known in every hamlet of Christendom as a synonym of descent from something worse than savages. If he could have foreseen Mr. Darwin's achievement, he would have considered it a thoroughly whiggish performance.

Deeply interesting indeed would it be to know how great an effect was caused in the mind of Darwin by this first meeting with the Fuegians. "The sight of a naked savage in his native land," Darwin said long afterward, "is an event which can never be forgotten." We all take it for granted that we have a fairly good mental picture of a primitive man; if we could suddenly be set

down upon bleak rocks ten thousand miles from home—
confronted with smeared bodies, gross salutations, fierce
willingness to kill a mate—then we should feel to the
bottom of our mind a shiver of new understanding of
what the human race is. I say so because I once had
the experience of encountering some beings who were all
but totally savage; the memory has not been dimmed by
the passage of forty years. I can guess at the effect on
Darwin.

December 20. "Mr. Darwin and a party set off to
ascend the heights, anxious to get a shot at the guanacos."

On December 22 we saw Cape Horn; passed close to
the southward of it.

On December 24, being off Cape Spencer, with
weather indicative of a gale, I determined to seek for an
anchorage, and stood into St. Francis Bay. We were
assailed by such a furious hail-squall that for many minutes it was quite impossible to see what was ahead of us.
. . . We anchored in seventeen-fathoms water, quite
close to a promontory at the south side of St. Martin's
Cove. . . . Our position almost under this black precipice was singularly striking. . . . I could hardly persuade myself that the ship was in security. Notwithstanding violent squalls, and cold damp weather, we
kept our Christmas merrily, feeling that we were in a
secure position, instead of being exposed to the effects of
a high sea and heavy gale. . . . At midnight such
furious squalls came down from the heights that the
water was swept up, and clouds of foam were driven
along the sea. We hardly thought ourselves in security
with three anchors down and plenty of chain cable out.

The anchors held. On December 27—the anniversary
of leaving Plymouth, the new birthday for Charles Darwin—the *Beagle* was still in a place where Volume II of
Lyell's *Principles* could be read in comfort.

Darwin might have been distracted from the interest

in Lyell if he had known what was happening at Maer. It seems that Emma Wedgwood "received four or five proposals of marriage about this time, after a girlhood passed entirely without any love affair." She once described this flood of proposals to her daughter: "We got quite weary of it. One of the rejected swains, a neighboring curate, walked Elizabeth round and round the Pool, half crying, and asking what Emma found to object to in him."

We do not know how the knowledge of a swarm of suitors for Emma would have affected Charles Darwin. No letters between them at this time have been published. Possibly none was written. The previous March Charles had said in a letter to his father, "I have not time to write to anybody else, so send to Maer to let them know that in the midst of the glorious tropical scenery I do not forget how instrumental they were in placing me there. . . . Give my love to every soul at home, and to the Owens"—one of whom was Fanny. No love was sent to Maer.

It is likely that during the Christmas season, while the gale beat down upon the *Beagle* from over the top of the black precipice, Darwin thumbed and reread and pondered parts of Volume II of Lyell.

The book had now been in his possession two months. He had been curious when he first opened it at Montevideo and read in the twelve-line Preface that "the present part brings to a close one distinct branch of the inquiry, the study of which will be found absolutely essential to the understanding of the theories hereafter to be proposed." The Preface showed that this branch of the inquiry had not been anticipated when Volume I was planned. What was the subject that had thrust itself forward so unexpectedly, that was so absolutely essential to geology, that had swelled to a whole volume of three hundred and thirty pages? It was stated in the Contents, Chapter I: "Changes of the Organic World now in progress—whether Species have a real existence in Nature—Sketch of Lamarck's arguments."

If Darwin was interrupted by a summons to go ashore just at the moment when he had glimpsed so much of Volume II, he had hard work to keep his mind on whatever he heard or saw. His mind was all agog about that question to be examined in Chapter I— "Whether species have a real existence?" It was as singular, proposed by a geologist, as if a naval architect had inquired "Whether masts have a real existence?" Why should Lyell, of all men—and in geology, of all subjects—write a volume to discuss the speculations of Lamarck? Lamarckian views were for old-fashioned mystics like his grandfather, or for enthusiastic specu- lators like Dr. Grant. But Lyell was hard-headed and matter-of-fact. Lyell had a mind that was con- tinually refreshing and fascinating because it cared only to observe things as they are, to visualize from these observations how unseen forces would have appeared to our eyes if we could have seen them operate.

"Is Lyell going to show that there is any sense in the Lamarckian views?" Darwin kept asking himself as he went down the ladder and was rowed ashore and visited a shop and loitered along a street and waited im- patiently on the dock for the return to the *Beagle*. "This Lyell is a perfect devil for examining a theory without passion. He describes it fairly. He argues it calmly and with the clearest logic. He is less liable to illusion than any geologist in the world. What is he go- ing to say about Lamarck and species?"

As soon as Darwin could sit down to Chapter I he found, as he knew would be the case, that Lamarck's theory (which Darwin then knew only by vague hear-

say) was outlined with the most judicial impartiality.
Yet occasionally there was irony. The chapter sounded
as if the highest type of gentlemanlike intellect, quite
self-assured and polite, was indicating to a reader that
he ought not to smile too soon, but should be courteous
to this Frenchman. On the second of the seventeen
pages of his chapter Lyell said of the Lamarckian theory, "Although this notion is not generally received, we
feel that we are not warranted in assuming the contrary,
without fully explaining the data and reasoning by which
we conceive it may be refuted." He then sketched the
theory with precision and perfect fairness.*

On page 14 the wondering Darwin could perceive
whither Lyell's argument would lead. The irony about
the Lamarckian system becomes almost supercilious:

Our readers will hardly, perhaps, be able to form a
perfect conception of so complicated a piece of mechanism, unless we exhibit it in motion, and show in what
manner it can work out, under the author's guidance,
all the extraordinary effects which we behold in the present state of the animate creation. We have only space
for exhibiting a small part of the entire process by which
a complete metamorphosis is achieved, and shall, therefore, omit the mode whereby, after a countless succession
of generations, a small gelatinous body is transformed
into an oak or an ape. We pass on at once to the last
grand step in the progressive scheme, whereby the orang-
outang, having already evolved out of a monad, is made
slowly to attain the attributes and dignity of a man.

Darwin was relieved by that passage and advanced
through the succeeding chapters with increasing pleas-

---

*The theory sounded so fantastic that in later editions Lyell added
a final paragraph to the chapter, assuring his readers that "the above
sketch is no exaggerated picture, and those passages which have probably excited the greatest surprise are literal translations from the
original." Lyell first read Lamarck's *Philosophie Zoologique* in February, 1827.

ure. He liked to reread and chuckle over the passage
during the Yuletide of 1832, while the tempest shrieked
about him and the *Beagle* tugged with all her might
against three anchors. It is delightful. In the century
since Lamarck died no man has penned an attack on the
evolution theory that is more accurate, more concise, or
more full of contempt. Darwin was happy about it. It
proved the silliness of Dr. Grant's high admiration of
Lamarck.

The chapter fully conceded the naturalness of the
very line of reasoning which had been causing Darwin to
wonder and waver about species as he increasingly
learned how difficult they were to distinguish—how they
shaded into one another. Lyell quotes vivid sentences
from Lamarck to show how unreal a species comes to
seem to a naturalist when his information has widened:

The more we advance in the knowledge of the different organized bodies which cover the surface of the
globe, the more our embarrassment increases, to deter-
mine what ought to be regarded as species. In proportion as our collections are enriched, we see almost every
void filled up, and all our lines of separation effaced.
. . . The more do we discover proofs that everything
passes by insensible shades into something else, that
even the more remarkable differences are evanescent.
. . . The study of species has become almost imprac-
ticable. When the species are arranged in a series, and
placed near to each other, they differ in so minute a degree from those next adjoining that they almost melt
into each other, and are in a manner confounded together. . . . Every naturalist, when he begins to study,
finds it an easy task to establish specific distinctions;
and it is only when his experience is enlarged, and when
he has made himself master of the intermediate links,
that his difficulties begin.

Darwin sympathized whole-heartedly with Lamarck's

description of a naturalist's experience. Darwin's mind was going through exactly such a transformation of opinion about a species, and could recognize the good sense with which Lamarck described it. Often he had been fuddled and skeptical as he grew better acquainted with the swarming, anomalous, unclassifiable creatures at Rio and Belgrano. But here was the firm mind of Lyell, admitting the complete justice of Lamarck's description of conditions, yet calmly preparing to demonstrate that Lamarck's theory was nonsense. Between October 27 and December 27 Darwin had absorbed all of Lyell's reasoning. It comforted him. It showed with thoroughgoing skill the likelihood that "species will never vary, and have remained the same since the creation of each species."

Lyell freely admitted all the puzzling variations which baffled classifiers. He devoted paragraphs to displaying these, especially in domestic plants and animals. But he contended that all variation was *within* each species, that the fluctuating forms were varieties *within* the boundaries of their one common group, their species.

What most strongly appealed to Darwin in Chapter I was three paragraphs of comment on Lamarck's theory:

We must here interrupt the author's argument, by observing that no positive fact is cited to exemplify. . . . There were no examples to be found; Lamarck gives us names for things, and resorts to fictions as ideal as the "plastic virtue" and other phantoms of the middle ages. . . . The gratuitous assumption of a point so vital to his theory was unpardonable.

Lyell was just in his severe charge. Lamarck does not offer any fact that could exemplify the working of his theory. Darwin was glad to learn on such authority that Lamarck's theory was mere fancy. As he read on through Volume II he found the following phrases applied to the Lamarckian views: "the *notion* of a gradual transformation; Lamarck appears to have *speculated;* Lamarck *imagined* that species are endowed with indefinite powers of modifying their organization; the *pretended* metamorphosis of one species into another; the *fancied* evolution of one species out of another; the *dreams* of those who have fancied that the orang-outang might have been transmuted into the human race."

One of Lyell's sarcasms against the Lamarckian theory set the tone for Darwin's lifelong ridicule of it. Lyell spoke of how the natives of Borneo trained apes to climb trees and gather cocoanuts: "It is for the Lamarckians to explain how it happens that those same savages have not themselves acquired—by dint of longing, for many generations, for the power of climbing trees—the elongated arms of the orang, or even the prehensile tails of some American monkeys." The "longing" or "desire" which caused evolution in the Lamarckian theory was always an absurdity to Darwin.

All the major problems of species with which Darwin was to struggle the rest of his life were proposed and discussed in Volume II. The book presented them definitely to his mind, so that they were always there, to be checked or queried or altered, while the wonders of four more years of observation were being mentally classified.

1. Hybrids had seemed to all evolutionists the great clue to alteration of species; it bulked large in Lyell's mind; it occupied a large share of Darwin's life, and was the most baffling of mysteries.

2. Lyell argued that there are fixed limits beyond which the descendants from common parents can not deviate: "There is no tendency to continual divergence from certain attributes with which the elephant was

originally endued—no ground whatever for anticipating that, in thousands of centuries, any material alteration could ever be effected." The difficulty of accounting for *continual* divergence was the greatest obstacle Darwin encountered, and the last one surmounted in working out his theory.

3. The phrase "struggle for existence" was several times used in Volume II and probably helped to crystallize in thought what Darwin's eyes perpetually saw.

4. One of the simplest, but one of the most startling, of Darwin's lines of reasoning was concerned with the marvelous ways in which seeds and eggs may be preserved and transported. Lyell offered some astonishing facts about modes of dispersal.

5. The most spectacular and romantic sort of evidence for evolution is the series of changes through which every organism goes when it is an embryo: in its own individual life it seems to pass through evolutionary stages. Lyell took stock of this evidence and argued that it is an illusion, a mere superficial resemblance.

6. Lyell had much to say about the variations caused in species by climate and other conditions of life; he argued that to some extent these variations might be transmissible to offspring. But he was cautious about speculating where Lamarck had recklessly made the most sweeping assumption. "The acquired habits derived from human tuition," said Lyell, "are rarely transmitted to the offspring." Darwin would have had a long hunt to find any other author in the world who had spoken so firmly on this side of the question. The question of inheriting acquired habits made Darwin's whole life uneasy and is still disputed among biologists.

The young naturalist in his hammock off Cape Horn would have liked to look into the future and see that Volume II would stand the wear and tear of criticism for fifteen years and would be confidently reprinted, almost verbatim, as Book III of the edition of 1847. He would have felt exhilarated if he could have foreseen that Book III would be enriched by many added illustrations, and that prominent among these would be some paragraphs beginning, "A vivid description has been given by Mr. Darwin," "Mr. Darwin observes," etc.

His great gain from Volume II was the conception that the history of the earth, so far as it can be read in the rocks, has been *uniform*. Uniformity of natural law was Lyell's great lesson to geology—as novel as it was fruitful. Catastrophes and deluges and cataclysms were henceforth regarded with strong skepticism by Darwin; all his observation was to make them seem more and more illusory. Lyell had applied this principle to rocks. Now in the second volume, he extended it to animals. He wished to show that all of nature, so far as the record goes, has always been what it is to-day—with about the same kinds of species, in the same sorts of environments, struggling for existence in much the same ways. This argument for uniformity of life was difficult and dangerous in the extreme—for three reasons, which are all phases of one reason.

In the first place, Lyell was indefinitely extending an admission that had made him trouble in Volume I. In Volume I he had admitted that the creation of man was a breach in the uniformity of natural law, but a breach in a very lofty sphere—in the creation of a moral being. Now, in Volume II, he was obliged to concede that *every* species had been specially created. He was peppering his grand uniformity with millions of mysterious "creations," and implying that a "creation" was a divine interference with natural law. The idea is dangerous for a doctrine of uniformity.

In the second place, Lyell knew as well as the most

rabid catastrophist that the species in the older rocks are different from the species in the younger rocks. He knew, as every geologist knew, that species must have originated frequently in the course of geologic ages, and that species had frequently become extinct. All students of rocks agreed perfectly that species had come and gone. The great majority of geologists believed that species had come in waves or bunches, that in the earliest age only lowly forms existed, that in the next age somewhat higher forms had existed, and so on, in an ascending series, to birds and mammals, and finally to man. This view made the ancient history of the earth very different from the later history; it pictured a whole population of the earth swept out of existence, to be followed by a catastrophic second population that was suddenly created wholesale, which was in turn destroyed by some cataclysm and succeeded by a later creation of a quite different population. This was not uniformity. This was a reliance on a grand world-wide miracle. Therefore it was repugnant to Lyell. Therefore he wrote Volume II. His argument had to be based on evidence that could be read two ways, and it was based on a *wish* to prove uniformity. It was not conceived in a spirit of curiosity to find out how species did come into existence. A wish is a dangerous foundation for reasoning.

The third reason why Lyell's argument was dangerous is that it had to deny "progressive development."* The usual theory of such development was a doctrine of sudden and sweeping alterations, great leaps in crea-

---

*In Lyell's correspondence there are two statements that might seem, to an unwary reader who took words in their modern connotation, to admit a belief in progressive development, and on these exceptional fragments Professor Judd has built his faith that Lyell was an evolutionist in 1831. But all the other letters and all of the *Principles* show unmistakably that Lyell was utterly opposed to an evolution theory. And even the two letters are not exceptional if rightly read. See the Appendix of this book, page 429, for some samples of the evidence.

tion—which was opposed to uniformity. Lamarck's theory provided slow uniformity, but it was not supported by any evidence and it led to the conclusion that man is descended from brutes. If Lyell had confined himself to opposing these two theories of development, he would have been on strong ground, which has since proved to be unassailable. But Lyell, alas, was much influenced by an emotion which had nothing to do with science. And this emotion ran through his argument like a vein of soft cement in a wall, endangering his whole superstructure. It was the same emotion that has influenced men ever since his day—the loathing of a brutish ancestry.

Lyell's hatred of descent from monkeys has been shown in the sarcasm already quoted. It appeared elsewhere in Volume II. He speaks of "the generally received opinion that all the leading varieties of the human family have sprung from a single pair, a doctrine against which there appears to me to be no sound objection." He argues that, since all the races of man belong to one species and since there is no evidence that one species can ever be transmuted into another, therefore man is not descended from a lower animal. He says, "Some speculators were bold enough to affirm that a scale might be traced from 'apes with foreheads villainous low' to the African variety of the human species, and from that to the European; . . . but the attempt to trace a graduated scale of intelligence through the different species of animals is a mere visionary speculation."

We do not have to depend on interpreting Lyell's statements. He wrote the full and frank confession of the fact to Darwin, March 15, 1863: "I remember that it was the conclusion Lamarck came to about man that fortified me thirty years ago against the great impression which his arguments at first made on my mind.

. . . When I came to the conclusion that . . . we must 'go the whole orang,' I reread his book, and remembering when it was written, I felt I had done him an injustice." Lyell's mind was unquestionably "fortified" when he wrote Volume II. His book was motived by dread. And dread will endanger any argument. It is hard to believe that Darwin was unaware of Lyell's weakness.

Yet in the main he must have approved what he read. His recollection of his opinion during the years in South America was that he had full faith in the fixity of species. He must have agreed that no evidence was in sight to oppose Lyell's conclusion: "I see, then, that there exist in organized beings *permanent* differences, which can not be referred to any one of the actual causes of varia- tion, and these differences are what constitute species." He must have understood, to his lasting profit, that the history of strata, their relative ages, can be read only by means of the fossil species imbedded in them. That was Lyell's fundamental reason for presenting at such length, in a treatise on geology, the vexed question "What is a species?"

There is every reason to suppose that Darwin fully agreed with Lyell's belief in supernatural design, as shown in the adaptations of animals and plants:

We may reasonably conjecture that such habits of the dogs *were given* with no other *view* than for the use of man and the preservation of the dog.

Some of the qualities of particular animals and plants may have been given solely with a view to the connexion which *it was foreseen* would exist between them and man.

Each species was *endowed,* at the time of its creation, with the attributes by which it is now distinguished.

If the Author of Nature had not *ordained* that the fluctuations should be in perfect harmony with each other.

Such belief in God's designing of creatures was just Paley's logic, which Darwin had fully approved in his last year at Cambridge.

But I wonder about one element of the supernatural in Lyell—the *creation* of species. For, to the Darwin mind, that subject would stand out garishly, as of quite different stuff from all the other matter of the book. Lyell's logic led inevitably to a special act of creation for every species: no one denied that new species have come into being; there were no facts to support Lamarck's theory that new species grew gradually out of old ones; therefore they must have been created. Lyell makes this conclusion unobtrusive, but he does not dodge it. Indeed it is essential to his whole picture of uniformity. He reckons that if, on the average, only one species became extinct and one new one were "to be called into being" every year, more than a million years would be required to change the population of the globe. That would be uniformity. Occasionally a species dies; occasionally a new one is born to take its place; the total extent of the history of life contains no catastrophes and no progress; there is very gradual and uniform change always going on—by the substitution of one species at a time.

It was a very reasonable hypothesis, much more in conformity with natural laws than Lamarck's or Buckland's. But it is an utterly different kind of hypothesis from anything else advanced in the eight hundred and forty-one pages that Darwin had seen. *It could not be visualized.* Darwin never would entertain a conception unless he could form some sort of mental picture to associate with it, and no picture of the creation of a species can be formed. Put yourself in the hammock below the deck of the lurching *Beagle* and try the experiment.

At some particular second—no matter if it was 753,-

819 years, 4 months and 17 days ago—at that particular second there was no such thing in the world as a certain kind of flat worm; then, the next second, under a particular piece of rotten wood weighing just so many grams and situated just so many inches north of the center of the Plaza in Maldonado, there *was* such a flat worm. It had been "called into being" at that moment, Lyell asserted, equipped with many extraordinary adaptations, fitted with a sex apparatus which could continue the species amidst a fierce struggle for existence. What took place at that instant of birth of a species? It is obvious that *nature* has no apparatus for *creating* a species. The creative power must be above natural law. That is what Lyell everywhere implies and nowhere denies.

Darwin could have granted that in the days of Noah the hand of God might have been visible to mortal eyes as it placed the new type of animal under the rotten wood. But how about now, in South America, in the presence of a naturalist who has been taught to regard only invariable natural law? Lyell's figures indicated that about once in ten years God's hand did deposit a new kind of creature in South America. Therefore it must be possible that a Charles Darwin, strolling about some day in a forest, might happen to be present at the birth of a species. Would atoms jump out of the air and the dead leaves? Would the new species descend from the sky? Or would God always take pains to manufacture the species where no human being could see what was going on? The effort to visualize a scientific hypothesis resulted in a picture that no scientist would dare to sketch before an audience, that could not be admitted to any scientific discussion—that Lyell himself left completely vague. Must the study of species resolve itself into a faith in a sort of miracle that not even Sedgwick would like to describe to a congregation in a church? No scientist has ever seen, not for one moment of his life, anything that could conceivably be interpreted as a part of any step in a "creation" of a species.

It is extraordinary that Darwin left no record of how Lyell's "creation" affected him then or later. It is much more extraordinary that Professor Judd should speak of the teaching of Lyell as "identical with evolution." Darwin could not have found a sentence in Volume II that tolerated evolution. Lyell's use of the word *creation* can not by any subtlety be twisted into the meaning of "created by an evolutionary process." Lyell's purpose was to prove that every species originated, fully formed, in a particular spot, at a particular moment, as a "first pair," which was to be the parents of all future members of that species. He does not flinch from concrete statement: "Let us consider what kind of evidence we ought to expect of the first appearance of new animals or plants."

"The mystery of mysteries" Lyell called a species. Darwin must have given assent as he threw Volume II on to the table below him, closed his eyes, and tried to imagine the facts. On this mystery hung all natural science. What is a plant or animal? What is geological history? And what is man? The answer to every question of natural science hung on the answer to one supreme question: What is a species? No one could ever know the nature of a species until he found out how it originated. The *origin* of species was the greatest riddle of science.

It was exciting enough to make a naturalist forget, at times, that perhaps three anchors would not hold the *Beagle* against the gale that blew down from the black precipice.

CHAPTER VI

The Second Year in South America

The eight hundred pages in which the chroniclers of the *Beagle* voyage tell about the years 1833-1835 do no more than sketch the principal impressions made upon Darwin's sensitive mind. In this book there can not be a tenth of that space used for outlining their outline. In my brief index to all the treasure that poured into Darwin's memory I can only point out some of the most striking and peculiar experiences. If you would realize the effects of the three years of adventure, you must lend your imagination to what Darwin saw, and your sympathy to the poor devil of an author who has to choose a few selected glimpses for his readers.

A large part of 1833 was spent ashore and is reported rather fully (as 1832 was not) in Darwin's *Journal*. The year was spent in three very different regions.

The first region was the inlets and islands northwest of Cape Horn, where the *Beagle* spent January and February. The Captain's business here was curious, considering that every day cost the Admiralty a considerable sum. He was returning three Fuegians to their native land after having them a year in England to instruct them in religion and agriculture. This missionary enterprise was a source of much amusement to all on board except the Captain. If the Admiralty had not allowed him to carry the Fuegians on the *Beagle*, he would have chartered a vessel to take them home at his private expense. He was in earnest about them.

109

In the summer of 1830, when the *Beagle* was on the southwest coast of Tierra del Fuego, some natives had stolen a boat; three of them were seized by Fitz-Roy as hostages; later another was bought for some beads and buttons; all four were taken to England, where one died; and for ten months the survivors were kept, at the Captain's expense, in the house of a schoolmaster in a London suburb. They were named York Minster, Jemmy Button, and Fuegia Basket. King William graciously summoned them for an audience, and Queen Adelaide graciously put a ring on little Fuegia's finger. In the autumn of 1831 a missionary, Matthews, was found to return with them; and a zealous missionary society sent loads of books and full sets of crockery to be stowed in the overfull *Beagle,* in the hope that the returned Fuegians would set up civilized housekeeping and be a nucleus of religion and virtue among their tribe. They had learned bits of English and other matters and were now, in January of 1833, to be restored to their homes.

For three weeks the *Beagle* tried in vain to beat a hundred and fifty miles west to the towering cape of York Minster, for which the oldest Fuegian had been named because he was captured near it. One day the sea ran so high that a wave forced the whole lee bulwark two feet under water. The captain of a sealing schooner reported that it was the worst gale he had known for twenty years; three vessels were totally wrecked off Tierra del Fuego. During the gale York decided not to return home, and told the Captain that he would like to settle with Jemmy and Fuegia in their native place a hundred miles north of Cape Horn. "I was very glad of it," says the Captain, because he felt it would be better to have all three civilizers left together; and he adds, "I little thought how deep a scheme master York had in contemplation." Accordingly the

Beagle was securely moored in a bay north of the Cape, and the yawl was loaded with crockery and tools. Darwin was one of the party of twenty-eight officers and men, three Fuegians, and the missionary Matthews, who were to work their way to Jemmy's home on Beagle Channel.

Beagle Channel, which had been discovered and charted by Fitz-Roy on his previous voyage, is one hundred and fifty miles south of the eastern entrance of the Strait of Magellan. It forms the southern edge of the largest island of Tierra del Fuego, running in a straight course one hundred and twenty miles west with a remarkably uniform width of about two miles. Snow-capped mountains rise on the north side, from which glaciers run to the Channel. As the ends of the glaciers advance and break off, they form icebergs, which varied the landscape for the occupants of the yawl and the three whaleboats from the *Beagle.*

The party entered the eastern end of the Channel on the 19th of January (which is midsummer in the Antarctic), and for the next eighteen days Darwin was in close contact with savages. His brain was struck with sights and feelings that grew more potent as the years passed by. They formed, at the time, a very curious background for Lyell's discourse on the divinity and gentlemanlikeness of the human species. They may have been, twenty years later, a deeper basis for reasoning about evolution than Darwin was conscious of. More than a twentieth of his *Journal* is devoted to these days with the Fuegians, which were less than a hundreth part of the time of the voyage. It will not be amiss for us to use our limited space in the same proportion.

A few sentences from the *Journal* will disclose, better than photographs could, the scenery through which the party passed.

Tierra del Fuego may be described as a mountainous land, partly submerged in the sea, so that deep inlets and bays occupy the place where valleys should exist. The mountain sides, except on the exposed western coast, are covered from the water's edge upwards by one great forest. The trees reach to an elevation of between 1000 and 1500 feet, and are succeeded by a band of peat, with minute alpine plants; and this again is succeeded by the line of perpetual snow.

The trees all belong to one kind. This beech keeps its leaves throughout the year; but its foliage is of a peculiar brownish-green color, with a tinge of yellow. As the whole landscape is thus colored, it has a somber, dull appearance; nor is it often enlivened by the rays of the sun.

There was a degree of mysterious grandeur in mountain behind mountain, with the deep intervening valleys, all covered by one thick, dusky mass of forest. The atmosphere, likewise, in this climate—where gale succeeds gale, with rain, hail, and sleet—seems blacker than anywhere else. The distant channels between the mountains appeared from their gloominess to lead beyond the confines of this world.

The climate is certainly wretched; the summer solstice was now passed, yet every day snow fell on the hills, and in the valleys there was rain, accompanied by sleet. The thermometer generally stood about forty-five degrees, but in the night fell to thirty-eight or forty degrees. From the damp and boisterous state of the atmosphere, not cheered by a gleam of sunshine, one fancied the climate even worse than it really was.

A few short passages from the *Journal* will picture the kind of people encountered by the party.

A group of Fuegians, partly concealed by the entangled forest, were perched on a wild point overhanging the sea. . . . It was without exception the most curious and interesting spectacle I ever beheld: I could not have believed how wide was the difference between savage and civilized man. . . . The party altogether closely resembled the devils which come on the stage in plays like Der Freischutz. [Since Edinburgh days Darwin has learned to spell the opera—except for the umlaut.]

These Fuegians in the canoe were quite naked, and even one full-grown woman was absolutely so. It was raining heavily, and the fresh water, together with the spray, trickled down her body. In another harbor not far distant a woman, who was suckling a recently-born child, came one day alongside the vessel, and remained there out of mere curiosity, whilst the sleet fell and thawed on her naked bosom, and on the skin of her naked baby! These poor wretches were stunted in their growth, their hideous faces bedaubed with white paint, their skins filthy and greasy, their hair entangled, their voices discordant, and their gestures violent.

The different tribes when at war are cannibals. From the concurrent, but quite independent, evidence of the boy taken by Mr. Low, and of Jemmy Button, it is certainly true that when pressed in winter by hunger, they kill and devour their old women before they kill their dogs; the boy being asked by Mr. Low why they did this, answered, "Doggies catch otters, old women no." This boy described the manner in which they are killed by being held over smoke and thus choked; he imitated their screams as a joke, and described the parts of their bodies which are considered best to eat. Horrid as such a death by the hands of their friends and relatives must be, the fears of the old women, when hunger begins to press, are more painful to think of; we were told that they then often run away into the mountains, but that they are pursued by the men and brought back to the slaughter-house at their own fire-sides!

Was a more horrid deed ever perpetrated than that witnessed on the west coast by Byron, who saw a wretched mother pick up her bleeding, dying infant boy, whom her husband had mercilessly dashed on the stones for dropping a basket of sea-eggs!

Like wild beasts, they do not appear to compare numbers; for each individual, if attacked, instead of retiring, will endeavor to dash your brains out with a stone, as certainly as a tiger under similar circumstances would tear you.

We were clothed, and though sitting close to the fire were far from too warm; yet these naked savages, though further off, were observed to be streaming with perspiration at undergoing such a roasting.

Early in the morning a fresh party arrived, belonging to Jemmy's tribe. Several of them had run so fast that their noses were bleeding, and their mouths frothed from the rapidity with which they talked; and with their naked bodies all bedaubed with black, white, and red, they looked like so many demoniacs who had been fighting.

The next morning after our arrival the Fuegians began to pour in and Jemmy's mother and brothers arrived. Their meeting was less interesting than that between a horse, turned out into a field, when he joins an old companion. They simply stared for a short time at each other; and the mother immediately went to look after her canoe. We heard, however, that the mother had been inconsolable for the loss of Jemmy and had searched everywhere for him.

Darwin's relief at "hearing, however" is obvious. He was quite as much interested in the higher and pleasanter traits of the savage nature as in their bestiality. On board the *Beagle* he had been intimate with Jemmy for a year. Who shall tell what thoughts about the nature of human beings were engendered in Darwin's mind by constant familiarity with this Jemmy— who wore gloves and knew something of three languages and had an immortal soul, but who had so lately been a demoniac savage?

The *Journal* frequently reveals that the relation between the human and the bestial was much in Darwin's thoughts:

The difference between savage and civilized man is

greater than between a wild and domesticated animal.

York Minster's affections were very strong towards a few friends on board; his intellect good.

It seems yet wonderful to me, when I think over all Jemmy's many good qualities, that he should have been of the same race, and doubtless partaken of the same character, with the miserable, degraded savages.

I do not think that our Fuegians were much more superstitious than some of the sailors; for an old quartermaster firmly believed that the successive gales were caused by our having the Fuegians on board.

If a Fuegian is not much more superstitious than a sailor, the next question might be "Is a sailor much more superstitious than Samuel Wilberforce, who firmly believes that bad weather may come as a result of a Great Spirit's anger?" Wilberforce was the artful and gentlemanlike debater of the Bethel Union at Oxford. Because of his smooth oratory his peers in Bethel had nicknamed him "Soapy Sam," and his peers in the House of Lords later confirmed the name. Mr. Wilberforce—already the author of volumes of hymns and stories, though only four years older than Darwin—hated unwelcome facts worse than Sedgwick did. Possibly there were only two slight degrees of superstitiousness between him and Jemmy Button. A Darwin could not have avoided some fleeting speculations of this sort.

On January 19 the thirty miles to the eastern end of Beagle Channel were covered, though part of the distance the yawl had to be "dragged along by strength of arm against wind and current." Fifty miles still remained to be covered, westward through the Channel, to reach Jemmy's home.

The following dated paragraphs are direct quotations from Fitz-Roy's *Narrative*.

January 20. Several natives were seen in this day's pull. . . . York laughed heartily at the first we saw, calling them large monkeys. Jemmy assured us they were not at all like his people. Fuegia was shocked and ashamed. It was interesting to observe the change which three years only had made in their ideas; for it turned out that Jemmy's own tribe was as inferior in every way as the worst of those whom he and York called "monkeys—dirty—fools—not men."

January 22. Being within a few hours' pull of Jemmy's own land, which he called Woollya, we all felt eager.

January 28. The yawl, with one whale-boat, was sent back to the *Beagle,* and I set out on a westward excursion, accompanied by Messrs. Darwin and Hamond, in the other two boats; my intention being to complete the exploration of the northwest arm of Beagle Channel; then revisit Woollya.

January 29. We enjoyed a grand view of the lofty mountain, now called Darwin, with its immense glaciers extending far and wide. [Mt. Darwin is slightly less than seven thousand feet high, but this height is impressive because the mountain rises directly from sea-level. The top of Pike's Peak is only nine thousand feet above the plain from which the mountain rises. The most sightly peak in Tierra del Fuego, Mt. Sarmiento, pictured twice in the *Narrative,* is of the same height as Mt. Darwin.]

We stopped to cook and eat our hasty meal upon a low point of land, immediately in front of a noble precipice of solid ice. . . . Our boats were hauled up out of the water upon a sandy point, and we were sitting round a fire about two hundred yards from them, when a thundering crash shook us—down came the whole front of the icy cliff—and the sea surged up in a vast heap of foam. . . . Had not Mr. Darwin, and two or three of the men, run to the boats instantly, they would have been swept away irrecoverably. Wind and tide would soon have drifted them beyond the distance a man could swim.

The advantage of following Fitz-Roy's *Narrative* is

that in Darwin's *Journal* there is no mention of the fact that Mr. Darwin was among those quick thinkers who ran instantly to save the boats. Nor is there any reference to a mountain that is "now called Darwin." Mr. Darwin was reticent about these and some other similar matters on the voyage of the *Beagle*. He does not, for example, tell his readers the following:

January 30. We passed into a large expanse of water which I named Darwin Sound—after my messmate, who so willingly encountered the discomfort and risk of a long cruise in a small loaded boat.

Neither Fitz-Roy nor Darwin tells us about the naming of Mt. Buckland, fifty miles northwest of Mt. Darwin. It must be a comical story, for Buckland's peak is only half as high as Darwin's. Why was no body of land or water named for Lyell? Probably Darwin did not feel at liberty to nominate an unknown geologist for such an honor.

The yawl explored the north shore of Darwin Sound, turned south, entered the southwest arm of Beagle Channel on its return to Woollya, and followed this to the point where the two arms divide.

February 4. On the south shore we met a large party of natives. . . . One of their women was far from ill-looking. . . . The sight of her linen garment, several bits of ribbon, and some scraps of red cloth, evidently recently obtained, made me feel very anxious about Matthews and his party.

February 6. At daybreak we were hastening toward Woollya. As we shot through the Murray Narrow, several parties of natives were seen, who were ornamented with strips of tartan cloth or white linen, which we well knew were obtained from our poor friends. . . . Our boats touched the shore. . . . Then, to my extreme relief, Matthews appeared, dressed and looking as usual. . . . Matthews gave a bad account of the prospect which he saw before him, and told me that he did not think himself safe among such a set of utter savages. No violence had been committed beyond holding down his head by force, as if in contempt of his strength; but he had been harshly threatened. . . . More than one man went out of his wigwam in a rage, and returned immediately with a large stone in his hand, making signs that he would kill Matthews if he did not give him what was demanded. . . . York and Fuegia fared very well, but Jemmy was sadly plundered, even by his own family. Our garden had been trampled over repeatedly. . . . It was soon decided that Matthews should not remain. . . . I then bade Jemmy and York farewell, promising to see them again in a few days. . . . Matthews must have felt almost like a man reprieved, excepting that he enjoyed the feeling always sure to reward those who try to do their duty.

February 7. About an hour after dark reached the *Beagle*—found all well, the ship refitted, and quite ready for her next trip.

February 26. We ran before a fresh gale towards the Falkland Islands. Towards evening we rounded to for soundings, but the sea was so high and short that a man at the jib-boom-end was pitched more than a fathom under water. He held on manfully, and as he rose above the water hove the lead forward as steadily as ever. My own feelings at seeing him disappear may be imagined —it was some time before we sounded again.

The second region in which Darwin spent part of 1833 was the Falkland Islands, two hundred and fifty miles east of the tip of Tierra del Fuego. During 1832 there had been a quarrel between the British and American governments over the case of some American sailors who had been detained by the British governor. A rash American captain of a corvette had landed, cut down the British flag, carried away the governor's agent in irons, and brutally destroyed the little colony. On the 2d of

January a British frigate had hoisted the British colors again—and they have flown over the islands ever since. It is likely that Darwin, arriving directly after this high-handed action by an officer from the Land of the Free, gained certain lasting impressions of the way in which primitive instincts clothe themselves in noble colors. Just where would the line be drawn between a marauding Fuegian and a righteous apostle of American liberty?

Darwin was at the Falklands from March 1 to April 7; again in March, 1834, he reached the Falklands for a four-week stay; and his *Journal* does not reveal which of his observations belong to each visit. Probably most of them were made, and with the fresh interest of novelty, during his first and longer visit; so that I am safe in treating them all as of 1833. There is a further good reason for including them all here: Fitz-Roy's *Narrative* is much concerned with the species question in 1833, but entirely concerned with the American atrocity in 1834.

The Falkland Islands have a greater area than Massachusetts; they are gloomy in appearance; in 1833 only a handful of people lived on them; and they are perpetually swept by sleety gales and smothered in clouds. "In their appearance," says Fitz-Roy, "there is very little either remarkable or interesting. About the greater part of the archipelago barren hills or rocky, surf-beat shores are the only objects which meet the eye. Scarcely any view can be more dismal than from the heights."

But Darwin was not dependent on scenery. He could find some entertainment in the people and shipping. The crew of a wrecked American schooner were brought into the Sound. Several recent wrecks were in sight, one of them a vessel that had been blown ashore right in the harbor. Thirty whale-ships were in the vicinity of the islands; many American sailors came ashore armed with rifles, and English sailors armed with sealing clubs; there were cutthroat Gauchos; Frenchmen vied with Americans in desiring to plunder what was left of the settlement of Port Louis. Captain Fitz-Roy's clerk was drowned and buried ashore with ceremony.

A matter of much interest to all on board the *Beagle* was the Captain's purchase of a one-hundred-and-seventy-ton schooner to assist in his labors. "I had often anxiously longed for a consort," he says; "but when I saw the *Unicorn* my wish to purchase her was unquenchable." The *Unicorn* was a sealer that had had a disastrous season; her captain was willing to sell for a fifth of the original cost; she was renamed *Adventure*, in memory of the *Beagle's* companion on the previous voyage; and thenceforth she added much to the efficiency of Fitz-Roy's expedition.

Of course Darwin's chief interest at this time was in applying Lyell's incomparable way of reading the history of the earth's crust. In the Falklands was a spectacle that put a severe strain on the uniformity theory—the "streams of rocks," which, as Darwin wrote, "have been mentioned with surprise by every voyager." They are like glaciers stretching down the hillsides, in some cases a mile wide, composed of sharp-edged blocks of whitish stone from a foot to forty feet in diameter. The mystery is that these streams of stone extend far into the almost level valleys, where the slope is so gradual that "it would not have checked the speed of an English mail-coach." It is not conceivable that the stones could have "flowed" down such a gradient. There are few geological problems which offer more defiance to Lyell. "Never," says Darwin, "did any scene so forcibly convey to my mind the idea of a convulsion, of which in historical records we might in vain seek for any counterpart. Yet the progress of knowledge will probably some day give a simple explanation." His hope has not yet been fulfilled. Whatever baffled Darwin in geology was likely to remain baffling for a long time.

The Captain may have been discussing the great species puzzle with his naturalist, for he devotes several pages of his *Narrative* to the cases that furnished Darwin so many good illustrations for his later reasoning. The Falklands are a laboratory for experiments in species. "Rats and mice," Fitz-Roy argues, "were probably taken to the Falklands by the earlier navigators. That they have varied from the original stock is to be expected, because we find that every animal varies more or less in outward form and appearance, in consequence of altered climate, food, or habits; and that when a certain change is once effected the race no longer varies while under similar circumstances." That is strict Lyellian doctrine. It is based on two natural assumptions: first, that there is a definite limit to variation; second, that the variation is *in consequence of* the surroundings. The assumptions looked proper to Lyell, who had never wandered in the maze of classification that Lamarck knew; they looked perfectly proper to a captain who was concerned with bargaining for a consort and rescuing the crew of the wrecked *Magellan* and maintaining English authority ashore. But to Darwin—— How could a naturalist feel sure about this mysterious *limit* of variation, which was defined only as the limit of an indefinite somewhat called a "species"? And by what process of natural law did food and climate *cause* variation? How could the gloomy dankness of the Falklands *cause* a rat's nose to grow longer? Or, if somehow a nose was lengthened, how did this new length get into the ovum of a mother rat? The effort to visualize these assumptions is too great for an experienced mind that has any curiosity about some other possibility. The guiding maxim for every good puzzle-solver is always the same: *look for another possibility*. Darwin followed that method by instinct when he consorted with New-haven oystermen; we may be sure that he was following it in the Falklands.

Why should the mist and cold of these islands put longer tails on mice? Why should incessant gales make the wild bulls so large? Just *how* had the peat bogs worked to make the wild horses weaker? What explana-tion of these processes, then undreamed of, might be found by some sleuth of a naturalist who could open his brain to some *other* possibility? Darwin scented his prey in these alterations of domestic animals during two centuries—a mere brief moment in geological time—only two centuries. Lyell's Volume II had drawn striking examples from the changes under domestication; now the Falklands put the very smell of them in his nos-trils. He never deserted the trail of them after March, 1833.

There was also an impressive exhibit of a wild species—the strange "wolf-fox." Fitz-Roy argued that it stood twice as high as an English fox because it did not have to steal along under branches. He had no doubt that this creature, though unknown elsewhere in the world, was an immigrant that had varied. "I can see nothing extraordinary in foxes carried from Tierra del Fuego to Falkland becoming longer-legged, more bulky, and differently coated. . . . Icebergs and trees, drifted by the current which always sets from Staten Land, af-ford the means of transport." To Fitz-Roy it appears obvious that these wild foxes have done just what do-mestic animals have done—they have varied in new sur-roundings. Darwin was never afterwards able to see a flaw in this part of Fitz-Roy's reasoning: the variations of wild and domestic animals seem the same sort of phenomena.

But another part of Fitz-Roy's reasoning led to a quagmire of opinion which he was ignorant of. Darwin knew all about it.* Darwin knew of a surety that the wolf-fox was a very distinct species, *canis antarcticus*. Fitz-Roy proclaimed with easy assurance that the wolf-fox was *magellanicus*, which had altered—within the limits of its species, as confidently explained by Lyell— into a new variety of its species. He did not understand that any classifier in Europe, confronted with this "variety," would unhesitatingly pronounce it a distinct species. He did not understand that his confident logic had transmuted one species into another, and so was in conflict with his whole creed about the fixity of species.

His belief in fixity was as uncompromising as Lyell's. His confusion if he had really examined the case of *antarcticus* vs. *magellanicus* would have been as complete as Lyell's. The world's stock of logic and knowledge was not sufficient for deciding the *limits* of variation of the wolf-fox. And the question of the limits of that variation went to the foundation of all conceptions of life— yes, of human life as well.

It is easy to see between Fitz-Roy's lines that he distrusts the whiggish, leveling tendencies of the naturalist. He is defending the tory cause of fixity of species. Probably Darwin, having learned a lesson from the dispute about slavery, avoided any argument on species. Indeed he had no grounds for opposing the Lyellian theory. Is it fanciful to suspect that his prejudices were somewhat roused against Lyell's fixity when he found that the theory was so very agreeable to a tory?

Darwin was intensely interested in the kinds of

*The discussion of the foxes, as written for the 1839 edition of Darwin's Journal, was left unchanged for the second edition.

changes to be seen in the animal life of the islands, and in observing the phases of life.*

1. These wild horses were introduced by the French in 1764. I was particularly curious to know what has checked their originally rapid increase.

2. It is interesting to find the once domesticated cattle breaking into three colors, of which some one color would in all probability ultimately prevail over the others.

3. The rabbit is another animal which has been introduced and which has succeeded very well. . . . The French naturalists have considered the black variety a distinct species. . . . The Gauchos laughed at the idea of the black kind being different from the gray, and they said that the two readily bred together. . . . Even Cuvier, on looking at the skull of one of these rabbits, thought it was probably a distinct species.

4. Within a very few years after these islands shall have become regularly settled, in all probability this fox will be classed with the dodo, as an animal which has perished from the face of the earth. [This is a good sample of Darwin's keenness. The last of the foxes was killed in 1875.]

5. One day I observed a cormorant playing with a fish which it had caught. . . . I do not know of any other instance where dame Nature appears so wilfully cruel.

6. The jackass penguin is a brave bird. . . . In diving its little wings are used as fins; but on the land as front legs. . . . When it dives so instantaneously I defy anyone at first sight to be sure that it was not a fish leaping for sport.

7. Thus we find in South America three birds which use their wings for other purposes than flight.

8. The "steamer" feeds entirely on shell-fish; hence the beak and head, *for the purpose* of breaking them, are

---

*Quotations 1, 2, and 5 contain ideas that were not in the first edition of 1839; quotation 9 has been rephrased for the second edition, but contains no new idea; the others are identical in the two editions.

surprisingly heavy and strong: the head is so strong that
I have scarcely been able to fracture it with my geological hammer.

9. In another elegant little coralline each cell was
furnished with a long-toothed bristle, which had the
power of moving quickly. Each of these bristles and
each of the vulture-like heads moved quite independently
of the others, but sometimes all on both sides of a branch
moved together coinstantaneously. In these actions we
apparently behold as perfect a transmission of will in
the zoophyte, though composed of thousands of distinct
polypi, as in any single animal. . . . The examination
of these compound animals was always very interesting
to me. . . . Surprising as this union of separate individuals in a common stock must always appear, every
tree displays the same fact, for buds must be considered
as individual plants. . . . The individuals propagated
by buds seem more intimately related to each other than
eggs or seeds are to their parents. . . . It is familiar
to everyone what singular and numerous peculiarities
are transmitted with certainty by buds, which by seminal
propagation never, or only casually, reappear.

Darwin was standing upon the brink of the mystery
of life, pondering heredity and variation. How could
the variations in a wolf-fox be so directed and so certainly conveyed to offspring by seminal reproduction?

The third region in which Darwin gathered knowledge during 1833 was Argentina. For more than two
months he lived ashore at Maldonado, and for four
months (August 3—December 6) he was spending much
of his time on horseback, covering more than eight
hundred miles. A long chapter could no more than sum-
marize the varied information that poured into Darwin's mind; and my portion of a chapter can only hint
at them as I rapidly describe his itinerary.

The *Beagle* left the Falklands April 6. Fitz-Roy

failed to find the two little schooners at the Rio Negro, but learned that Corporal Williams had been drowned. The *Beagle* was moored off Maldonado on the 28th. Captain Fitz-Roy was now occupied with the outfitting of a fourth consort, the *Constitucion*, of one hundred and seventy tons.

Darwin took quarters on shore, and for ten weeks busied himself with inland excursions for collecting—and with thinking about species. He describes the mole-like animal which makes a queer noise underground—a succession of four nasal grunts like tu-cu-tu-co, from which it is named. The tucutucos have eyes, but these are generally useless, and Darwin comments: "Lamarck would have been delighted with this fact, had he known it, when speculating (probably with more truth than usual with him) on the gradually acquired blindness of the Aspalax and the Proteus. . . . No doubt Lamarck would have said that the tucutuco is now passing into the state of the Aspalax and Proteus."

A reader who wishes to know of Darwin's other reflections at Maldonado—such as his thoughts about a "parasitical" ostrich—will go to pages 48-62 of the *Journal*. My narrative must make speed.

On August 3 Darwin said good-by to the *Beagle* at the mouth of the Rio Negro, and went ashore, to begin a long excursion northward. A glance at the map opposite page 110 will show where he rode.

Behind him, to the south, was the great plain of Patagonia, a series of barren plateaus, rising at intervals in abrupt terraces from the Atlantic to the Andes, an expanse of gravel and boulders. Seven hundred miles of this desolation lay between him and the Strait of Magellan, so unknown to explorers that Fitz-Roy could only print across his map "inhabited by wandering tribes of Indians." South of the little town of Carmen on the Rio Negro there was no settlement, not even any military outpost of civilization.

Before him, to the north, was the plain of Argentina, the Pampas. Buenos Ayres lay five hundred miles away.

Before he left Carmen he examined a salt-lake and grew curious about the fetid odor of the mud at its border. "The mud in many places was thrown up by numbers of some kind of worm. How surprising it is that any creatures should be able to exist in brine, and that they should be crawling among crystals of sulphate of soda and lime! And what becomes of these worms when, during the long summer, the surface is hardened into a solid layer of salt? . . . Thus we have a little living world within itself, *adapted* to these inland lakes of brine." I select this sample of Darwin's observations on the Argentine trip because of its pettiness: an investigation of an evil-smelling mud led to a lifelong interest in earthworms and to an exposition of the astounding geological powers of these unnoticed animals. It led also—as every observation of Darwin's did—to the marvels of adaptation in nature. What is an adaptation? A cluster of adaptations is called a species, and a species is what? The question was never out of his thoughts.

But he did not obtrude the mystery much in his *Journal.* He told of the Indians that had recently been somewhat scared away by the little army of General Rosas, whose hope had been to exterminate them. The General had marched his troops from Buenos Ayres across the Pampas and left behind a series of small posts, forty miles apart, each garrisoned by a squad of cavalry. But for this protection Darwin could not have seen the Pampas. Even now his route was by no means secure; Indians sometimes rode in between the posts; and Darwin's guide was thoroughly alarmed one day.

At Carmen, August 11, Darwin joined an English-

man and five Gaucho soldiers for the ride across the
Pampas. "This was the first night which I passed under an open sky, with the gear of the recado for my bed.
There is high enjoyment in the independence of the
Gaucho life—to be able at any moment to pull up your
horse and say, 'Here we will pass the night!'" On
August 12 he queried: "What cause can have altered,
in a wide, uninhabited, and rarely-visited country, the
range of animal like this Agouti?" So, every day, there
were similar queries about habitats.

The government at Buenos Ayres—mindful of the
quick retribution brought by H. M. S. *Druid* for discour-
tesy to the *Beagle*—commanded General Rosas to extend every courtesy to the roving naturalist. Hence a
good reception and assistance everywhere awaited Darwin along his route.

The first eighty miles (to the Rio Colorado) was
across the northern edge of the Patagonian shingle.
"The pebbles are chiefly of porphyry, and probably owe
their origin to the rocks of the Cordilleras." Here he
was facing the same mystery of erratic boulders that
had so impressed him when Mr. Cotton solemnly explained about the bell-stone of Shrewsbury; and the
world's knowledge of geology was not then sufficient to
say how the pebbles were transported from the Andes
four hundred miles to the seashore. The solution was
so incredible that the cautious Lyell, even in his edition
of 1847, dared accept only a tincture of it. All that
Darwin could do in 1833 was to wonder—and to doubt
the efficacy of Noah's Flood.

But Lyell's guidance emboldened him to trust his
senses for an explanation of the sand-dunes. He saw
"absolute proofs of the recent elevation of the land,"
just as he had seen undubitably that Tierra del Fuego
had subsided. So long as he was in South America he

continued to see, as if he were looking at photographs of scenes in past ages, the proofs of the rising and falling of large regions. The grandeur of these movements of the earth's crust, and the meaning of them in reading geological history, was henceforth a perpetual exhilaration to him. His careful but fearless notations of great fluctuations of level became one of the treasuries of geology.

He passed close to the fort of Argentina, which he had visited a year before with Fitz-Roy, and rode to the harbor in Bahia Blanca, where he was to rendezvous with the *Beagle*. At this time he was relishing an armadillo roasted in its shell, and was digging for fossil armadillos in "a perfect catacomb of extinct races." It was curious to see—very curious indeed—how armadillos had been "created" so different in size, so similar in pattern. At just what moment, by what means, had this recent species been "called into being"?

All manner of ancient monsters were exhumed. There was "an extinct kind of horse." There was "the Toxodon, perhaps one of the strangest animals ever discovered. How wonderfully are the different *Orders*— at the present time so well separated—blended together in different points of the structure of the Toxodon!" Such blending of *orders* really seemed a bit freakish for the handiwork of a "creative force."

Darwin was visualizing these monsters as they secured their food: "With their great tails and their huge heels firmly fixed *like a tripod* on the ground, they could freely exert the full force of their most powerful arms and great claws. . . . The Mylodon, moreover, was furnished with a long extensile tongue like that of the giraffe, which by one of those beautiful provisions of nature, thus reaches with the aid of its long neck its leafy food." Darwin wanted to picture the vegetation on which the Mylodon fed. He thought this need not have been luxuriant, and speaks out with a sudden conviction that startles a reader: "That large animals require a luxuriant vegetation has been a general assumption which has passed from one work to another; but I do not hesitate to say that it is completely false, and that it has vitiated the reasoning of geologists on some points of great interest in the ancient history of the world." The words sound rash. But they had been carefully weighed. It is doubtful whether any similar bold challenge in Darwin's published work was ever found false. At least it was always based on thorough and acute observation.

Read the *Journal* for the following weeks and realize what pictures of the ways of life were being hung in Darwin's mental gallery. If you lack time to read, imagine. Nothing so spectacular as a Toxodon was encountered every week during the next three months, but Darwin had no need of monstrosities to stimulate his mind. His endless curiosity could find rewards just as rich by poking into mud, or watching ostriches take to the water, or examining a bird that was a combination of quail and snipe. Always he vivified and personified what he saw. The casaritas, birds which bore six feet in the ground for a nest, continued to perforate a mud wall: "I do not doubt that each bird, though they were constantly flitting over the low wall, as often as it came to daylight on the opposite side, was greatly surprised at the marvelous fact." He observed something about rattlesnakes that seemed to him very curious and instructive: "Every character, even though it may be in some degree independent of structure, has a tendency to vary by slow degrees." He found a little toad: "If we imagine, first, that it had been steeped in the blackest ink, and then, when dry, allowed to crawl over a board freshly painted with the brightest vermilion, so as to color the soles of its feet and parts of the stomach, a good idea of its appearance will be gained. . . . It is a fit toad to preach in the ear of Eve." He heard how Indians fight: "One dying Indian seized with his teeth the thumb of his adversary, and allowed his own eye to be——"

But I have no space for a catalogue of what Darwin heard and saw. On September 8 he hired a Gaucho to guide him from the head of Bahia Blanca to Buenos Ayres, four hundred miles across the Pampas, nearly the whole way through an uninhabited country. Now he was riding over clay and limestone, an utterly different formation from the gravel and boulders of the first three days. About him in every direction were "only scattered tufts of withered grass, without a single bush or tree to break the monotonous uniformity."

By evening he had reached the mysterious mountain called Ventana. "I am not aware that any foreigner, previous to my visit, has ascended this mountain; and indeed very few of the soldiers at Bahia Blanca knew anything about it. Hence we heard of beds of coal, of gold and silver, of caves, and of forests, all of which inflamed my curiosity, only to disappoint it. . . . I do not think nature ever made a more solitary, desolate pile of rock. The mountain is steep, extremely rugged, and broken, and entirely destitute of trees, and even bushes. The strange aspect of this mountain is contrasted by the sea-like plain, which abuts against its steep sides. . . . Here nature shows that the last movement before the bed of the sea is changed into dry land may sometimes be one of tranquillity." No object of Darwin's curiosity was enjoyed simply for itself, but for what it showed about the forces that operate in rocks and species.

Darwin tells of how one night, when he was en-

camped with a troop of soldiers and they were sitting
round the fire playing cards, "I retired to view such a
Salvator Rosa scene." It was an anxious night, for Indians had recently routed the garrison of the nearest
post, and the soldiers listened to every slight sound.

What a life of misery these men appear to us to lead!
. . . I used to think that the carrion vultures, while
seated on the little neighboring cliffs, seemed by their
very patience to say, "Ah! when the Indians come we
shall have a feast."

On September 16 one of the soldiers at the seventh
post had found thirteen deer killed by a hailstorm; at
night there was puma for dinner. On the 18th he had to
ride for many miles through a country flooded with
water above the horse's knees. But this was a slight
matter. The great affair was a flood of a certain plant
imported from Europe, which had prospered so ruth-
lessly that not a plant of any other species could now live
over an area of several hundred square miles. "I doubt
whether any case is on record of an invasion on so grand
a scale of one plant over aborigines." Quite a document,
this, in the records of the struggle for existence. Compare it with the case of the horses below.

On September 20 the party reached Buenos Ayres.
"On September 27 I set out on an excursion to Santa Fe,
which is situated nearly three hundred English miles
from Buenos Ayres, on the banks of the Paraná. . . .
I had a letter of introduction to an old Catalonian
Spaniard."

Of the record for the thirty days of this trip I will
offer only two items:

1. Certainly it is a marvelous fact in the history of
the Mammalia that in South America a native horse

should have lived, and disappeared, to be succeeded in after ages by the countless herds descended from the few introduced with the Spanish colonists!

2. The mosquitos were very troublesome. I exposed my hand for five minutes, and it was soon black with them; I do not suppose there could have been less than fifty, all busy sucking.

Early in November Darwin rejoined the *Beagle* at Montevideo, but found that another month would be necessary to complete the repairs of the consort *Adventure*, to work up the charts, and to provision the two vessels for a nine-month expedition to Tierra del Fuego. So there was a chance for another excursion. He left Montevideo November 14 on a triangular course: westward along the north bank of the Plata to a point opposite Buenos Ayres, thence north along the Uruguay River, then directly home by the long side of the triangle. He was gone two weeks and covered about four hundred miles.

It was early in this trip that he saw the strange bull-dog cattle, the "niata" breed, which furnished him such good material for his later writing on variation: "Their lower jaws project beyond their upper. . . . Their bare teeth and upturned nostrils give them the most ludicrous self-confident air of defiance imaginable." He carefully listened to testimony about the ways in which the niata characters are transmitted in breeding, and learned how ill-adapted the race is for feeding during a time of drought. The race *would not survive* in the struggle for existence if a drought were sufficiently prolonged. "This strikes me as a good illustration of how little we are able to judge from the ordinary habits of life on what circumstances, occurring only at long intervals, the rarity or extinction of a species may be determined."

One night Darwin was in talk with a man who owned a ranch thirty miles square and with an army captain. These gentlemen "expressed unbounded astonishment at the globe being round, and could scarcely credit that a hole would, if deep enough, come out on the other side." After much scientific talk the captain very seriously pledged Darwin to answer a question truthfully.

I trembled to think how deeply scientific it would be; it was: "Whether the ladies of Buenos Ayres were not the handsomest in the world." I replied like a renegade, "Charmingly so." He added, "I have one other question: Do ladies in any other part of the world wear such large combs?" I solemnly assured him that they did not. They were absolutely delighted. My excellent judgment in combs and beauty procured me a most hospitable reception.

It may be that the naturalist tells this story just as a bit of comic relief: he never could resist humor. But I am as serious as the captain when I quote it. I want my readers to bear it in mind when they hear how Darwin, as a reverend sage forty years later, answered some inquiries that were put to him by scientists who had less knowledge than they supposed they had. Darwin remained a diplomat to the end of his days. He was always ready to be a renegade of this amiable sort—if he was doing no harm and if he could procure a more hospitable reception for his theory of the origin of species. Some commentators on Darwin have interpreted his remarks as trustfully as the Argentine ranchero did.

Darwin had been bred to the utmost kindness and courtesy; if his whole life had been passed amid gentle English surroundings, he would have regarded the English standard of feeling as the norm of human nature. On the ride to the Uruguay he learned something else about human nature. He fell behind the party because his horse was tired. When the leader shouted, "Spur him," Darwin replied that the animal was exhausted. "Never mind," yelled the leader; "it is *my* horse."

I had some difficulty in making him comprehend that it was for the *horse's* sake that I did not choose to use my spurs. He exclaimed with a look of great surprise, "Que cosa!" It was clear that such an idea *had never before entered his head.*

On his way back to Montevideo he was told of some "giant's bones" at a ranch-house, and bought the head of a Toxodon for eighteen pence. Of course these bones were considered to be the remains of a human giant. The theology of England a century previous had required that mastodon bones should be human; long after 1833 it was still necessary for Professor Silliman of Yale to try to persuade Americans that mastodon bones were not human. Experiences like these with giant's bones and a flat earth taught Darwin how little difference there is intellectually between a South American ranchero and a Rev. William Buckland of Oxford who wrote (in 1823) a famous treatise on *Organic Remains Contained in Caves Attesting the Action of a Universal Deluge.* The treatise was still influential and a pride to its author—real scientist though he was—in 1833. Darwin was learning a sympathy for him and all the host of Goliath in England, but it was a sympathy of which Buckland could not be proud.

"December 6. The *Beagle* sailed from the Rio Plata, never again to enter its muddy stream. . . . I often towed astern a net made of bunting, and thus caught many curious animals. Of Crustacea there were many strange and undescribed genera. . . . One is very re-

markable from the structure of its hind pair of legs.
. . . I suppose this beautiful and most anomalous
structure is *adapted* to take hold of floating marine
animals.''

"The guanacos appear to have favorite spots for
lying down to die. . . . I remember having seen in a
ravine a retired corner covered with bones of the goat.
. . . .I mention these trifling circumstances because in
certain cases they might explain the occurrence of a
number of uninjured bones in a cave." As an example
of one of these possible cases: an elaborate theological
argument, based on *Organic Remains in Caves* might
have to be altered if some observant naturalist should
keep his eyes open for several years in South America.

Perhaps you object to being swung ashore so abruptly when you supposed you were under full sail for Beagle
Channel. But Darwin was no respecter of his reader's
comfort when he assembled data about the ways of life.

By December 23 the *Beagle* had covered only three-
fourths of the way to Jemmy Button's home. A very
pleasant Christmas Day was spent at Port Desire. The
crews of the *Beagle* and the *Adventure* went ashore and
had a field-day of racing, jumping and wrestling. It was
here that Darwin spent the second birthday of his new
life, December 27, 1833.

CHAPTER VII

The Third and Fourth Years in South America

DARWIN spent the last forty-five years of his life writing books in England. The meaning and value of his life is in those books. Hence it may seem queer that a biographer should so magnify the space devoted to four youthful years of excursions in South America—a mere lark, it might seem, compared with the momentous achievements of ten times that number of years which followed. But in truth the great career of thought is all sketched, outdoors and romantically, in this youthful period. The studious decades that succeeded only amplified, by reading and experiment, the thoughts engendered in South America. If we are familiar with the years of travel, we can easily and quickly understand all the others. I am not lengthening out the *Beagle* period in order to make a better story, but to convey a better knowledge of the life of Charles Darwin.

1834

The first half of 1834 was spent in the now familiar regions of the southeast coast; the latter half was in a new scene, the west coast.

When the *Beagle* was working out of Port Desire, January 4, she struck heavily against a rock. "I was instantly convinced," says Fitz-Roy, "that we had hit the very rock on which the *Beagle* struck in 1829, in the night—a danger we never again could find by daylight till this day." The accident is of interest to us because later the *Beagle* had to be beached for the repair of the damage, and at this time the artist of the expedition was moved to draw the only authentic picture we have of the vessel that carried Darwin (opposite this page).

What Darwin was about during the next three months will appear in a few excerpts from Fitz-Roy's *Narrative*:

January 9. One day Mr. Darwin and I undertook an excursion from Port San Julian, two hundred miles south of Port Desire, in search of fresh water. After a very fatiguing walk not a drop could be found. I lay down on the top of a hill, too tired and thirsty to move farther, seeing two lakes of water, as we thought, about two miles off, but unable to reach them. Mr. Darwin thought he could get to the lakes. We watched him anxiously, saw him stoop down, but immediately leave it, and we knew by his slow returning pace that the apparent lakes were "salinas." . . . About dusk I could move no farther . . . and lay down to sleep. . . . Towards morning we all got on board, and no one suffered afterwards from the over-fatigue except Mr. Darwin, who had had no rest during the whole of the thirsty day—now a matter of amusement, but at the time a very serious affair.

[During January and February the *Beagle* was sounding and reckoning longitude between Port Desire and the Strait of Magellan, working back and forth.]

February 27. Crossed Nassau Bay, and the following day entered Beagle Channel.

March 5. The *Beagle* anchored at Woollya. The wigwams in which I had left York, Jemmy, and Fuegia were found empty, though uninjured. They seemed to have been deserted many months. . . . In the other canoe was a face which I knew, yet could not name. . . . A sudden movement of the hand to his head (as a sailor touches his cap) at once told me it was indeed Jemmy Button—but how altered! I could scarcely restrain my feelings, and I was not the only one so troubled by his squalid, miserable appearance. . . . York and Fuegia left him some months before our arrival, and the last act of the cunning fellow was to rob poor Jemmy of all his clothes, nearly all the tools, and various other necessaries.

After witnessing this failure Darwin considered it useless to send missionaries to the Fuegians. So would you or I or any ordinary person. The state of mind is not worth recording. What most of us could not do would be to reverse our judgment when our prejudice was thirty-five years old, send five pounds sterling to the Fuegian mission, and an annual check thereafter. That was Darwin's way of dealing with new evidence.

The *Beagle* sailed from Woollya to the Falklands for the second time, remaining there a month. It was a gloomy visit. There had been a mutiny of the Indian and Gaucho soldiers, who had murdered five of the twenty-three settlers, driven the rest to live on shell-fish, and pillaged the houses. The survivors were saved by a detachment of marines from H. M. S. *Challenger*, a vessel whose record was to be spread at great length in Fitz-Roy's log of the following year. Fitz-Roy found the body of the governor's agent, Brisbane, and thus comments:

He was murdered by villains; he was mangled by them to satisfy their hellish spite; dragged by a lasso, at a horse's heels, and left to be eaten by dogs.

Darwin was learning by direct contact those fearful truths about human nature which most of us have to gather dimly from cold type. We can gauge the effect on his compassionate mind by the fierceness of Fitz-Roy's words. Fitz-Roy was not a tender-hearted college student; in an age of harshness at sea he was noted for the severity and testiness of his discipline; yet even he was moved to passion by the sight of what human beings had done on the Falklands. I would not argue that any particular episode like this had a definite effect on Darwin's mode of thought. I am indicating how five years of such episodes wrought in his mind the alteration from pleasant assumptions to stern realization. It was a change never brought about in Sedgwick or Buckland or Owen—or even in Lyell.

One of those who escaped the mutineers was a Scotchman named Low, the captain of a sealer, who entered Fitz-Roy's service on the *Adventure.* He knew, from long years of following his trade, more about Tierra del Fuego than any other man in the world, and was of great use to Fitz-Roy and Darwin.

Just before leaving the Falklands (April 6) Fitz-Roy buried a lieutenant from the *Challenger,* who had been drowned three months previously, but whose body could not then be found. Fitz-Roy had the grave dug alongside the grave of his clerk Hellyer.

Darwin's visits to the Falklands have since been commemorated by naming after him a harbor and a station of the Falkland Islands Company.

One of the most notable of Darwin's geological experiences was a three-week expedition up the Santa Cruz River, April 18—May 8. If you look at a map of South America and run your eye southward from the Rio Negro to the Strait of Magellan, you will see eight large streams flowing into the Atlantic, and the Santa Cruz, just below the fiftieth parallel of latitude, seems one of the smallest. But some of these are "arroyos," watercourses which may carry great floods for brief seasons, but are otherwise dry beds; and others of them, though magnificent on a map, may at times dwindle to very small volume. Fitz-Roy assures us that "south of the Negro only the Santa Cruz flows with a full and strong stream throughout the whole year." No white man had

ever ascended it. The Captain resolved to explore it.
After laying the *Beagle* ashore at the flood of a forty-foot
tide and repairing the injury to her hull, Fitz-Roy
moored her in the estuary. He made up a party of
eighteen sailors, five officers, and Mr. Darwin; and fitted
out three light and specially strengthened whale-boats.
These had to be towed the whole distance above the
estuary.

Half the party at a time, spelling each other in
hour shifts, walked the shore like canal-boat mules,
pulling the string of boats by means of a canvas harness
across each man's chest. Officers and Mr. Darwin "willingly took their share of the work with the men, and
stood watch-duty at night." The current of blue water
from the melting snow of the Andes had a temperature
of forty-five degrees—colder than the glacier-chilled
water of Beagle Channel. Small wonder that the party
"shunned their usual ablutions." The stream was from
three to four hundred yards broad, seventeen feet deep
in the middle, and flowed seven miles an hour. Against
such a current only two miles an hour could be made by
the party that towed, or "tracked," on shore.

Tracking was difficult and tedious; many were the
thorny bushes through which one half of the party on
the rope dragged their companions. Once in motion,
no mercy was shown: if the leading man could pass, all
the rest were bound to follow. Many were the duckings,
and not few the wear and tear of clothes, shoes, and skin.
. . . We had to contend against high cliffs, over whose
upper edges it was difficult to convey the tow-line. . . .
This day we passed some earthy cliffs between two and
three hundred feet high, and where they came in our
way it was extremely difficult to manage the tow-line;
but by veering out at times a great length of tow-line our
object was accomplished without any disaster. . . .
Difficult places to pass—delays caused by embarking and

disembarking frequently to change banks . . . occupied so much time that we did not average more than twelve miles in one day; and even that small distance was not accomplished without making both shoulders and feet sore.

What impressed the explorers most—barring, of course, geology—was the cold. Mr. Darwin's net was frozen so stiff one night that it was difficult to stow. The sextant was injured by the frost. Sleep was broken by the cold; men wanted to be first at the rope in the morning, to warm up. "Scarcely could we find bushes enough to make our nightly fires. . . . There may be honor among thieves, but there was little to be found during a cold night among our party, for the fire of those who happened to be on watch was sure to blaze cheerily, at the expense of the sleepers."

A lookout for Indians was constantly necessary: "We had not advanced an hour this morning, when fresh tracks of Indians on horseback, trailing their long lances, aroused our utmost vigilance."

So for ten days the party followed the winding stream, obliged to cover two miles for every mile of progress toward the Andes. The utter monotony of the scenery called forth all Fitz-Roy's power of description. Darwin hits it off thus: "We watched for the most trivial signs of change. The drifted trunk of a tree or a boulder was hailed with joy, as if we had seen a forest."

I quote from the Captain's *Narrative:*

April 29. Mr. Stokes and Mr. Darwin descried distant mountains in the west, covered with snow. At last, then, the Andes were in sight.

May 3. In the distant west the Cordillera of the Andes stretched along the horizon. During three days we had advanced towards those distant mountains, seeing them at times very distinctly; yet this morning our distance seemed nearly as great as on the day we first saw their snow-covered summits.

May 4. Our provisions being almost exhausted, and everyone weary and footsore, I decided upon walking overland to the westward, as far as we could go in one day, and then setting out on our return to the *Beagle*. . . . At noon we halted on a rising ground, made observations, rested and eat our meal, on a spot which we found to be only sixty miles* from the nearest water of the Pacific Ocean. . . . We were about a hundred and forty miles, in a straight line, from the estuary of the Santa Cruz. . . . and about thirty miles from the Andes.

The return trip, down the swift current, was made in three days.

Darwin is extraordinarily brief in his account of this journey, and for a good reason: the profound geological meaning of it could not be made entertaining to general readers. So he appeals to them with an account of the condors. As he watched them wheeling and soaring for hours he grew curiously forgetful of the struggle for existence and imagined himself circling in the clear air: "On some occasions I am sure that they do this only for pleasure." He tells of an experiment he carried out at Valparaiso to test their power of scent, which is naturally supposed to be highly refined:

The condors were tied in a long row at the bottom of a wall; and having folded up a piece of meat in white paper, I walked backwards and forwards, carrying it in my hand at the distance of about three yards from them, but no notice whatever was taken. I then threw it on the ground, within one yard of an old male bird; he looked at it for a moment with attention, but then regarded it no more. With a stick I pushed it closer and closer, un-

---

*Even on Fitz-Roy's own map the distance seems twice this; and I can not make it less by recent maps. How Fitz-Roy calculated is not explained, but he may have measured from the spot to the eastern end of a stream flowing into the Pacific.

til at last he touched it with his beak; the paper was then instantly torn off with fury, and at the same moment every bird in the long row began struggling and flapping its wings. Under the same circumstances it would have been quite impossible to have deceived a dog.

If I had made such an experiment, I should have supposed that I had settled the question of a condor's power of scent. The Darwinian mind is different.

The evidence in favor of and against the acute smelling powers of carrion-vultures is singularly balanced. Darwin could remain eternally curious. He was forever inventing ingenious experiments of convincing simplicity, always framing theories to account for the results— but never in love with his solution, never allowing it to harden into conviction.

He examined the condor's flight with minute attention.

I intently watched, from an oblique position [i. e., as the Ancient Mariner "looked sideways up"], the outlines of the separate and great terminal feathers of each wing; and these separate feathers, if there had been the least vibratory movement, would have appeared as if blended together; but they were seen distinct against the blue sky.

His interest was not centered on the mechanics of flight, for he concludes:

However this may be, it is truly wonderful and beautiful to see so great a bird, hour after hour, without any apparent exertion, wheeling and gliding over mountain and river.

If a man could understand the operation of one bird's wing-feathers, he would have a clue to all adaptations for

locomotion in the air or water. If he could understand
how a condor was adapted for securing food, he might
see far into other puzzles of the struggle for existence.
The condor is in the severest competition with hawks and
pumas for detecting bodies of guanacos; the fox lives by
somehow detecting the whereabouts of mice; mice eat
each other. Any animal of Patagonia which was a little
less keen than others might perish in the struggle for
existence. Hence any detailed knowledge of a condor's
flight or scent or vision might reveal a great, unexpected
field of further knowledge. You never can tell what
casual shred of a fact may show where the wind of truth
blows. If you are a Darwin, you will always be quest-
ing for facts, as naturally and zealously as a hound will
sniff at every slot.

If you are a Darwin you will realize that some basalt
blocks in the Santa Cruz River may furnish a clue to a
part of the species problem. For it will be evident to
you that the mystery of species ramifies everywhere and
can be dissected only by prying at every obstacle to any
sort of knowledge of natural forces. Species, you see,
have always been dying out—because they were not well
enough adapted? Perhaps so. Species have forever
been "created"—possibly by natural law? The record
of fossils tells us about ancient species, which were somehow "called into being" and flourished and dwindled and
died out. Lyell says that all this vast history of the
rocks is to be read by observing natural forces *now* in
operation. Here is a great force, the turbulent might
of a river, which has evidently transported basalt blocks.

From the first starting I had carefully examined the
gravel in the river, and for the last two days had noticed
the presence of *a few small pebbles* of a very cellular
basalt. . . . This morning, however, pebbles of the
same rock *suddenly* became abundant. . . . Above that

limit immense fragments of primitive rocks were equally numerous. None of the fragments of any considerable size had been washed *more than three or four miles* down the river below their parent source. . . . This example is a most striking one of *the inefficiency of rivers* in transporting even moderate-sized fragments.

For a hundred and forty miles Darwin had seen evidence that the whole plain of Patagonia was a mass of gravel and boulders which had been carried eastward from the Andes. He had seen, as obviously as if he had looked at a piece of layer-cake in a pantry, that a mighty sheet of lava—increasing uniformly in thickness from one hundred and twenty feet on its eastern edge to three hundred and twenty feet where the party turned back— had been cleft where the river ran. He could see, as plainly as we can see ripple-marks of an ebbing tide on a beach, the successive coast-lines of former ages, rising in steppes from east to west. Some long history was to be read here. At every stage of it new species had been created, as an integral part of the history. How could the writing of nature be deciphered?

If I had space, I could prove that South America was here formerly cut off by a strait, joining the Atlantic and Pacific Oceans, like that of Magellan. . . . No possible action of any flood could thus have modeled the land. . . . It is, I believe, quite impossible to explain the transportal of these gigantic masses of rock so many miles from their parent source on any other theory except that of floating icebergs.

How Darwin laughed at himself fifteen years later for not *seeing* how the boulders of Patagonia and the bell-stone of Shrewsbury had been transported. Yet he had almost seen what the gravel-beds placarded before his eyes. He had at least not imagined that Noah's flood could have transported boulders. It was true in 1834 that no other theory than that of Lyell's icebergs was worth considering. And young Darwin could hardly be blamed for not divining a cause which made every geologist gasp when he first heard it proposed. Darwin committed himself to the best explanation available, announced it boldly, and longed for a better one.

The cross-section of Patagonia, cut by the Santa Cruz River, had shown him something more valuable than facts: it had shown the immense difficulty of learning anything about species. For the history of the warfare of oceans and mountains can only be read, in the last analysis, by understanding the history of the fossil species imbedded in rocks. When an inquirer has learned the full intricacy of his task he is prepared for it. On the trip up the Santa Cruz Darwin got an inkling of the greatness of the question which was before him.

For a month after the trip the *Beagle* was busy near the eastern end of the Strait of Magellan. Then she sailed half-way through it, worked her way out from the southern bend of it, passed the Furies, and then went through a stretch of sea where the waves break on such a multitude of islets that the region is named The Milky Way. "One sight of such a coast," says Darwin, "is enough to make a landsman dream for a week of shipwrecks, perils, and death; and with this sight we bade farewell forever to Tierra del Fuego." The *Beagle* stood out into the Pacific with every inch of canvas set.

For four hundred miles the coast on the right presented a continuous array of glaciers. Darwin noted that even in low mountains, not over four thousand feet high, in a latitude no farther from the pole than the English lake region, "every valley was filled with streams of ice descending to the coast." Almost every arm of the sea, northward to a latitude as low as that of Paris, was terminated by "tremendous and astonishing glaciers." He notes that "some of the icebergs were loaded with blocks, of no inconsiderable size, of granite and other rocks, *different from the clay-slate of the surrounding mountains*." Here was demonstration of Lyell's theory. "These facts are of high geological interest with respect to the climate of the northern hemisphere at the period when the boulders were transported." Quite so. But why not go one step further with an equally obvious fact? "Few geologists now doubt that those erratic boulders which lie near lofty mountains have been pushed forward *by the glaciers themselves*." Then why not speculate about possible glaciers on the eastern slope of the Andes? So near was Darwin to disclosing the greatest secret of geology. His failure to take the last little step was the best lesson of his life for all attempts at reading nature.

On June 27 the purser died, "and we committed the body of our companion to the seaman's grave." At midnight of the 28th the *Beagle's* anchor was let go in the harbor of San Carlos, on the north end of the island of Chiloe, in latitude forty-two degrees, close to the coast of Chile. July 22 she was in Valparaiso, then a town of five thousand population. Here the Captain spent four months in working up his records. It was a time of severe despondency for him, because he could no longer afford to maintain the *Adventure* at his own expense and the Admiralty had refused to assume the cost. Fitz-Roy describes himself as dispirited, mortified, in ill health, careless about making the best bargain for the sale of the *Adventure*. The invaluable pilot Low had to be used aboard a whale-boat for exploring inlets.

From August 14 to September 27 Darwin made a four-hundred-mile horseback trip. His course was, very roughly, an ellipse: twenty miles north of Valparaiso, thence east fifty, thence south one hundred and seventy (through the city of Santiago), thence to the coast and thence north to the starting-point. He set forth from the Valparaiso home of an old schoolmate, visited an estate that formerly belonged to an English lord, was diverted by a Cornish superintendent of a copper mine, and was entertained by an American operator of a gold mine. His readers are regaled with all sorts of anecdotes and descriptions: of the sap of palms that will not exude down hill, of the Guasos who are not gentlemen like the cutthroat Gauchos, of wallowing through snow-drifts piled up by a storm that came down upon them, of orange orchards, of rawhide suspension bridges that "oscillated rather fearfully," of floating islands that act as ferry-boats for cattle, of a German naturalist who was arrested because he impiously planned to turn caterpillars into butterflies.

All this assortment of trinkets is for amusement. His own heart, of course, was in the panorama of geology.

The proofs of the elevation of this whole line of coast are unequivocal. . . . I was much surprised to find under the microscope that the vegetable mould is really marine mud. . . . These basins, I have no doubt, are the bottoms of ancient inlets and deep bays, such as *at the present day* intersect every part of Tierre del Fuego and the western coast. Chile must formerly have resembled the latter country in the configuration of its land and water. The resemblance was occasionally shown strikingly when a level fog-bank covered, as with a mantle, all the lower parts of the country: the white vapor, curling into ravines, beautifully represented little coves and bays; and here and there a solitary hillock, peeping up, showed that it had formerly stood there as an islet.

Who can avoid wondering at the force which has upheaved these mountains, and even more so at the countless ages which it must have required to have broken through, removed, and leveled the whole masses of them? When in Patagonia I wondered how any mountain-chain could have supplied such masses, and not have been utterly obliterated. We must not now reverse the wonder, and doubt whether all-powerful time can grind down mountains—even the gigantic Cordillera—into gravel and mud.

At the first glance of this view it was quite evident that the plain represented the extent of a former inland sea.

Toward the close of this excursion Darwin reports that "although very unwell, I managed to collect from the tertiary formation some marine shells." All the rest of his life he was to be very unwell, struggling against weakness and pain. During October he was in bed at his schoolmate's home in Valparaiso.

Chapter XIII of his *Journal* begins thus:

November 10th. The *Beagle* sailed from Valparaiso to the south, for the purpose of surveying the southern part of Chile, the Island of Chiloe, and the Chonos Archipelago. On the 21st we anchored in the bay of S. Carlos, the capital of Chiloe.

While Darwin listened to the anchors rattling down, the one-hundred-and-eighty-ton brig *Pilgrim*, ninety-nine days out of Boston, bound to California for a cargo of hides, was two hundred miles to the west of the *Beagle*, heading for Robinson Crusoe's island. On board was a young man who had changed his Harvard frock for a sailor's checked shirt and was spending two years before the mast. Four days previous the *Pilgrim* had lost George Ballmer overboard and had scored the "black day" in her log. Four days later Dana was one of the lucky squad told off to row ashore for water on San Juan Fernandez. It is doubtful whether either of these adventurers ever knew that the other had been near him in the Pacific.

Through the autumn of 1834 Darwin was especially struck by the distribution of species. He saw the dominant beech of the southern islands thin out and grow stunted, so that he could mark rather exactly its northern limit. In Tierra del Fuego the luxuriant kelp on every rock sustained a teeming world of life.

A great volume might be written, describing the inhabitants of these beds of sea-weed. . . . The leaves are thickly encrusted with corallines. . . . Innumerable crustacea frequent every part of the plant. . . . Often as I recurred to a branch of the kelp I never failed to discover new animals of a new and curious structure. [He describes what would happen if the kelp were destroyed.] Amidst the leaves numerous species of fish live, which nowhere else could find food or shelter; with their destruction the many cormorants and other fishing-birds, the otters, seals, and porpoises, would perish also; and lastly the Fuegian savage, the miserable lord of this miserable land, would redouble his cannibal feast, decrease in numbers, and perhaps cease to exist.

But a few hundred miles north of Tierra del Fuego, though the climate seems very similar, the kelp is not the basis of all life, and the economy of nature is profoundly different. Darwin was taught, as if in a specially prepared museum, that very slight and intricately adjusted changes in an environment may "call into being" a new fauna, and that the interrelations of life are past finding out. Of a great bay south of Chiloe he remarks:

The number of seals which we saw was quite astonishing: every bit of flat rock, and parts of the beach, were covered with them.

Of course Darwin could have read about similar cases of prolific swarming of a certain species in a certain locality, but reading can not convey the knowledge that is gained by hearing the yapping of thousands of seals which plunge off rocks on every hand. How comes it that they are so marvelously adapted to *this* locality, and that they were not created in many similar places? How comes it that a certain species of parasite is adapted to a certain species of beech in one region, that a related species is adapted to a related species of beech in another part of the world, and that a third species of the genus is adapted to a third species of the beech genus in a third portion of the world?

How does it happen that species vary so marvelously on neighboring islands? Darwin wonders if a mouse sometimes escapes from the nest of a hawk which has carried it from its habitat and thus distributed the species: "Some such agency is necessary to account for the distribution of smaller gnawing animals." He wonders about the "great proponderance of certain common genera, such as the finches," in any given district. His mind was at work on finches. It was preparing for a very strange distribution of these birds that was to be encountered next year. They seem to play so insignificant a part in the great scheme of nature that "one is apt to wonder why they were created." He was soon to find far deeper reason for wondering about the "creation" of any species.

He wondered at the wild potato in the Chonos Islands: Professor Henslow said that it was only a variety of the Valparaiso potato, but that some authorities thought it was a distinct species. Darwin comments:

It is remarkable that the same plant should be found on the sterile mountains of central Chile, where a drop of rain does not fall for six months, and within the damp forests of these southern islands.

A species may range widely through varying environments, or a species may be crowded out of existence by a very slight change of environment. Distribution is a singular element in the species mystery.

But was the potato of Valparaiso the same as the potato of Chonos? It was not exactly the same. It was a "variety." Some judges thought it was so different as to be a species. These judges and Professor Henslow seemed to take no interest in agreeing upon any limit for a variety. One specialist felt in his soul that the two potatoes were varieties within a species; another specialist had an intuition that the two potatoes were sundered by an impassable chasm of "creation," so that they were essentially as different as kelp and beech trees. But neither specialist could define his limits. All the distinctions were intangible matters of what somebody "thought." If the two potatoes were only varieties, the difference between them was negligible; if they were species, the difference between them was a mighty and eternal barrier of creation.

Lyell could sit at his desk and construct excellent logic about the profound distinction between a variety and a species. If Lyell had rowed in a whale-boat to the island of Lemuy for a potato, if he had then ridden into the high Andes for another potato, if he had laid them side by side for study, then he could not possibly have told whether they were varieties or species. But in his study he could philosophize about the abysm that separated the abstraction called a variety from the abstraction called a species. Between these two abstractions a great gulf of logic was fixed. Between the two potatoes not a crack of logic could be made. Lyell argued for the abstractions, while Darwin cared more for observing potatoes. That is the difference between the Lyells and the Darwins in science.*

If Lyell had conceded that a variety of potato could not be distinguished from a species, he would next have had to concede that man could not be biologically distinguished from an orang-outang. This was revolting to gentlemanlike instincts. But Darwin was not interested in preserving his biological status; he was just curious about *the limit* beyond which a variety was elevated to the mysterious peerage of "species." What is a species of potato? Night and day the query was never out of his mind. As the midsummer of December came on, he looked with ever-increasing wonder at the variant types of life which he found in water, on rocks, under trees, and in air.

He learned of curious dogs that are employed to kill pumas: "They are born with a particular instinct for this sport." Of the singular Turco bird he says, "It requires little imagination to believe that the bird is ashamed of itself." The Turco is so outlandish a creature that it looks "like a vilely stuffed specimen escaped from some museum." Its structure is so anomalous that "it seems to connect the thrushes with the gallinaceous order." Darwin suspects that the naturalist Molina omitted this very common Turco from his detailed descriptions of all the birds of Chile because he was at a loss how to classify it. Darwin describes a petrel as "an example of those extraordinary cases of a bird evidently belonging to one well-marked family, yet both in its habits and structure allied to a very distinct tribe." He judges that certain plants, "though possessing a very close general resemblance to the English species of the

---

*If you have a conception of Lyell that makes this seem a hasty remark, suspend judgment until you have read Chapter XII.

same genera, are different." All sorts of plants and animals were everlastingly different from other closely allied species. Who could guess at *the limit* where these differences become great enough to deserve the sacred name of "species"? In the Chonos Islands there was a beaverlike animal, but it had a round tail and lived only in salt water. There was a barking-bird: "I defy any-one at first to feel certain that a small dog is not yelping somewhere in the forest."

Some of the birds flourished incredibly. "A second species of petrel frequents the inland sounds in very large flocks. . . . Hundreds of thousands flew in an irregular line for several hours in one direction." Yet a certain fox was known to live on only one island and to be very scarce even there. How curious that the creative force, which Lyell said "foresaw" the needs of each species, should make a bird so prolific and a fox so unable to multiply. Was the creative power entertain-ing itself by lavishing gifts on the most rapacious of birds, while barely allowing a timid fox to perpetuate it-self? It was all very queer.

The fox furnished an illustration of Darwin's ability to find specimens of even the rarest animals. If I were to charter a steamer and spend a year among the Chonos Islands, I should fail to come upon the animals I most coveted. Darwin knew how to coax rare birds out of the thicket by standing perfectly still and letting their curiosity draw them to him. Darwin saw one of these hitherto undescribed foxes, which was absorbed in watch-ing two officers working the theodolite on the beach; he stole up quietly and knocked the fox on the head with his hammer. "This fox, more curious or more scientific than the generality of his brethren, is now mounted in the museum of the Zoological Society."

On the 20th of December "we bade farewell to the

south and with a fair wind turned the ship's head northward." But foul and boisterous weather soon followed,
and the *Beagle* was kept prisoner in a harbor that was
none too safe. "This Christmas," says Fitz-Roy, "was
a somber period. All looked dismal around us; our
prospects for the future were sadly altered; and our
immediate task was the surveying of a place swampy
with rain, tormented by storms, without the interest even
of a population."

But a most extraordinary human interest was encountered only three days later. Five men were seen signal-
ing from a point of land as the *Beagle* anchored off
Chiloe. "A boat was sent to them, and directly she
touched the land they rushed into her, without saying
a word, as men would if pursued by a dreadful enemy."
For fourteen months these deserters from a New Bed-
ford whaler had succeeded in living, bare-handed against
nature, in the thickets along the shore; for the past
seven months they had not seen a single sail. "Yet these
five men were in better condition than any five individuals belonging to our ship." They were an interesting exhibit in Darwin's panorama of the struggle for
existence.

1835

The first eight months of this year were spent in the
neighborhood of Valparaiso; the last four months included the memorable visit to the Galapagos and the
first part of the homeward passage across the Pacific.

In the middle of January Darwin saw, from the harbor at the north end of Chiloe, an eruption of one of the
volcanos of the Andes. Later he learned that on the
same night a great volcano four hundred miles to the
north had erupted, and also a third volcano that had
been dormant for twenty-six years. At the same time

an earthquake was felt over the whole region. This night's happenings were the beginning of a long series of bold but judicious efforts to explain the coincidence of eruptions and earthquakes. By reasoning from the lava *now* flowing and the effects of earthquakes *now* felt, he attempted to reconstruct the chapters of mountain-making history written in the Andes. What most excited him was the *succession* of events, the *chronicle*: here had been a flow of lava; this had hardened and been eroded; then another flow had come; later there had been an elevation of the whole region. He was inquisitive about earthquakes as symptoms of dislocation of parts of the earth's crust while it was being forced upward—gradually, uniformly—into a mountain chain.

Eight months of continual deciphering of these histories, in a region which no European geologist had been able to visit, netted some great help to his master Lyell, and thus to the science of geology. For no other man was so great a power as Lyell in diffusing sound ideas about rocks. When Lyell read the reports that went to Henslow from this amateur observer in Chile, he knew with instant conviction that Darwin's work was dependable and shrewd. This young Darwin had the rare faculty of looking at the evidences before his eyes, and not being blinded by the shimmer of pre-conceived theories.

In proportion as science could learn how mountains were upheaved, it could deal more surely with the records of former life imbedded in the uplifted strata—that is, with species. In proportion as Darwin grew more familiar with uniformity in all the history of rock-making, his mind was less able to conceive those strange little miracles of "creation" of species, those millions of small catastrophes that were outside of any uniform natural law which could be detected in Chile.

By curious good fortune Darwin felt another earthquake a month later, believed to be the most severe one ever experienced on the coast. A biographer who expatiated on the effect that this produced in Darwin's mind might be accused of working for a dramatic effect. Darwin has relieved a biographer of the need of imagining.

A bad earthquake at once destroys our oldest associations: the earth, the very emblem of solidity, has moved beneath our feet like a thin crust over a fluid—one second of time has created in the mind a strange idea of insecurity, *which hours of reflection would not have produced*.

No number of hours of imagining crustal movements can produce the knowledge born of a minute of experience. In this way the earthquake typifies the whole of Darwin's observations in South America: one minute in which he heard savages yell, or sighted a strange genus in his net, or realized how a fox varied, or saw that an island had been raised ten feet in a moment—one such minute could thrust into his mind a seed of thought which no book or lecture would ever have planted there. It is astonishingly true that none of us conceive the forces of nature until we see and feel them.

Darwin felt the earthquake while he was lying down in a wood. The motion made him almost giddy.

The whole coast was strewed over with timber and furniture as if a thousand ships had been wrecked. . . . I believe this convulsion has been more effectual in lessening the size of the island of Quiriquina than the ordinary wear and tear of the sea and weather during the course of a whole century. . . . Both towns presented the most awful yet interesting spectacle I ever beheld. . . . It is quite impossible to convey the mingled feelings which I experienced. The strongest language of several officers of the *Beagle* failed to give a just idea of the scene of desolation. . . . In my opinion we have scarcely beheld, since leaving England, any sight so deeply interesting. . . . The most remarkable effect of this earthquake was the permanent elevation of the land. There can be no doubt that the land round the Bay of Concepcion was upraised two or three feet. . . . Captain Fitz-Roy found beds of putrid mussel-shells *still adhering to the rocks* ten feet above high-water mark. . . . At Valparaiso similar shells are found at the height of thirteen hundred feet; it is hardly possible to doubt that this great elevation has been effected by successive small uprisings, such as that which accompanied or caused the earthquake of this year. . . . The island of Juan Fernandez was violently shaken, and a volcano burst forth under water close to the shore. . . . We may confidently come to the conclusion that the forces which slowly and by little starts uplift continents, and those which at successive periods pour forth volcanic matter, are identical.

Darwin was to see in 1835 two sights more interesting than the effects of an earthquake. The first of these was the view from the top of the Andes, March 21. Fate seems to have contrived to educate Darwin for this ascent. At Cambridge she had fired him with a passion to climb Teneriffe, which is only twelve thousand feet high and offers only a view of an expanse of ocean; whereas the Andes carried him to a height of fourteen thousand feet, where kingdoms of mountain and ocean and plain were spread below him. Fate had instructed him, by months of riding and towing, how to conceive the wide, sunburned expanse of Pampas clay and Patagonian boulders as a unit. Fate had then made him familiar, through months of hardship in the rain-soaked, matted forests of the Chilean islands, with the details of the coast on the west. Last, she had given him demonstrations of how the Andes were slowly upraised through the ages. When he set out from Santiago, attended by a pack-train of ten mules, he was prepared, as no other climber of the Andes has ever been, to feel the full harmony of vast details over which his eye swept at one view.

It is familiarity with details that gives inspiration in a wide scene. If Darwin had been whisked to the top of the Andes by a railway as soon as he first stepped on South American soil, he could not really have seen the views. Let me illustrate by a petty episode, which will be a slight help in imagining what Darwin felt at the summit of the Piuquenes ridge. From a range of mountains less than four thousand feet high I once saw at sunset, when the air was perfectly clear and the conditions just suitable, an arch of rock that was forty miles away, across a channel of salt water. I had formerly been near this arch in a schooner and knew it was not fifty feet high; I knew of a man who had been drifted in a rowboat through the channel that was twenty miles wide; I knew intimately the twenty miles of land between me and the channel. So the view had a fulness of meaning that it could not have had for one who was a stranger to the region.

Lift up your imagination from this small scene to visualize Darwin at a height more than three times as great, looking three times as far, across the huge parallel ridges that melted softly down to the Pacific Ocean. A telescope might have shown him the *Beagle*. The record of the ages of rock-making lay legibly before him, telling the wonder-story of the uniformity of natural law.

When we reached the crest and looked backwards a glorious view was presented. The atmosphere resplendently clear; the sky an intense blue; the profound valleys; the wild broken forms; the heaps of ruins, piled up during the lapse of ages; the bright-colored rocks, contrasted with the quiet mountains of snow—all these together produced a scene no one could have imagined. Neither plant nor bird, excepting a few condors wheeling around the higher pinnacles, distracted my attention from the inanimate mass. I felt glad that I was alone: it was like watching a thunderstorm, or hearing in full orchestra a chorus of the Messiah.

From this ridge Darwin had to descend nine thousand feet and then climb ten thousand to reach the greatest height of the Portillo Pass, from which the east slope of the Andes drops precipitately to the Pampas. At the summit a cloud enveloped him. But lower down he got the full view.

This was a spectacle to which I had always looked forward with interest, but I was disappointed: at the first glance it much resembled a distant view of the ocean, but in the northern parts many irregularities were soon distinguishable. The most striking feature consisted in the rivers, which, facing the rising sun, glittered like silver threads, till lost in the immensity of the distance.

Perhaps one of the silver threads, just visible far to the south, was the headwaters of the Colorado, which he had crossed when he rode to Buenos Ayres.

He descended to the Pampas, turned north to the forlorn town of Mendoza and feasted on watermelons at a half-penny each, returned across the Andes by the lower pass where the trans-Andean railway now runs, and reached Santiago on April 8. "My excursion cost me twenty-four days, and never did I more deeply enjoy an equal space of time."

A few quotations will indicate the stimulus given to Darwin's imagination by this excursion. In the first one he is speaking of the roar of the mountain streams as they roll stones down their beds.

The thousands and thousands of stones, which, striking against each other, made the one dull uniform sound, were all hurrying in one direction. It was like thinking on time, where the minute that now glides past is irrecoverable. So it was with these stones; the ocean is their eternity, and each note of that wild music told of one more step towards their destiny. . . .

As often as I have seen beds of mud, sand, and shingle accumulated to the thickness of many thousand feet I have felt inclined to exclaim that causes such as the present rivers and the present beaches could never have ground down and produced such masses. But, on the other hand, when listening to the rattling noise of these torrents, and calling to mind that whole races of animals have passed away from the face of the earth, and that during this whole period, night and day, these stones have gone rattling onwards in their course, I have thought to myself, "Can any mountains, any continent, withstand such waste?" . . .

It is an old story, but not the less wonderful, to hear of shells which were once crawling on the bottom of the sea, now standing nearly fourteen thousand feet above its level. . . .

Daily it is forced home on the mind of the geologist that nothing, not even the wind that blows, is so unstable as the level of the crust of this earth. . . .

From this resemblance I *expected* to find silicified wood. . . . I was gratified in a very extraordinary manner. In the central part of the range, at an elevation of about seven thousand feet, I observed on a bare slope some snow-white projecting columns. These were petrified trees, eleven being silicified. . . . Mr. Robert Brown has been kind enough to examine the wood; he says it belongs to the fir tribe, partaking of the character of the Araucarian family, but with some curious points of affinity with the yew. . . . It required little geological practice to interpret the marvelous story which this scene at once unfolded, though I confess I was at first so much astonished that I could scarcely believe the plainest evidence. I saw the spot where a cluster of fine trees once waved their branches on the shores of the Atlantic, when that ocean (now driven back seven hundred miles) came to the foot of the Andes. I saw that they had sprung from a volcanic soil which had been raised above the level of the sea, and that subsequently this dry land, with its upright trees, had been let down into the depths of the ocean. In these depths the formerly dry land was covered by sedimentary beds, and these again by enormous streams of submarine lava—one such mass attaining the thickness of a thousand feet; and these deluges of molten stone and aqueous deposits five times alternately had been spread out. The ocean which received such thick masses must have been profoundly deep; but the subterranean forces exerted themselves, and I now beheld the bed of that ocean, forming a chain of mountains more than seven thousand feet in height. . . . Vast and scarcely comprehensible as such changes must ever appear, yet they have all occurred within a period recent when compared with the history of the Cordillera; and the Cordillera itself is absolutely modern as compared with many of the fossiliferous strata of Europe and America.

You will note how the *species* of fossil firs, which are in some ways curiously like yews, are an inseparable part of this story.

The species question is fundamental in all natural history. Darwin reveals that it was ever present in his thoughts while he listened to the symphonies of the mountains. As a footnote to a comment on the strange difference between the species on the two slopes of the Andes he remarks, apropos of "the admirable laws first laid down by Mr. Lyell":

The whole reasoning, of course, is founded on the assumption of the immutability of species; otherwise the difference in the species in the two regions might be considered as *superinduced during a length of time.**

Already he was thinking of the possibility that differences between species might be "superinduced." But by what agency? The agency which Lamarck assumed had not shown a vestige of itself in South America. The lives of all plants and animals had shown that they were marvelously *adapted* to secure a living in the struggle for existence. The agency that brought about the adaptations was shrouded completely. To conceive that in 1835 Darwin had much faith in Lyell's creation is difficult. It is likely that he was silently regarding it with astonishment.† For he has told us that in 1837 he "had *long* reflected on the origin of species"—and *long* would surely mean as much as two years.

The second sight more interesting than an earthquake in 1835 was the distribution of species on the Galapagos Islands, which Darwin reached in the middle of September.

Yes, I am omitting five months of Darwin's life in South America, months crowded with information and excitement. If I were writing a chronicle of the *Beagle*, I should tell of how she rescued the crew of H. M. S. *Challenger*, which went ashore three hundred and fifty miles south of Valparaiso, and of how she surveyed north of Valparaiso. I should enjoy telling at length how it happened that she picked up Mr. Darwin four hundred miles north of Valparaiso on the Fourth of July. He had spent two months in riding thither, making numerous side excursions, and seeing every day new

---

*This footnote was in the first edition, 1839.

†Sir Francis Darwin, in his preface to *The Foundations of the Origin of Species*, argues convincingly for the earliness of his father's doubts of fixity, notwithstanding his father's statement about "not recalling that I doubted."

phases of the mystery of species, especially of the human species. But I am not a chronicler. I omit all narrative unless it gives new light on what Darwin was about while he made books for forty-five years. I will note only two bits of comments made during the five months of adventure and sight-seeing from Valparaiso to Lima.

It is curious to observe how the seeds of the grass and other plants *seem* to accommodate themselves, as if by an acquired habit, to the quantity of rain.

Lamarck's easy-going theory is mere seeming. Lyell's smooth philosophy is not worth mentioning.

My geological examination of the country created a good deal of surprise amongst the Chileans. . . . Some (like a few in England who are a century behindhand) thought that all such inquiries were useless and impious.

Goliath always considers that a Darwin's curiosity is impious. As Darwin said, quoting the Chilenos: "It was quite sufficient that God had made the mountains." A scientist, if he wants to know the steps by which God evolves a butterfly out of a caterpillar, will seem an atheist to Goliath.

On September 15 the *Beagle* sighted the easternmost point of the Galapagos Islands. This group lies on the equator six hundred miles west of the coast. In early days it was a favorite resort of pirates. Ecuador had established sovereignty over it only three years before the arrival of the *Beagle*. By far the largest island is Albemarle, which has an area nearly as great as Delaware; there are five other islands which range downward from a fourth of this size, and nine that continue the dwindling to mere rocks. All are volcanic; the largest peaks are five thousand feet high. Their name is derived from the monstrous turtles (ga-lap'-a-gos) that are here found in abundance, but that exist nowhere else in the world.

The turtles are only the most spectacular of the exhibits of species that nature has arranged on these islands. Darwin devoted thirty pages of his *Journal* to exclaiming about the "truly wonderful" facts and the "remarkable" facts of which he "never could have dreamed."

More wonderful than the species of the Galapagos was the providence which had educated this particular man for this special task. It is not likely that there was in the world another naturalist who combined in one brain the boldness and inquisitiveness and carefulness that Darwin brought to bear on the distribution of the plants and animals of these strange islands. And even his penetrating curiosity could not have detected the significance of the variations from island to island if he had not been trained by four years of observing and pondering in tropical forests and dreary plains and swampy islands and snowy summits and bare intermountain valleys. It was Lyell, the keenest of all observers of geology, who most feelingly witnessed to his own blindness at first view of any place, and to the revelations of a second view after an interval of training in seeing what rocks declare. Any dull amateur observer knows how a cliff on a shore or some bushes in a desert can be vivified and made to tell audible stories after he has had a little training. Every professional naturalist is amazed to realize how much more he can learn to detect as the years of experience pass. The mind that detected *Flustra* at Newhaven when it was sixteen years old had been continually exercised in novelties for four years. It was prepared for the Galapagos.

If Fitz-Roy could have known what unseemly ideas

about evolution were taking shape here in Darwin's mind, he could not have written with more feeling about the generally diabolical aspect of the islands.

Our eyes and imagination were engrossed by the strange wildness of the view; for in such a place Vulcan might have worked. Amidst the most confusedly heaped masses of lava, black and barren, as if hardly yet cooled, innumerable craters showed their very regular, even artificial-looking, heaps. It was like immense iron works, on a Cyclopian scale! . . . From a height near Tagus Cove dismal indeed was the view. . . . To reflect that at some one period all was activity and dreadful combustion was very impressive.

Darwin's chapter on this archipelago is like a play in structure. The six opening pages are descriptive, to give the setting; the next twenty-one pages run steadily upward to a dramatic climax; the last three drop to the pleasant level of the tameness of the birds; the very end is a clear, quiet announcement of the center of the mystery—"hereditary instincts adapted to the stranger's craft or power."

Since some of my readers may be so incurious as never to read Darwin's Chapter XVII, and since there is not space to reprint it here, I must offer a few mangled fragments to indicate the direction which Darwin's mind took during the five weeks on the Galapagos. Even these will furnish some interest for a sympathetic reader who bears in mind:

1. That Darwin, from his youth up, had cared for nothing so much as a puzzle.
2. That he was confronted by "the mystery of mysteries."
3. That only two solutions had been offered by the world's best thinkers, and that he had seen no evidence which made either one possible.

4. That all the modern biological sciences were shaped by Darwin's solution.

Nominally he appears to accept Lyell's "creation," but he is wondering what rational meaning can be attached to the words "varieties produced by surroundings."*

The natural history of these islands is eminently curious, and well deserves attention. Most of the organic productions are aboriginal creations, found nowhere else. . . . Considering the small size of these islands, we feel the more astonished at the number of their aboriginal beings and at their confined range. . . . Within a period geologically recent the unbroken ocean was here spread out. Hence, both in space and time, we seem to be brought somewhat near to that great fact—that mystery of mysteries—the first appearance of new beings on this earth. . . . I can hardly doubt that this rat is merely a variety, produced by the new and peculiar climate, food, and soil, to which it has been subjected. Although no one has a right to speculate without distinct facts, yet even with respect to the Chatham Island mouse it should be borne in mind that it may possibly be an American species imported here. . . .

The other twenty-five birds consist, firstly, of a hawk, curiously intermediate in structure between a buzzard and the American group of carrion-feeding Polybori. . . . The remaining land-birds form a most singular group of finches, related to each other in the structure of their beaks, short tails, form of body, and plumage. . . . The most curious fact is the perfect gradation in the size of the beaks in the different species of *Geospiza* [a genus of the finches], from one as large as that of a hawfinch to that of a chaffinch. . . . There are no less than six species with insensibly graduated beaks. . . .

_____

*The following quotations about the Galapagos are taken from the second edition (1845). The substance of them was in the first edition (1839), but the chapter has been largely rewritten and the marvels of the distribution emphasized. The greatest difference in the second edition is the account of the tortoises: in the first edition Darwin politely accepted Fitz-Roy's idea of transportal on ships for food. For a comparison of the two editions see page 207.

Seeing this gradation and diversity of structure in one small, intimately related group of birds, one might really fancy that from an original paucity of birds in this archipelago one species had been taken and modified for different ends. . . .

Hence it would appear probable that the same causes which here make the immigrants of some species smaller make most of the peculiar species also smaller. . . . We may therefore conclude that the usual gaudy coloring of the intertropical productions is not related either to the heat or light of those zones, but to some other cause, perhaps to the conditions of existence being generally favorable to life. . . . Of toads and frogs there are none: I was surprised at this, considering how well suited for them the temperate and damp upper woods appeared to be. . . .

The absence of the frog family in the oceanic islands is the more remarkable when contrasted with the case of lizards, which swarm on most of the smallest islands. May this difference not be caused by the greater facility with which the eggs of lizards, protected by calcareous shells, might be transported through salt water than could the slimy spawn of frogs?

It would appear as if this lizard had been created in the center of the archipelago, and thence had been dispersed only to a certain distance. . . . The aquatic species is by far the most remarkable, because it is the only existing lizard which lives on marine vegetables. . . .

The fifteen kinds of sea-fish which I procured here are all new species. . . . Of land-shells I collected sixteen kinds (and two marked varieties), of which, with one exception, all are peculiar to this archipelago. . . . Mr. Cuming, before our voyage, procured here ninety species of sea-shells. . . . Of the ninety no less than forty-seven are unknown elsewhere—a wonderful fact, considering how widely distributed sea-shells generally are. . . . At the Galapagos we have a halting-place, where many new forms have been created, and whither these two great conchological provinces have each sent several colonists. . . .

Dr. Hooker informs me that the flora has an undoubted Western American character; nor can he detect in it any affinity with that of the Pacific.

The following paragraph merits the closest attention and two readings. It challenges the assumption—made by all previous reasoners about evolution—that similar environments will produce similar results on life. It asks why a creative power should so strangely limit its inventiveness to South American models.

We see that this archipelago, though standing in the Pacific Ocean, is zoologically part of America. If this character were owing merely to immigrants from America, there would be little remarkable in it; but we see that a vast majority of all the land animals, and that more than half of the flowering plants, are aboriginal productions. It was most striking to be surrounded by new birds, new reptiles, new shells, new insects, new plants, and yet by innumerable trifling details of structure, and even by the tones of voice and plumage of the birds, to have the temperate plains of Patagonia, or the hot, dry deserts of northern Chile, vividly brought before my eyes. Why, on these small points of land, which within a late geological period must have been covered by the ocean, which are formed of basaltic lava and therefore differ in geological character from the American continent, and which are placed under a peculiar climate—why were their aboriginal inhabitants . . . created on an American type of organization? It is probable that the islands of the Cape de Verd group resemble, in all their physical conditions, far more closely the Galapagos Islands than these latter physically resemble the coast of America; yet the aboriginal inhabitants of the two groups are totally unlike; those of the Cape de Verd Islands bearing the impress of Africa, as the inhabitants of the Galapagos archipelago are stamped with that of America.

Darwin now proceeds to a still greater marvel—the distribution of animals within the archipelago.

I have not as yet noticed by far the most remarkable feature in the natural history of this archipelago; it is that the different islands to a considerable extent are inhabited by a different set of beings. . . . I never dreamed that islands—about fifty or sixty miles apart, and most of them in sight of each other, formed of precisely the same rocks, placed under a quite similar climate, rising to a nearly equal height—would have been differently tenanted; but we shall soon see that this is the case. . . .

My attention was first thoroughly aroused by comparing together the numerous specimens, shot by myself and several parties on board, of the mocking-thrushes, when, to my astonishment, I discovered that all those from Charles Island belonged to one species *(Mimus trifasciatus);* all from Albemarle Island to *parvulus;* and all from James and Chatham Islands (between which two other islands are situated as connecting links) belonged to *melanotis.* These two latter species are closely allied and would by some ornithologists be considered as only well-marked races or varieties; but the *trifasciatus* is very distinct. . . .

If we now turn to the flora we shall find the aboriginal plants of the different islands wonderfully different. I give all the following results on the high authority of my friend Dr. J. Hooker. . . . Hence we have the truly wonderful fact that in James Island, of the thirty-eight Galápageian plants, or those found in no other part of the world, thirty are exclusively confined to this one island; and in Albemarle Island, of the twenty-six aboriginal Galapageian plants, twenty-two are confined to this one island. . . . This fact will perhaps be rendered even more striking by giving a few illustrations: *Scalesia,* a remarkable arborescent genus of the Compositae, is confined to the archipelago; it has six species; not one of these six species grows on any two islands. Again, *Euphorbia,* a widely distributed genus, has here eight species, of which seven are confined to the archipelago, and not one found on any two islands; *Acalypha* and *Borreria* have respectively six and seven species, none of which have the same species on two islands.

The next paragraph goes to the heart of the "creation" idea with this query: Why should a creative power deal with such slight and imitative and graduated differences of species? Why is it not manifested in a more creative way—that is, by such large differences as those which distinguish genera?

The distribution of the tenants of this archipelago would not be nearly so wonderful if, for instance, one island had a mocking-thrush and a second island some other *quite distinct genus;* if one island had its genus of lizard and a second island another distinct genus, or none whatever; or if the different islands were inhabited, not by representative species of the same genera of plants, but by *totally different genera.* . . . But it is the circumstance that several of the islands possess their own species of the tortoise, mocking-thrush, finches, and numerous plants—these species having the same general habits, occupying analogous situations, and obviously filling the same place in the natural economy of this archipelago—that fills me with wonder. It may be suspected that some of these representative species, at least in the case of the tortoise and of some of the birds, may hereafter prove to be only well-marked races; but this would be of equally great interest to the philosophical naturalist. . . . I must repeat that neither the nature of the soil, nor height of the land, nor the climate, nor the general character of associated beings—and therefore their action one on another—can differ much in the different islands.

The next paragraph offers the key to the distribution —namely, that in three different ways (which I have numbered) the islands are thoroughly separated, and that each has therefore been very much isolated from its neighbors.

The only light which I can throw on this remarkable difference in the inhabitants of the different islands is

(1) that very strong currents of the sea must separate, as far as transportal by the sea is concerned, the southern islands from the northern ones. (2) As the archipelago is free to a most remarkable degree from gales of wind, neither the birds, insects, nor lighter seeds would be blown from island to island. (3) And, lastly, the profound depth of the ocean between the islands, and their apparently recent volcanic origin, render it highly unlikely that they were ever united. . . . Reviewing the facts here given, one is astonished at the amount of creative force, *if such an expression may be used,* displayed on these small, barren, and rocky islands; and still more so at its diverse yet analogous action on points so near each other. I have said that the Galapagos Archipelago might be called a satellite attached to America, but it should rather be called a group of satellites, physically similar, organically distinct, yet intimately related to each other, and all related in a marked, though much lesser degree, to the great American continent.

It would seem fairly safe to predict that Darwin will not long continue to think "creative force" a proper expression to use. Probably he will soon be astonished—not at the amount of such a force, but at the idea that any geologist should talk about it without trying to visualize it.* Everything in the Galapagos points to a creative force, but to one that operates by Lyellian uniformity and that obeys natural law. What can it be?

Fitz-Roy also recorded his opinion about the species question as he prepared to leave the Galapagos. He uses Lyell's idea of "a Creator who endows."

All the small birds that live on these lava-covered islands have short beaks, very thick at the base. This

*The only reference to "Creation" in the MS of the Journal written while Darwin was at the Galapagos is the following; the quotation marks around "centre of creation" are Darwin's: "September 26. It will be very interesting to find from future comparison to what district or 'centre of creation' the organized beings of this archipelago must be attached."

appears to be one of those admirable provisions of Infinite Wisdom by which each created thing is adapted to the place for which it is intended. . . . It is rather curious, and a striking instance of the short-sightedness of some men, that these tortoises should have excited such remarks as, "Well, these reptiles never could have migrated far," when there is no other animal in the whole creation so portable, so likely to have been carried, for food, by the aborigines. . . . Honest Dampier immediately reverted to the tortoises of the West Indies and of Madagascar when he saw those of the Galapagos. He had observed too many varieties caused by climate, soil, food, and habits to entertain a doubt of their being other than a variety of the tortoise kind.

Goliath never has been able to see why people should worry about species; his horse-sense can see well enough how short-sighted the Darwins are.

Shortly before the *Beagle* sailed from the Galapagos Darwin made an entry in his journal (not published) which is interesting as an example of the frequent hardships which were later not considered worth complaining about in print: "Oct. 12-16. We should have been distressed if an American whaler had not very kindly given us three casks of water (and made us a present of a bucket of onions). Several times during the voyage Americans have showed themselves at least as obliging, if not more so, than any of our countrymen would have been. Their liberality, moreover, has always been offered in the most hearty manner."

By the sheerest good fortune the *Beagle* received mail from a little schooner just a few hours before she was to leave Charles Island forever. The next day she called at Albemarle Island to take the naturalist on board.

The day we re-embarked Mr. Darwin there was a man missing, belonging to an American whale-ship, and his ship-mates were seeking for him. Men have been lost hereabouts, and it is said that some of the bodies never were found. . . . Next day (October 20) at sunset we made all sail and steered to get well into the southeast trade wind, so as to expedite our passage towards the dangerous archipelago of the Low Islands, and thence to Tahiti.

Tahiti was reached November 15. It would be pleasant to remain here a while, seeing the cliffs that Darwin scaled, attending the parliament which Fitz-Roy addressed in reference to an indemnity that was due the British Government, watching the entertainment of the Queen aboard the *Beagle,* and hearing Darwin's ultra-whiggish comment on her. But such trifles might distract us from the serious business of species.

A month later the *Beagle* was on the coast of New Zealand. Fitz-Roy's record reads:

December 25. Being Christmas day, several of our party attended Divine service at Paihia. Very few natives were present, but all the respectable part of the English community had assembled. The services extended to such a length that we could scarcely help feeling much fatigued.

Darwin has much to say about the recently Christianized natives, all favorable to the missionaries. He makes many racy remarks on social customs, of which I will cite only one specimen. A missionary had all but persuaded a chief not to go to war; "but at length it occurred to the chief that a barrel of his gunpowder was in a bad state, and that it would not keep much longer. The idea of allowing so much good powder to spoil was not to be though of; and this settled the point."

Amidst the fourteen pages of such cheerful journalism there is only one remark about species, but it is as weighty as it is brief.

It is a most remarkable fact that so large an island, extending over more than seven hundred miles in latitude, with land of all heights from fourteen thousand feet downwards, did not possess (with the exception of a small rat) one indigenous species [of mammals].

Truly this is remarkable. In the small and uniform area of the Galapagos a creative force has called into being hundreds of unique species; in the large and diversified area of New Zealand a creative force has refrained from acting. Why should a great and dignified principle of life be so capricious?

CHAPTER VIII

Six Years of Coral Islands and Species

1836—1841

New Zealand is half-way round the world from England. On the first day of 1836 the *Beagle*, setting out to cover those one hundred and eighty degrees of longitude, headed for Sydney. Darwin stepped to Australian soil on January 12, made an excursion to a place one hundred and twenty miles inland, and sailed for Tasmania on the 30th. There, in Hobart, he got an inkling of how steam-power had developed in the world during his years of species work, and he recorded it with an exclamation mark:

> I crossed the bay in a steamboat, two of which are constantly plying backwards and forwards. The machinery of one of these vessels was entirely manufactured in this colony!

From Hobart the *Beagle* went to the southwest corner of Australia (longitude one hundred and seventeen degrees east), where Darwin went on a kangaroo hunt. He saw a hundred bushmen dance a corroboree, and treated them (as Fitz-Roy betrays) to "an immense mess of boiled rice, with sugar."

From here the course was laid northwest, to the Keeling Islands, thirty-five hundred miles away, in longitude ninety-seven degrees east. These are a lonely

177

group of coral islands, less than ten miles in diameter, rising from water so deep that Fitz-Roy's longest line would not touch bottom, and surrounding a lagoon. They are of profound interest in Darwin's life.

The species in the Keeling Islands give no suggestion of a creative force. Contrast them with the species in the Galapagos. In the Galapagos most of the species were unique, unknown elsewhere in the world; and the distinguishing features of each group of species shaded into one another by fine gradations. A Lamarck who examined them would feel irresistibly that "species" is a mere name, a convenient fiction; for the kinds of finches or turtles can be arranged in a continuous series where no definite boundary is to be seen between two varieties or between a variety and a species. A Darwin who examined the Galapagos species could see plainly that some sort of force had originated new types on each island, though modeling them on familiar lines, with no novelties of structure.

But in the Keeling Islands all was absolutely different. This cluster of coral islets was more isolated than the group of Galapagos volcanos, yet no creative force had operated. The species of plants and animals were few in number, and they were exactly the same as the species to be found on the nearest large bodies of land, Sumatra and Java. Some of the plants are of exactly the same varieties as those on the tiny coral islands of the Radak chain, five thousand miles to the east. Have the same species been made twice, on these distant pin-points of land? Not even Lyell believed so. Even the cautious Lyell felt confident in affirming that no species was ever created twice. All authority and observation that Darwin could bring to bear made him feel sure that every given species of life had been called into being at one time, in one place, and had never been duplicated.

There was never any serious effort among naturalists or philosophers to uphold the idea of duplicate creation.

So there was only one possible conclusion as to the origin of the species on the Keelings: they had been brought from somewhere else; they were immigrants. On this point Darwin and Fitz-Roy and Lyell could all agree. Darwin considered the probability so complete that he did not trouble to offer any other explanation: "All the productions now living here must have been transported by the waves of the sea." Darwin's words were published in 1839 and are universally accepted now. A fuller knowledge of life on islands has shown every stage of population, from an uninhabited volcano a few days old to the well-stocked Galapagos that are millions of years old. On the very youngest of these no instance of creation of a species has ever been remotely suggested: its first life is transported to it over the waves or through the air. As an island's age increases it is stocked by arrivals of immigrants. These are due to the accidents of currents and gales. The immigrants are of widely different kinds—not simply of different genera, but of different *families* or *orders*. Darwin found that the species of the Keelings belonged to widely separated forms of life.

In startling contrast to the small number of species on land was the swarming multitude of them in the sea. The kinds of plants and animals that could migrate freely through the water were as numerous here as off the shores of Sumatra. But the kinds that had to be rafted over the waves, exposed to all hazards and aided only by the rarest chances, were very few. Thus the absence of creative force on the islands was shown with impressive distinctness.

But the presence of a creative force was just as distinct on the Galapagos. The immigrants there gave the impression of having arrived long, long ago, and of having *altered gradually* during ages of residence. That was merely an impression. But it was one which instantly commanded the attention of every man who had a full knowledge of the distribution of plants and animals. It must have struck Darwin with a force and sharpness that laid his mind open to new conceptions. Put yourself in his place; confront the exhibits of Galapagos and Keelings; choose the most likely of the only four possible explanations:

1. That God makes each species, by a fiat.
2. That a creative force calls each new species into being at some instant of time, at some particular spot, in accordance with some utterly unknown natural law.
3. That great populations of large portions of the globe are suddenly created, at once, by divine fiat, after a previous population is entirely destroyed. This was the opinion most generally held by geologists in 1836. It accounted for the origin of species by "catastrophe."
4. That species grow gradually out of one another by some process of uniform natural law which science can investigate.

Of course there were numerous variations and combinations of these four theories, but no really different one had even been proposed, or can now be conceived. What is the likelihood of each?

1. If God makes each species, there can be no biological science of any sort; for no natural laws of life can ever be observed.
2. A "creative force" is unlike anything else known to science, and no slightest evidence for it has ever been detected.
3. Creation by catastrophe is opposed to every-

thing that Lyell holds dear; the geological evidence for it is very dubious; it is out of line with everything else known to science; it can not offer a shred of explanation for the contrast between the Galapagos and the Keelings.

4. Everything that Darwin had seen of species could be rationally explained by Lamarck's theory. Species *do* appear to grow out of one another everywhere, and not to have been created anywhere. They appear to flow from one another by some uniform natural law of a kind that would be dear to Lyell. But by what law? There is the core of the mystery. That must be investigated patiently and carefully in the coming years.

The coral islands that spring up steeply from great depths, forming isolated dots of land in the Pacific and Indian Oceans, had always been uncanny things in geology. Darwin had often climbed a mast to see them as he crossed the Pacific to New Zealand, and had marveled at their low and helpless look. The rings of land were only a few hundred yards wide, and the diameter usually only a few miles. On the outer side the breakers incessantly roared upon the friable dead coral as if they expected to annihilate the little ring in a few days. Yet they never made any impression. As the centuries went by the insignificant thin barrier was always there, gently waving its cocoa palms at the fury of the ocean; the vivid green of the water in its lagoon was never ruffled. What operation of geological law could account for

1. The steep and very lofty cones which rose like submarine Teneriffes from the ocean floor?

2. The very slight and uniform projection of these huge cones above the surface of the ocean?

No geologist knew of anything but volcanos that could form the cones. It was obvious that the top of the cones

was built by minute coral polyps. Hence it was natural
to suppose that coral began to grow on the tops of old
submerged volcanos, and built its structure upwards till
it came to the surface. No objection was known to this
theory. Even to Lyell it seemed adequate.

But Darwin noticed something. It was a wee little
bit of a something, no bigger than a thousand other
trifles like the wing-feathers of a condor. Philosophical
minds would never have stooped to it. Geologists had
never inquired about it. Darwin wondered how deep the
coral animals could live.

The answer to this simple query is now a classic
proof of the blindness and futility of human reason when
it is not based on observation. Coral polyps can not
build at a depth greater than one hundred and fifty feet.

Yet nobody doubted that the atolls were solid coral
to a depth of many hundreds of feet. Darwin longed
with unutterable yearning for a proof of the depth. And
my story will be clearer if I say now that he got it some
years later. A costly expedition, financed by three governments, drilled eleven hundred feet down through a
coral reef—and found nothing but coral. If you belonged to the Puzzlers' League, you would now close this
book and try to guess how—exclusive of divine intervention—the coral which is so far below the surface was
ever formed.

If you were as bold as Darwin and as direct in your
mental processes, you would reach his conclusion: that
the foundation on which the first polyps began to build
sank gradually while they kept at work. It appeared to
Darwin that a large area of ocean-floor must have subsided very slowly and uniformly—say a small fraction
of an inch a year—and that the coral-builders kept pace
with the subsidence, heaping up their skeletons as fast
as the land sank. When he made for himself a mental

picture of this supposed operation, he could see that it would result in both kinds of coral structures: (1) the rings that encircled lagoons, (2) the reefs that run parallel with shores, either so close as to "fringe" them or so far away as to be an outlying "barrier." He resolved to study the matter after he reached home. He wondered whether Lyell would accept such a beautiful addition to his uniformity theory of geology, or whether he would puncture it with some fact unknown to an amateur.

The *Beagle* left the Keeling atoll April 12, and in seventeen days reached Mauritius, east of Madagascar, where Darwin was only fifty-seven degrees from the Greenwich meridian. The entrance to the harbor was through dangerous coral reefs, and on an expedition ashore Darwin saw ancient coral that had been elevated to form part of a hill. Coral occupied his thoughts, but he regaled his readers with the astonishing fact that operas were excellently sung and large book-shops flourished in Port Louis, and that he had a ride on an elephant.

On the last day of May the *Beagle* anchored at the Cape of Good Hope, and Darwin dined with the famous astronomer Sir John F. W. Herschel, who had wanted Lyell to be more outspoken about "creation" as a natural process.

On July 8, Darwin landed at St. Helena for four days. Here he was less interested in Napoleon's tomb than in "the extremely curious" alterations in life that had been caused by the destruction of the trees. "There can be little doubt that this great change in the vegetation affected not only the land-shells, but likewise a multitude of insects. . . . St. Helena, in the midst of a great ocean and possessing a unique flora, excites our curiosity. The eight land-shells, though now extinct, are peculiar species found nowhere else"—and so on. Now you see this creative force, and now you don't.

Thence the *Beagle* bore northwest to the lonely little island of Ascension, where he examined the rats that were supposed to have been called into being on a volcano.

I can hardly doubt that these rats have been imported and have varied from the effect of the new conditions to which they have been exposed. [This opinion was not in the first edition, but the quotation in the previous paragraph was there.]

Even after the experiences in the Pacific he still finds his curiosity excited by the so-called "native" rat and by the "little world within itself" of flora and fauna. The idea of rats varying from the effect of conditions perplexed him all the rest of his life—and indeed is still perplexing some of his critics. How can an animal be made to vary *by* the environment? How can climate and food enter into an egg so as to cause the new individual to vary? The answer is the difference between Lamarckism and Darwinism.

From Ascension the *Beagle* sailed west to Pernambuco, in Brazil, and remained there during the first four days of August.

I was glad to find my enjoyment of tropical scenery had not decreased, even in the slightest degree. . . . When quietly walking along the shady pathways and admiring each successive view, I wished to find language to express my ideas. . . . In my last walk I stopped again and again to gaze on these beauties, and endeavored to fix in my mind forever an impression which at the time I knew sooner or later must fail. . . . On the 19th of August we finally left the shores of Brazil. I thank God I shall never again visit a slave country. . . . On the last day of August we anchored for the second time

in the Cape de Verd archipelago; thence we proceeded
to the Azores. On the 2nd of October we made the
shores of England, and at Falmouth I left the *Beagle,*
having lived on board the good little vessel nearly five
years.

Our voyage having come to an end, I will take a short
retrospect of the advantages and disadvantages of our
circumnavigation of the world. . . . The pleasures
gained at the time do not counterbalance the evils. It is
necessary to look forward to a harvest, when some fruit
will be reaped, some good effected.

The harvest of Darwin's voyage was to be reaped
twenty-three years later, when he published *The Origin
of Species.* Some such intellectual reaping must have
been planned before he debarked in the Cornish town
and wished that he could be whisked to Shrewsbury by
one of the new "railroads" instead of having to crawl
in a stage-coach. He must have betrayed something of
his purpose to the tory Captain during their long, close
intimacy, though his policy even with scientific friends
was cautious secrecy. For it can not be an accident that
Fitz-Roy's last chapter of his long *Narrative* was entitled "A Very Few Remarks with Reference to the Deluge."* There is something so comical about this per-
oration by a captain against his naturalist messmate that
it is worth quoting for pure entertainment.

But I quote it for the instruction it conveys about the
host of Philistia that Darwin was going to encounter.
As the feeling of a naval officer, it deserves no space in
this book. As an expression of the almost unanimous
feeling of educated England, it reveals the meaning of
Darwin's life. It shows what Sedgwick and Buckland
and Wilberforce were fighting for. It shows why the
great Philistine scientists, Owen and Mivart, thirsted for
Darwin's blood. It exhibits the dread of refined souls

---

*Compare his speech at Oxford in 1860, page 312.

like Henslow and Asa Gray. It reveals what Gladstone, the Grand Old Man, was still contending for when Darwin died, and what an army of fundamentalists still clamor for. Darwin's crop of theory was to outrage deep feelings. Fitz-Roy wished to take the offensive against the Darwinian evil. He foresaw that a blow in behalf of Genesis was "not irrelevant to the narrative" of a seaman. He was right. He and his vessel are now familiar names in every college because of their connection with the story of Noah—the Deluge and the species in the Ark. In Noah's day, as in Fitz-Roy's, the questions of geology and species were inseparable. Fitz-Roy politely refrained from mentioning Darwin's name, and he pretended that he was merely addressing young seamen.

To account for offering a few remarks on a subject so important as that of the Deluge, I beg to say that reflections, arising out of facts witnessed during the *Beagle's* voyage, have occasioned them; and, as results of that expedition, it has appeared to me that they are neither irrelevant to the narrative, nor likely to be altogether uninteresting to young men in the navy. . . .
While led away by skeptical ideas, and knowing extremely little of the Bible, one of my remarks to a friend, on crossing vast plains composed of rolled stones bedded in diluvial detritus some hundred feet in depth, was "This could never have been effected by a forty-days' flood"—an expression plainly indicative of the turn of mind and ignorance of Scripture. I was quite willing to disbelieve what I thought to be the Mosaic account, upon the evidence of a hasty glance, though knowing next to nothing of the record I doubted. . . . These remarks would be useless, were it not that they may reach the eyes of young sailors, who have not always access to works of authority. . . .
Some men of rare abilities have thought that the "days" of creation were indefinite periods. . . . Can we think that "day" means one space of time in the for-

mer part, and another space of time in the latter part, of that one verse? . . .

Anomalies such as these appear to be endless in most geological theories. Instead of ascribing these effects to the universal deluge, many geologists say that the earth is in a continual, though gradual, state of change; that in consequence of this general mobility places now far above the sea were once beneath it; that districts, or countries, may have been inundated in one quarter, and other regions elsewhere, but that an universal deluge never could have happened. This is implied plainly enough, if not asserted, in several geological works.

In the *Beagle's* examination of the southern parts of South America I had opportunities of observing immense tracts of land, composed solely of fossil shells, bones, and an earth which looked like dried mud. [He argues that the fossils might have been deposited by the Deluge, quoting two passages from Lyell, on which he comments:] In reflecting upon these passages it appears to me that Mr. Lyell has supposed what may not always take place in a deep sea—namely, that sand and mud sink to the bottom. . . .

Hence, therefore, if Patagonia was covered to a great depth, all the world was covered to a great depth; and from those shells alone my mind is convinced (independent of the Scripture) that this earth has undergone an universal deluge. . . .

[The following paragraph was preceded by a quotation from a published letter of Darwin to Henslow and was followed by a quotation from Lyell, 1838 edition, in which Lyell cites Darwin.] These wonderful alternations of the consequences of fire and flood are, to me, indubitable proofs of that tremendous catastrophe which alone could have caused them—of that awful combination of water and volcanic agency which is shadowed forth to our minds by the expression "The fountains of the great deep were broken up, and the windows of heaven were opened." . . .

If my few remarks tend, even in the least, to warn young persons of my profession against assenting hastily to new theories—while they induce a closer ex-

amination into the Record of truth—my object will be
fully attained.

Fitz-Roy's tone is so gentle and devout that we may
not realize the warlike state of mind which it represents.
Darwin described the case concisely to his sister: "The
object of Captain Fitz-Roy's most devout abhorrence is
one of the d—d scientific whigs."

Darwin had been in a "dead and half-alive state"
during the last days on board, and was weak when he
got into the mail-coach on Sunday evening, October 2.
But he grew exhilarated as the hours passed. He was
feeling with redoubled force what he had written home
two years previously about "the geological castles in the
air which I have been building for the last two years."
He had said, after crossing the Andes, "I cannot express the delight which I felt at such a famous winding-
up of all my geology in South America." He felt more
than enjoyment (he explained); he felt purpose. He had
spoken of "those talking giants, Whewell and Sedgwick," and his words were friendly enough. But he
knew, when the whip cracked and the horses leaned to
their collars, that his business henceforth was to be
giant-killing.

All day Monday and Tuesday he bowled along toward
Shrewsbury. How different the world had grown in
five years! Now every shrub beside the road spoke of a
virility that could go overseas and spread itself against
the competition of plants in Argentine or New Zealand.
These decorous ornaments of a placid English landscape
were warriors now. A hare that scurried off the road
was a notable fighter in the struggle for existence, a
species that could vary, a descendant from ancestors en-
tombed in the ancient pyramids of nature. The hills—
which used to be curiosities—were now a part of the
grand symphony of lofty Andes and deep-sunk, coral-

crowned peaks. Every pebble or autumn leaf told of
roaring torrents or petrified forests that still stand on
their ancient seashore in the mountains.

The arrival at Shrewsbury was so late at night that
Darwin slept at an inn. The next morning he walked
into The Mount before breakfast. When the first excitement of greeting was over, and the servants were drinking hilariously in honor of Master Charles's return, his
father exclaimed, "Why, the shape of his head is quite
altered!" Of course no physician should have spoken
so unscientifically: Charles's cranium had not changed
by a millimeter in any dimension. But Charles knew
that the exclamation was another proof of his father's
sagacity: the mind within the head was quite altered.
The eyes that looked so sternly from under their deep
ledges of brow were seeing the world in a new way and
reporting to a mind reorganized. The poco curante
Charles had become the most implacable of seekers for
natural law.

The next two years were the busiest that Darwin
ever spent, for he was in a whirlpool of duties that all
needed immediate attention. He must see Henslow and
arrange to have the specimens attended to by competent
classifiers; he must write a *Journal* to be part of the official report on the *Beagle's* voyage; he must prepare
papers on geology and zoology, to be read in learned
society meetings; he burned to study all the charts of
coral islands; he wanted to dive into the species question.

His first move was to visit Henslow and arrange to
live in Cambridge for a time. Late in October he attended to unloading his specimens from the *Beagle* at
Greenwich and shipping them to Cambridge.

Emma Wedgwood confessed to a sister-in-law that
she was growing impatient for a visit from Charles.
"We all ought to get up a little knowledge for him. I

have taken to no deeper study than Captain Head's *Rapid Journeys across the Pampas.* I am afraid it won't instruct me much.''

She was well aware of the humor of coaching herself to talk with such a geological lion. She knew that Charles was already a marked man. Two years previously Sedgwick had predicted to Dr. Darwin that his son would take a place among the leading scientists. Henslow had been spreading his fame. Lyell was anxious to meet this disciple who was bringing such trophies for uniformitarianism. How he must have searched the bronzed face of Darwin when they first met in London, wondering in his skeptical way what weakness or illusion lurked behind those steady eyes. For every geologist had in him some taint of fanaticism or was blind to some set of facts. Lyell knew. Lyell wondered what would prove to be wrong with Darwin.

And how Darwin's instinct fenced for an opening in the guard of this most adroit and polished champion. What sort of mentality could this be that perceived geological truth as if by divination, yet argued about species like a mystic in a cloud of incense? What Darwin saw was a man of medium height, somewhat stooped, whose eyes were always drawn quizzically at the corners, as if they were saying, ''You can hardly expect me to believe that.'' Above the eyes was a full, broad brow, where a large intellect resided. Lyell's manner was courtly; when he leaned over to peer with near-sighted eyes he seemed bookish; his voice was low, very softly modulated, and somewhat hesitant. So an undiscerning critic would have supposed that Lyell was a carpet-knight. But Darwin observed the hard hands and the spring in the step; he knew that Lyell could have outwalked him in the Andes.

These two men, the stoutest foes of Goliath in all the

world, measured each other and found each other admirable. Seldom has a friendship been formed so quickly, so surely, so lastingly. Yet there was a reservation in it. Darwin soon found that the intellect of Lyell had formed an impregnable conception of the species question; it was useless to confide revolutionary guesses to such a gentlemanlike mind.

We shall better understand Lyell and the species question if we take two glimpses at the social life to which he had long been accustomed; they are average samples:

December, 1827. I am on a visit here to an uncle, where some of my sisters are staying, and for a short season am to be in a continual round of dinners and balls.

April, 1828. I chaperoned Mrs. Somerville to Sir George Phillips's on Sunday evening, after a dinner at Dr. Somerville's. Sir G., who is one of the new baronets, is an M. P., as is his son. A room full of Sir J. Reynolds's and other good pictures, and a famous living gallery of portraits. The party was—Sir Walter Scott, Cooper (the American novelist), Mrs. Marcet and daughter, Sir J. Mackintosh, Rogers the poet, Dumont the Genevese jurisconsult, "Conversation" Sharp, Lady Davy, Spring Rice, M. P., Dr. Wollaston, Newton the American artist, Mr. and Mrs. Lockhart, Scott's son and unmarried daughter, etc.

Yet Lyell was not a social butterfly, nor had he any interest in tuft-hunting. He contrived all manner of devices to prevent having his time wasted by dinners and receptions. His passion was geology. His joy was to wage battle against philistine delusions. He cared more for Darwin's new knowledge than for a roomful of coronets and champagne. He had been fired with hope by a preliminary report of Fitz-Roy's on the Chilean earthquake. While the *Beagle* was approaching New Zealand he had written to Sedgwick, "How I long for the return of Darwin! I hope you do not mean to monopolize him at Cambridge.'' In every way he encouraged and cultivated the new geologist, arranging for his membership in societies, sponsoring his astounding reports about glaciers and land elevations and coral islands, persuading specialists (who had pleaded lack of time) to classify Darwin's specimens. It is pleasant to learn that one specialist gladly volunteered to classify corallines—the old Edinburgh friend, Dr. Grant, now a professor at the University of London.

Early in November Darwin described to his cousin, Fox, the stay in town while having his treasures shipped from the *Beagle*.

My London visit has been passed in most exciting dissipations amongst the Dons in science. All my affairs are indeed prosperous; I find there are plenty who will undertake the description of whole tribes of animals of which I know nothing. . . . It is quite ridiculous what an immensely long period it appears to me since landing at Falmouth. The fact is I have talked and laughed enough for years instead of weeks, so my memory is quite confounded with the noise. . . . Amongst the great scientific men no one has been nearly so friendly and kind as Lyell. I have seen him several times, and feel much inclined to like him. You cannot imagine how good-naturedly he enters into all my plans. . . . Be it known, I was proposed to be a Fellow of the Geological Society last Tuesday.

Darwin was grieved to find how many strong reasons there were why he should soon have to take up a residence in ''this dirty, odious London.'' He was horrified at ''the mean, quarrelsome spirit'' shown in a meeting of the Zoological Society, ''where the members were snarling at each other in a manner anything but like that of gentlemen.'' But there was exhilaration and high hope in the attention shown to him on all hands. ''Mr.

Yarrell has asked me to dine with the Linnæan on Tuesday, and on Wednesday I dine with the Geological, so that I shall see all the great men."

From this babel of greatness and meanness he was glad to slip, in November, to Maer. Emma Wedgwood wrote an account of his visit on November 21.

We enjoyed it uncommonly. We had been very handsome in inviting all the outlyers of the family to meet him. . . . Charles talked away most pleasantly all the time; we plied him with questions without any mercy. . . . Caroline looks so happy and proud of him, it is delightful to see her. [Caroline was his sister.]

Emma appears to have been prejudiced in favor of the *Journal* before much of it was written:

I am convinced Dr. Holland is mistaken if he thinks it not worth publishing. I don't believe he is any judge as to what is amusing or interesting. Cath. [another of Darwin's sisters] does not approve its being mixed up with Capt. Fitz-Roy's.

Then Emma was off to Edinburgh for a gay two months with her cousin Lady Gifford, whom she found "blazing with gas in a handsome house." Next spring she heard a rumor that Charles was engaged.

The rumor was false; he had passed the winter at Cambridge classifying his geological specimens. How important his fossils were may be seen when we know that only two genera of extinct mammals had previously been described; Darwin had brought four new genera to England. In March, 1837, he moved to quarters in London, about half a mile southwest of the British Museum, on Great Marlborough Street; and for six months worked on the *Journal* every day for as many hours as health would permit.

Late in June his sister Caroline became engaged to Emma's brother Josiah. "It is delightful to see," said Emma, "how much attached he is to her. Whenever I have talked to him alone he has burst out in a way as if he could not contain himself about her exquisite charm."

Poor Charles slaved in London. As soon as he had finished reading the proof of the *Journal,* he set himself definitely to the study which was to occupy all the rest of his life:

In July I opened my first notebook for facts in relation to the origin of species, about which I had long reflected. . . . Nor did I ever intermit collecting facts bearing on the origin of species; and I could sometimes do this when I could do nothing else from illness.

But species had to be a side-issue for the present. He had to plan four scholarly reports on the zoology of his voyage; there was pressure upon him to write up the technical details of his geological observations; he had to prepare a paper on earthworms. The papers that he read "were favorably received by the great guns, and this gives me much confidence, and I hope not a very great deal of vanity, though I confess I feel too often like a peacock admiring his tail. . . . My life is a very busy one at present, and I hope may ever remain so; though heaven knows there are many serious drawbacks to such a life, and chief amongst them is the little time it allows for seeing one's natural friends. For the last three years I have been longing and longing to be living at Shrewsbury, and after all now in the course of several months I see my dear good people at Shrewsbury for a week." Poor devil! He wanted to be in the country, but he was doomed to "this vile, smoky place—I do hate the streets of London."

He was bound to vile London by his ambition. Here

only could he meet the men who would help him along in a scientific career. For one example, by starting the right influences to work, through Henslow and Lyell, he secured from the Treasury a grant of one thousand pounds sterling for the publication of the *Zoology of the Voyage of the Beagle*. An illustration of the keenness of his ambition is seen in a ludicrous picture that he drew of himself enjoying his first sheet of proof, in November. He had experienced that worst nightmare of authors: "Mr. Colburn employed some goose to revise, and he has multiplied, instead of diminishing, my oversights." The thrill of authorship is affecting his backbone: "In the summer before I started if anyone had told me that I should have been an angel by this time, I should have thought it an equal impossibility. . . . I sat the other evening in silent admiration at the first page of my own volume."

Amidst the pleasure of authorship and the vileness of London he passed the rest of 1837.

Early in 1838 he was made secretary of the Geological Society, and in June set out to attack the most peculiar problem in British geology. From Glasgow he went north seventy-five miles, through the *Lady of the Lake* region, to the Caledonian Canal. The Canal follows a series of lakes that almost cut Scotland in two, from Inverness on the North Sea to the Atlantic Ocean west of Glasgow. A few miles to the east of it, about midway of the length, is the valley of Glen Roy, descending toward the highest mountain in Great Britain, Ben Nevis. Along the sides of the valley run three parallel and absolutely horizontal lines, marking terraces on the face of the mountains, which the natives call "roads." To a geologist they are obviously the marks of the borders of a body of water—there was no debate about that. The debate was about the nature of the body of water:

had it been a lake or an arm of the ocean? Darwin, fresh from the marvels of South American shore-lines in the Andes, pronounced in favor of the ocean, and published his reasoning in the *Philosophical Transactions*.

His reasoning was so well grounded that it persuaded Lyell for twenty years. But it was wrong, so wrong that his error was of lifelong value to him in reasoning about species. No geologist, then or later, denied the acuteness of his observation or the clearness of his logic. The trouble was that he worked on the principle of "exclusion." When (in the previous chapter) I asked my readers to judge which of the four possible explanations of Galapagos species was most likely, I proposed a principle of exclusion—which is safe for us after the puzzle is solved. But it is just the wrong principle for a man who is investigating, since it keeps his mind off some other possible element that he is ignorant of. Darwin, though he had astonished the geologists by his reports of South American glaciers, neglected to ask himself, "Might glaciers have dammed this lake?" No other failure of his scientific life was so humiliating to him, or so instructive in his great work, as this early blindness to a geological cause that nature had advertised to him in Wales and Scotland and Chile. The evidence at Glen Roy was so strong that it fairly cried out for Darwin's attention. But he was blind and deaf to it. Even in 1846, when he spoke of the theory that the lake had once been dammed by ice, he declared that "there never was a more futile theory."

But he recognized all the while that his opinion might be based on ignorance. What is more, he was right in his reasoning: he said that the lake never could have been dammed by rocks washed down by a stream. That was correct. It was dammed by something else. Until Agassiz taught the world what the something else was, no sound argument could dislodge Darwin from his position.

Darwin was always chagrined that Agassiz—the foe of his species theory and a believer in catastrophes—should have been the man to prove him all wrong about the Parallel Roads. Yet he never allowed chagrin to interfere with acquiring truth. In 1847 he wrote to a geologist: "I plead quite guilty to your rebuke. . . . I am very much staggered in favor of the ice-lake theory of Agassiz and Buckland." And to Mrs. Lyell he wrote in the same year, "How Buckland will crow over me." Finally, in 1861, he yielded completely, and confessed to Lyell: "I am smashed to atoms about Glen Roy. My paper was one long gigantic blunder from beginning to end. Eheu! Eheu!" He had had to yield to the two men whose mode of thought was—in most ways—abhorrent to him. No discipline could have been better for a man who was trying to discover the origin of species. Only one other episode in his life shows his mental quality to better advantage.

The trip to Glen Roy had been taken because he needed a holiday. His health was failing. Nine months previously he had confessed to Henslow: "I have not been very well of late, with an uncomfortable palpitation of the heart, and my doctors urge me *strongly* to knock off all work." Throughout the rest of his life he had to make similar confessions. Always he yearned to work, always his health was precarious; there was nausea and palpitation, especially if he was excited by company; and often he was driven away from work by a physician to an enforced holiday at Maer or the seashore or some water-cure establishment.

The outing in Scotland improved his health and spirits. Shortly after his return to town he was further benefited by a visit from Emma Wedgwood and his sis-

ter Catherine, who stopped in London on their way home
from a trip to Paris. Emma reported:

Robert Mackintosh dined with us or came in the
evening every day, and Charles used to come from next
door, so we were a very pleasant, merry party. . . .
Mr. Carlyle dined with us in Marlborough St. which you
won't care about.

Another pleasure came in August, a copy of Lyell's
new *Elements of Geology*. In the appreciative letter
that Darwin wrote to Lyell about it he summed up what
seemed its greatest merit: "It must do good; the heretics against common-sense must yield." Now he was
fully allied with the world's leading geologist in a war
against philistinism. The frequent references that Lyell
had made in the *Manual* to his young companion exhilarated the ambitious Darwin: "You will see I am
in a fit of enthusiasm, and good cause I had to be, when
I find you have made such infinitely more use of my
Journal than I could have anticipated."

A much stronger fit of enthusiasm was justified in
another letter that he wrote to Lyell in November. The
occasion was one which had caused him to enter November 11 in his diary as "the day of days." The sentences
which describe it sound like an outpouring from a small-
necked jug.

I write because I cannot avoid wishing to be the first
person to tell Mrs. Lyell and yourself that I have the
very good, and shortly since very unexpected fortune, of
going to be married. The lady is my cousin, Miss Emma
Wedgwood, the sister of Hensleigh Wedgwood, and of
the elder brother who married my sister, so we are connected by manifold ties, besides on my part by the most
sincere love and hearty gratitude to her for accepting
such a one as myself.
I determined when last at Maer to try my chance, but

I hardly expected such good fortune would turn up for me. I shall be in town the middle or latter end of the ensuing week. I fear you will say I might very well have left my story untold till we met. But I deeply feel your kindness and friendship towards me, which in truth, I may say, has been one chief source of happiness to me ever since my return to England: so you must excuse me. I am well sure that Mrs. Lyell, who has sympathy for everyone near her, will give me her hearty congratulations.

Two days after Charles became engaged his father thus expressed himself to Emma's father:

Emma having accepted Charles gives me as great happiness as Jos having married Caroline, and I cannot say more.

On that marriage Bessy said she should not have had more pleasure if it had been Victoria, and you may assure her I feel as grateful to her for Emma as if it had been Martineau herself that Charles had obtained.

To this Emma's father replied:

I could have parted with Emma to no one for whom I would so soon and so entirely feel as a father, and I am happy in believing Charles entertains the kindest feelings for his uncle-father.

I propose to do for Emma what I did for Charlotte and for three of my sons, give a bond for £5000, and to allow her £400 a year as long as my income will supply it, which I have no reason for thinking will not be as long as I live.

And Emma wrote a postscript:

I have begged a bit of Papa's letter to thank you from my heart for the delightful way in which you have received me into your family, and to thank my dear Marianne and Susan for their affectionate notes, which gave me the greatest pleasure.

My narrative of scientific warfare must not pause for love-letters, but I should like to slip in a few sentences from a long epistle that Charles sent to Emma three days after the day of days:

There was never anyone so lucky as I have been, or so good as you. Indeed I can assure you many times since leaving Maer I have thought how little I expressed how much I owe to you; and as often as I think this, I vow to try to make myself good enough somewhat to deserve you. . . . My chief fear is that you will find, after living all your life with such large and agreeable parties as Maer only can boast of, our quiet evenings dull. You must bear in mind, as some young lady said, "all men are brutes," and that I take the line of being a solitary brute, so you must listen with much suspicion to all arguments in favor of retired places. . . . I can fancy I am sitting by the side of my own dear future wife, and to her own self I do not care what nonsense I talk—so let me have my way, and scribble, without caring whether it be sense or nonsense. . . . My father echoes and re-echoes uncle Jos's words, "You have drawn a prize." . . . My own dear Emma, I kiss the hands with all humbleness and gratitude, which have so filled up for me the cup of happiness—it is my most earnest wish I may make myself worthy of you.

And perhaps I shall be pardoned if I print a few sentences from Emma's letter to her Aunt Jessie (Madame Sismondi) describing what happened on the 11th of November.

When you asked me about Charles Darwin I did not tell you half the good I thought of him for fear you should suspect something. . . . He came down again last Thursday with aunt Fanny, and on Sunday he spoke to me, which was quite a surprise, as I thought we might go on in the sort of friendship we were in for years, and very likely nothing come of it after all. I was too much bewildered all day to feel my happiness and there was a large party in the house, so we did not tell anybody except Papa and Elizabeth and Catherine. Dear Papa, I wish you could have seen his tears of joy, for he has always had a great regard for Charles. . . . I went into their rooms at night, and we had a large party talking it over till very late, when I was seized with hunger, and Hensleigh went down to forage in the kitchen and found a loaf and 2 lb. butter and a carving knife, which made us an elegant refection. . . . He is the most open, transparent man I ever saw, and every word expresses his real thoughts. He is particularly affectionate and very nice to his father and sisters, and perfectly sweet tempered. . . . I am so glad he is a busy man. . . . I bless the railroad every day of my life, and Charles is so fond of Maer that I am sure he will always be ready to steam down whenever he can. . . . I don't think it of as much consequence as Aunt Sarah does that Charles drinks no wine, but I think it a pleasant thing. The real crook in my lot I have withheld from you, but I must own it to you sooner or later. It is that he has a great dislike to going to the play, so that I am afraid we shall have some domestic dissensions on that head. On the other hand he stands concerts very well. He told me he should have spoken to me in August but was afraid, and I was pleased to find that he was not very sure of his answer this time. It was certainly a very unnecessary fear. . . . I went straight into the Sunday School after the important interview, but found I was turning into an idiot and so came away.

How often Mrs. Darwin must have marveled, during the forty-three years of her husband's unremitted and health-destroying labor, at those words of a fiancée—"I am glad he is a busy man." How often through the quiet, monotonous years she must have felt the crook in her lot. Yet there were never any domestic dissensions. Charles did not have a dislike to plays, but only an inability to combine plays with his warfare against the heretics. If a man is destined to be a field-marshal of the forces of common sense, how can he spare any of his small amount of strength for the play? Emma Wedgwood made the usual wifely sacrifice. She gave, and in return received, a completeness of devoted love.

During the rest of 1838 Darwin's thoughts were much distracted from science. He was hunting a house and writing frequently to Maer.

I positively can do nothing, and have done nothing this whole week, but think of you and our future life. . . . On Saturday I dined with the Lyells, and spent one of the pleasantest evenings I ever did in my life. Lyell grew quite audacious at the thought of having a married geological companion, and proposed going to dine at the Athenaeum together and leaving our wives at home. . . . By the way, if you take my advice, you will not think of reading Lyell's *Elements,* for depend upon it you will hereafter have plenty of geology. On Sunday evening Erasmus took me to drink tea with the Carlyles*; it was my first visit. One must always like Thomas, and I felt particularly well towards him, as Erasmus had told me he had propounded that a certain lady was one of the nicest girls he had ever seen. Jenny sent some civil messages to you, but which, from the effects of an hysterical sort of giggle, were not very intelligible. It is high treason, but I cannot think Jenny is either quite natural or lady-like. . . .

And now for the great question of houses. Erasmus and myself have taken several very long walks; and the difficulties are really frightful. Houses are very scarce and the landlords are all gone mad, they ask such prices. . . .

What can a man have to say who works all morning in

---

*Carlyle once wrote a character sketch of Erasmus, Charles's brother, in which he explained that Erasmus's carriage was often at Mrs. Carlyle's disposal and that she "discerned him to be a perfect gentleman."

describing hawks and owls, and then rushes out and walks in a bewildered manner up one street and down another, looking out for the words "To Let." I called, however, to-day on the Lyells. I can not tell you how particularly pleasant and cordial Lyell's manner has been to me: I am sure he will be a steady and sure friend to both of us. . . . Lyell and Madame gave me a very long and *solemn* lecture on the *extreme* importance, for our future comfort during our whole London lives, of choosing slowly and deliberately our visiting acquaintance: every disagreeable or commonplace acquaintance must separate us from our relations and real friends, for the evenings we sacrifice might have been spent with them *or at the theater.*

Emma wrote to Sismondi on December 28:

I have been away to London to help Charles to look for a house. . . . Our gaieties were first going to the play, which Charles actually proposed to do himself, but I am afraid it was only a little showing off. It was the *Tempest,* and we all thought it very tiresome.

No distraction of the theater or a new home prevented Darwin's mind from engaging itself with species: "The crossing of animals is my prime hobby; and I really think some day I shall be able to do something in that most intricate subject, species and varieties." The species were merely side-tracked part of the time for house-hunting.

He found a tolerable home at length. It was on Gower Street (which runs north from the western side of the British Museum), near the present number 112, about half a mile from the entrance to the Museum. Because of the rather outlandish colors of its furniture and decorations Darwin named it Macaw Cottage. A letter to Emma on New Year's Day announced that his bachelor chattels had been moved to the new abode.

By half past three we had two large vans full of goods well and carefully packed. By six o'clock we had them all here. There is nothing left but some few dozen drawers of shells, which must be carried by hand. . . . The little garden is worth its weight in gold.

During January, 1839, Darwin was scribbling numerous unscientific letters to Maer.

Jan. 7. I wish the awful day was over. I am not very tranquil when I think of the procession: it is very awesome. . . . Mr. Stewart wanted me to have a blue coat and white trousers, but I vowed I would only put on clothes in which I could travel away decently.

Jan. 20. My own dearest Emma, I earnestly pray you may never regret the great, and I will add very good, deed you are to perform on *the* Tuesday. My own dear future wife, God bless you.

My good old friend Herbert sent me a very nice little note, with a massive silver weapon, which he called a Forficula (the Latin for an earwig) and which I thought was to catch hold of soles and flounders, but Erasmus tells me is for asparagus—so that two dishes are settled for our first dinner, namely soup and asparagus.

Jan. 26, from Shrewsbury. My last two days in London were rendered very uncomfortable by a bad headache, which continued two days and nights, so that I doubted whether it ever meant to go and allow me to be married. The railroad yesterday, however, quite cured me.

They were married very quietly on Tuesday, January 29, at Maer Church and steamed at once to London.

Mrs. Darwin to her mother, Jan. 31. The house was blazing with fires and looked very comfortable, and we are getting to think the furniture quite tasteful. . . . I have been facing the Cook in her own region to-day, and found fault with the boiling of the potatoes,

which I thought would make a good beginning and set
me up a little. On Monday or Tuesday we are going
to give our first dinner-party to the Hensleighs and
Erasmus.

Mrs. Darwin to her sister, Feb. 2. Yesterday we
trudged out again, and half ruined ourselves at the
plate shop, and in the evening we actually went to the
play, which Charles thinks will look very well in the
eyes of the world. . . . I am cockered up and spoilt as
much as heart can wish and I *do* think, though you and
Char. may keep this to yourself, that there is not so affectionate an individual as the one in question to be
found anywhere else.

Mrs. Darwin to her sister, March 15. We had Ellen
Tollet to dine with us yesterday and go to the play, and I
think it has cured Charles; at least he is much better to-
day, and he was very much interested and clapped and
applauded with all his heart. It was the new play of
Richelieu. It is an interesting play and very well acted,
but Macready tottered and made himself too old. . . .
I expect Charles to get quite fond of the theater, but as
to dinners and parties he gets worse I think, and I don't
care how few dinners we go to either. . . . Next week
we dine at Dulwich and go to Blagrove's concert, which
I am afraid will be a great deal too deep for Charles.

Mrs. Darwin to her sister, March 29. Mr. Sedgwick
called and was very pleasant; there is something remarkably fresh and odd about him. The Henslows come
on Monday, and Charles is much more alarmed at the
thought of them than I am. On Monday the Lyells dine
with us. . . . The cook is pretty good so I am not
afraid about the dinners.

Mrs. Darwin to her sister, April 2. I must tell you
how our learned party went off yesterday. Mr. and Mrs.
Henslow came at four o'clock and she, like a discreet
woman, went up to her room till dinner. The rest of the
company consisted of Mr. and Mrs. Lyell and Leonora
Horner, Dr. Fitton and Mr. Robert Brown. We had
some time to wait before dinner for Dr. Fitton, which
is always awful, and, in my opinion, Mr. Lyell is enough
to flatten a party, as he never speaks above his breath,

so that everybody keeps lowering their tone to his. Mr. Brown, whom Humboldt calls "the glory of Great Britain," looks so shy, as if he longed to shrink into himself and disappear entirely; however, notwithstanding those dead weights, viz., the greatest botanist and the greatest geologist in Europe, we did very well and had no pauses. Mrs. Henslow has a good, loud, sharp voice which was a great comfort, and Mrs. Lyell has a very constant supply of talk. Mr. Henslow was very glad to meet Mr. Brown, as the two great botanists had a great deal to say to each other. Charles was dreadfully exhausted when it was over, and is only as well as can be expected to-day.

Charles was always vivacious in company, a joy to his guests. Professor Judd describes the feeling he inspired:

I never knew any one who had met him, even for the briefest period, who was not charmed by his personality. Who could forget the hearty hand-grip at meeting, the gentle and lingering pressure of the palm at parting, and above all that winning smile which transformed his countenance—so as to make portraits, and even photographs, seem ever afterwards unsatisfying! Looking back, one is indeed tempted to forget the profoundness of the philosopher in recollection of the lovableness of the man.

The social evenings left Darwin no better than could be expected the following days, but they seldom kept him from a long forenoon of work at a book on coral-reefs, or grubbing out evidence about species, or driving at the book on the zoology of the voyage. The *Journal* appeared during the early summer, and copies were sent freely to men in strategic positions. Darwin was always a propagandist and anxious to establish relations with leading scientists. The copy of the *Journal* in the Yale library is inscribed:

Dr. Silliman
&c   &c   &c
With the respectful Compliments of the Author

Silliman, thirty years older than Darwin, was the most
noted chemist and geologist in the United States at the
time. His penciled note on a fly-leaf is dated Feb. 11,
1840.

Perused at Boston reading a chapter at once late at
night—my amusement and instruction after the hard
work of the lectures was over. I think it a most excellent work.

This first edition of the *Journal* contains every essential observation that is to be found in the second edition published six years later—except the passage about
the Galapagos tortoises. The variation in the Falklands,
the gradation and uniqueness in the Galapagos, the contrast between the Galapagos and the Keelings—all are
here. Moreover, no essential comment is lacking. But
the excitement about the species on the Galapagos is
pretty much suppressed, because it would have been dis-
courteous to Fitz-Roy, in whose name the three volumes
appeared (Darwin's *Journal* was Volume III). The chief
additions to the later edition were some results of classifying the specimens and an epitome of his book on coral-
reefs. But these were mere amplifying; all the essen-
tials, both of information and of theory, were in the first
edition.

Darwin's first child was born December 27, 1839 (the
eighth anniversary of the beginning of the *Beagle's* voyage), and was christened William Erasmus. The first
name was in honor of the earliest known ancestor, William Darwin of Marton, a contemporary of Columbus.
The middle name was for "dear old Ras," the bachelor

brother who had been Charles's companion for a year at
Edinburgh and for whom Charles had an abiding affection.

There was a third way in which the year 1839 marked
the beginning of Darwin's new life—the meeting with
Joseph Dalton Hooker. It was a casual meeting. Darwin gave it no thought at the time, and later in life he
asked Hooker, "Can you remember how we ever first
met? It was in Park Street, but what brought us together?" Hooker, however, remembered the meeting
perfectly. All through the summer* of 1839 he had been
waiting for H. M. S. *Erebus* to be fitted for sailing in the
Medway; he had wanted to be the naturalist of a surveying expedition, as Darwin had been on the *Beagle;* but
had to be content with an appointment as surgeon and
botanist. He had read proof sheets of Darwin's *Journal*
(passed to his father by Lyell's father) and took the new
book with him on the voyage just as Darwin had taken
Lyell's *Principles*. One day as he was walking in Tra-
falgar Square with a naval officer they met Darwin.
Hooker describes the encounter:

I was walking with an officer who had been his ship-
mate for a short time in the *Beagle* seven years before,
but who had not, I believe, since met him. I was introduced; the interview was of course brief, and the memory of him that I carried away and still retain was that
of a rather tall and rather broad-shouldered man, with
a slight stoop, an agreeable and animated expression
when talking, beetle brows, and a hollow but mellow
voice; and that his greeting of his old acquaintance was
sailor-like—that is, delightfully frank and cordial. I
observed him well, for I was already aware of his at-
tainments and labors, derived from having read various
proof-sheets of his then unpublished *Journal*.

---

*But Gray's account of meeting Darwin would make it appear that
Hooker had met Darwin previously in January. See page 277.

The intimacy with Hooker, which began after the four-year voyage of the *Erebus,* was to be the most useful and encouraging friendship of Darwin's life.

In 1840 Darwin had much contact with a man who was later to be the most discouraging enemy in his career—Richard Owen. This man, five years his senior, was the leading anatomist in England. He had been keenly interested in Darwin's fossils; indeed his study of extinct mammals began with them. In 1840 he was preparing a book on the subject, Volume II of the *Zoology of the Voyage,* for which Darwin wrote an introduction. His prodigious industry may be seen in the fact that he was at the same time beginning to publish a great work on the teeth of animals. In wideness of knowledge and skill of observation he was unrivaled. He had administrative abilities of a high order, becoming superintendent of the natural history collections in the British Museum, and later establishing them in their splendid new home at South Kensington. Throughout Darwin's life he was advancing from strength unto strength in his professional position. And increasingly he became the foe of Darwin's allies. At length he became so much dreaded by them that he seemed, in his own person, to be the Goliath who mocked at true science. How Hooker grew to despise him! When the stone sank into Goliath's forehead at Oxford twenty years later, Hooker thus described Owen's part of the fray:

Soapy Sam got up and spouted for half an hour with inimitable spirit, ugliness, and emptiness and unfairness. I saw he was coached up by Owen.

But in 1840 Owen was the obliging and learned great anatomist; Hooker was a forgotten young surgeon venturing into the southern ice-pack to study the scanty flora.

Master William Erasmus was all that a first baby should be. He was known to his parents as Hoddy Doddy and was thus described by his mother: "He has very dark blue eyes and a pretty, small mouth; his nose I will not boast of, but it is very harmless as long as he is a baby."

During his infancy his father was very unwell: "He has certainly been worse for the last six weeks, and has been pretty constantly in a state of languor that is very distressing, and his being obliged to be idle is very painful to him. He is consulting Dr. Holland, but without much good effect."

At the close of 1840 Maria Edgeworth (an old friend of the Wedgwood family, then seventy-three years old) described a call she made on Mrs. Darwin: "She has her mother's radiantly cheerful countenance, even now, debarred from all London gaieties and all gaiety but that of her own mind by close attendance on her sick husband."

I will venture to record another domestic item in the chronicle of 1840, because it marks the addition of perpetual comfort to the Darwin family all the rest of their days. This was the finding of a butler. Madame Sismondi, a competent critic, considered him at the beginning of his service "the most amiable, obliging, active, serviceable servant that ever breathed." As long as there was a Darwin household, Parslow was a valued member of it.

One sentence from a letter of Darwin's in 1840 will explain the position that Lyell was to hold in his esteem during the coming twenty years of species study: "You are the one man in Europe whose opinion of the general truth of a toughish argument I should be always most anxious to hear." Darwin was already fashioning his most tough argument with a view to persuading Lyell.

Every observation or experiment was checked by trying
to imagine what flaw the skeptical eyes of Lyell might
detect in it. If Lyell's strong prepossession could be
overcome and turned into the new channel, Darwin felt
sure that the world's opinion would follow.

The domestic history of 1841 may be indicated by a
letter which Darwin wrote on the first of July from
Shrewsbury. He had taken William Erasmus to visit
the grandfather, while Mrs. Darwin went to Maer with
the second child, Anne Elizabeth, now four months old.

Dear old Doddy—one could write forever about him.
. . . He has had *half a cup of cream* every morning,
which my father says is one of the most injurious things
we could have given him. . . . Last night Susan went
into Doddy's room and found no water by his bedside.
. . . I tell you these disagreeablenesses that you may
feel the same necessity I do of our own selves looking
and not trusting anything about our children to others.
I hope and suppose I shall hear tomorrow about yourself
and little Kitty Kumplings, who is not so bad a girl as
might be expected of Doddy's rival. . . . Right glad I
shall be to see you on Tuesday.

Lyell grew to care more and more for the friendship
with his disciple. In 1841 he began an extended tour in
the United States, visiting Silliman at New Haven and
lecturing to a class of two thousand enthusiasts at Boston. Shortly before he sailed he expressed his affection
to Darwin: "It will not happen easily that twice in
one's life a congenial soul so occupied with precisely the
same pursuits and with an independence enabling him
to pursue them will fall so nearly in my way."

During the residence in London Darwin continued to
meet leading scientists. He dined with Herschel, "for
whom I felt a high reverence." He saw a good deal of
the eminent botanist Robert Brown. The great Hum-

boldt (whose descriptions had first fired the young naturalist with a desire to travel), when he visited the geologist Sir Roderick I. Murchison in London, wished to meet Darwin. Murchison had Darwin to dinner, to oblige his distinguished guest; and Darwin was "a little disappointed." No wonder he was, for Hooker's first impression was this: "I saw to my horror a punchy little German instead of a Humboldt."

Darwin's acquaintance was not limited to scientists. He learned from Buckle how a young historian of civilization gathers facts for a new kind of history before he knows what sort of facts are going to be useful. Darwin, ploughing through files of breeders' journals for facts of variation, could sympathize with a youth who had to index for unknown needs. He met the amusing Sydney Smith; he met famous historians at the literary dinners given by the fourth Earl Stanhope. The third Earl asked him, "Why don't you give up your fiddle-faddle of geology and turn to the occult sciences?"

It is amusing to read how regularly Darwin found that the great men were monopolistic talkers. Buckland "left no gaps." "As there was only one other man, at dinner, I had a grand opportunity of hearing Macaulay converse." "Carlyle silenced everyone by haranguing during the whole dinner on the advantages of silence." "Humboldt talked beyond all reason."

The dinners were not frequent during 1841, for "I grow very tired in the evenings and am not able to go out at that time, or hardly to receive my nearest relatives."

His hope for each day was that he might have leisure and strength for amassing more details about hybrids and sports and small variations. What he said in January was true of the whole year.

I continue to collect all kinds of facts about "Varieties and Species," for my some-day work to be so entitled; the smallest contributions thankfully accepted. Don't forget, if your half-bred African cat should die, that I should be very much obliged for its carcass sent up in a little hamper. Any cross-bred pigeons, fowl, duck, etc., etc., will be more acceptable than the finest haunch of venison.

"Variation under domestication" was Darwin's great inquiry at this time, but it had to suffer much interference from a subject of immediate importance—the coral islands. He had been working for months at the British Museum and the Admiralty office, searching through all available charts, sailing-directions, and narratives of voyages, gathering data from which he could construct a map of the coral islands and reefs of the world. Each atoll was colored dark blue, the barrier-reefs pale blue, the fringing-reefs red, and the active volcanos vermilion. If volcanos are a sign of a rising area of land, there should not be any atolls near them; for the theory is that atolls can be formed only on wide areas that are slowly subsiding. Nor should there be any barrier-reefs near volcanos; for this sort of reef is essentially like an atoll; that is why these two kinds of coral formation are colored blue. But fringing-reefs are, by the theory, formed on land that is stationary or is rising; hence the regions of fringing-reefs should be near the regions of volcanos; hence these two regions should be similarly colored. We may imagine the absorbing interest with which he had plotted the reds and blues, point by point as he gathered the bits of information, and had watched the areas grow on his map. Would there be cantankerous blue spots that would force themselves into the red area where they would spoil a theory? Would any red or vermilion dots have to be marked in a blue region?

Of course there were complications. Such world-wide phenomena of interrelated forces could not be expected to settle themselves smoothly into so simple a prearrangement. But through the autumn of 1841, as Darwin devoted two hours a day to assorting and explaining the groups of facts, he rejoiced in results that grew ever more clean-cut. By the end of the year he could exclaim to himself (as he later did in print) "I defy anyone to explain this map in any other manner."

He would hardly have ventured to be so confident if his theory had not been sanctioned by Lyell. Strangely enough, though Lyell's *Principles* had given Darwin his fundamental idea, Lyell had explained coral islands in a way that he now admitted was quite wrong. When he made the next revision of his *Principles* he recanted completely and gave Darwin full credit for the new explanation. For seventy years the Darwin theory was almost unanimously accepted by geologists, but is now believed to be wrong in one important particular; there seem to be some coral islands that have been formed on rising areas of ocean bed.

This exception does not impair the influence of Darwin's theory. For Darwin was not engaged in a mere explanation of how coral is built; he was using coral-reefs as a demonstration of the prime law of geology, that great areas slowly and uniformly rise and sink as the ages pass. The crust of the earth heaves up and down as if it were the chest of a sleeper who breathes once in each geological period.

The copy for his book, called *Coral-Reefs,* was ready in January of 1842. The book is an illustration of Darwin's method throughout his life. By observing a small and simple fact, that polyps can not live at a greater depth than one hundred and fifty feet, and by applying this observation to the problem of reef-building, he had

reached a demonstration that all "catastrophic" geology
was idle speculation. He had revealed the basis of the
science of geology. By the same sort of attack—beginning with the humble facts of cross-bred fowls—he hoped
to discover the basis of all biological sciences.

CHAPTER IX

FOUR YEARS OF SPECIES AT DOWNE*

1. Downe House; 2. Joseph Dalton Hooker; 3. The Sketch of 1844; 4. Vestiges of Creation.

1. Downe House

BEFORE Darwin had been two years on Gower Street it became apparent that he could not continue to live in odious London. Though there seemed to be a return of health in the summer of 1842, so that he was able to tramp in Wales, "it was the last time I was ever strong enough to climb mountains or take long walks." Some hereditary weakness (not any illness caused by sea-sickness or confinement) now clutched him for the rest of his life. He had no strength for the increasing social duties. There were too many dinner invitations which could not be refused, too many callers in the evening; the excitement of meeting people, much as Darwin enjoyed it, grew more distressing. It was resolved to go to the country, but to some place fairly near London where Darwin might keep up acquaintances and attend occasional meetings of societies.

Many places were talked about and examined; none excited enthusiasm. Finally, despairing of finding a home that would be entirely to their liking, Darwin

---

*The name of the village is spelled *Downe* in the *Postal Guide,* on the Ordnance Map, in Baedeker, and on the gate-posts of Downe House; Mrs. Darwin and her daughters usually wrote it so. Darwin and his sons preferred *Down*; and the spelling was the subject of much family banter. *Down* is used in all the books about Darwin and in *Who's Who*; but I do not see that I have a right to it.

bought an eighteen-acre estate in Kent. He described
the purchase to his sister in July, 1842.

Village about forty houses with old walnut trees in
the middle where stands an old flint church and the lanes
meet. Inhabitants very respectable—all touch their hats
and sit at their open doors in the evening: no high road
leads through the village. The little pot-house where
we slept is a grocer's shop, and the landlord is the carpenter—so you may guess the style of the village. . . .
House ugly, looks neither old nor new. . . . Capital
study 18 x 18. Dining-room 21 x 18. Drawing-room can
easily be added to: is 21 x 15. Three stories, plenty of
bedrooms. We could hold the Hensleighs and you and
Susan and Erasmus all together. . . . I believe the
price is about £ 2200. . . . Emma was at first a good
deal disappointed, and at the country round the house;
the day was gloomy and cold with N. E. wind. She likes
the actual field and house better than I do; the house is
just situated as she likes for retirement. . . . She was
dreadfully bad with toothache and headache in the evening and Friday, but in coming back yesterday she was so
delighted with the scenery for the first few miles that it
worked a great change in her.

The bargain was made. The Darwin family moved
into Downe House September 14. A stone under a
great yew tree in the tiny churchyard tells the story of
the first three weeks of residence.

IN MEMORY OF
Mary Eleanor
Born Sept. 23, died Oct. 16, 1842
and of
Charles Waring
Born Dec. 6, 1856, died June 28, 1858
Children of Charles Darwin

The village of Downe is fifteen miles, in an air line,

southeast of the British Museum. It is in Kent, but only
two miles east of the Surrey line. When Darwin wished
to visit London he had to be driven more than eight miles
by his careful old gardener to the railway station (at
Croyden or Sydenham), whence he continued ten miles
by train. So retired is the village that even now the
most convenient railway station is four miles away (Or-
pington). Even though a Sunday bus now runs within
two miles of Downe (Farnborough), the pilgrim will find
that those last two miles are on winding, up-and-down
lanes, between high hedges, and so narrow that in many
stretches two cars could pass only with difficulty. If
he motors from London, he will hear his driver make
several anxious inquiries about how to find the unknown
hamlet. Downe House is a quarter of a mile south of
the church.

For the remainder of his life Darwin lived here constantly. I quote from his *Autobiography*.

Few persons can have lived a more retired life than
we have done. Besides short visits to the houses of relations, and occasionally to the seaside or elsewhere, we
have gone nowhere. During the first part of our residence we went a little into society, and received a few
friends here; but my health almost always suffered from
the excitement, violent shivering and vomiting attacks
being thus brought on. I have therefore been compelled for many years to give up all dinner-parties; and
this has been somewhat of a deprivation to me, as such
parties always put me into high spirits. From the same
cause I have been able to invite here very few scientific
acquaintances.

My chief enjoyment and sole employment throughout
life has been scientific work; and the excitement from
such work makes me for the time forget, or drives quite
away, my daily discomfort. I have therefore nothing to
record during the rest of my life, except the publication
of my several books.

A biographer must record the birth of children. In September, 1843, the fourth child, Henrietta Emma, was born; she became Mrs. Litchfield and edited *Emma Darwin: a Century of Family Letters*. George Howard was born in July, 1845; he became a professor of astronomy at Cambridge.

2.   *Joseph Dalton Hooker*

While the Darwins were spending their first night in Downe House, Hooker was sleeping under the battened hatches of H. M. S. *Erebus,* which was hove to in a fierce gale that was driving her east when she wanted to go west. He had been three years away from England on an Antarctic expedition commanded by the famous polar explorer Sir James Clark Ross. If you look at a map of the South Polar region, you will see the red lines that show how far Ross carried Hooker in 1839-42. For the rest of the century this remained the record of farthest south. Ross discovered the land from which later explorers set out to reach the Pole.

Ross's business was to keep daily records of compass variation, on certain days to keep a record every five minutes, and to locate the South Magnetic Pole as closely as possible. He had once seen the needle stand vertical over the North Magnetic Pole, and it was now his ambition to see the same sight in the Antarctic.

In the autumn of 1839 he headed for the South Atlantic by the same course that the *Beagle* had taken: south to the Madeira and the Cape Verde Islands, then to St. Paul's Rocks, though a high surf prevented Hooker's landing. Thence the course was laid, via the Cape of Good Hope, to the loneliest bit of land on the globe, Kerguelen Island. This is a volcanic mass of an area somewhat greater than Rhode Island, which lies just north of latitude 50°, on the other side of the world from Cape Horn. The first day that Hooker spent ashore he discovered thirty new species of plants; and he continued botanizing every day of the ten-week visit, while Ross worked at his magnetic-observation camp.

Kerguelen is largely covered by glaciers, but once it was the home of the luxuriant vegetation that was formed into coal. The vegetation of Kerguelen is peculiar, having some relationship with the plants of Australia, but none with the plants of Africa. There is a peculiar kind of duck in Kerguelen, and some most peculiarly constructed insects. The birds were so tame that one day when Hooker was sitting on a rock, whistling, "upwards of twenty of these sheathbills were gradually approaching, and would even perch on my foot, rocking their heads on one side in the most interesting manner. . . . Some penguins allowed me to take them by the beak." Hooker was seeing the same sort of extraordinary sights that Darwin had seen ten years previously, and was seeing them with eyes as keen as Darwin's. His mind was not occupied with any speculations about what a species is, but it was continually alert to the remarkable facts of the distribution of species.

Captain Ross named a mountain in Hooker's honor (only a third as high as Mt. Darwin) and left for Tasmania on July 20, 1840.

Hooker was never sea-sick an hour on the *Erebus,* and his captain did not consider him a "damned scientific whig," as we see from Hooker's letters home.

Almost every day I draw, sometimes all day long and till two and three in the morning, the Captain directing me; he sits on one side of the table, writing and figuring at night, and I on the other, drawing. Every now and then he breaks off and comes to my side to see what I am after. . . .

It would have amused you to have come into the cabin and seen the Captain and myself with our sleeves tucked up picking seaweed roots, and depositing the treasures to be drawn, in salt water, in basins, quietly popping the others into spirits. Some of the seaweeds he lays out for himself, often sitting at one end of the table laying them out with infinite pains, whilst I am drawing at the other end till 12 and 1 in the morning, at which times he is very agreeable and my hours pass quickly and pleasantly.

Perhaps Captain Ross would not have been so chummy with a young man whose father was a mere physician. Hooker's father was Sir William; he was director of the Royal Botanical Garden at Kew; and he was a friend whom Ross admired. The Hookers and Ross had similar opinions about keeping the Sabbath, as Joseph shows in this apology to his father, written from Tasmania:

I got a few specimens after service on Sunday, though Lady Franklin did not like it, and very properly, but I thought it excusable as being my only chance of gathering *Anopterus glandulosus*. Do not think this is my habit. Captain Ross is too strict, were there no other reasons.

In the Antarctic summer of 1840-41 Ross's vessels went into the ice-pack—that great field of floating icebergs, some of them miles in diameter, which surrounds the Antarctic continent. Hooker first saw the ice on New Year's Day, 1841. On January 12 Captain Ross took possession of some land that he discovered, naming it Queen Victoria's Land and serving out grog to all hands while they cheered. For many weeks of the trip no stars were visible, and the log of the *Erebus* recorded eleven storms. But Hooker enjoyed it all.

The next Antarctic summer the second expedition was made into the ice-pack. The weather was even worse than the year before. At one place the vessels maneuvered forty-six days to get clear of ice. In March they collided while trying to avoid an iceberg, and "for three-quarters of an hour the *Erebus* lay among the breakers, striking her masts against the berg as she rolled, each ship threatening to send the other to the bottom."

When the *Erebus* reached the Falkland Islands after this expedition, April 6, 1842, she had been out of sight of land for one hundred and thirty-five days. It is not surprising that Ross stayed five months at the Falklands. He had no controversy with Hooker about the variations of animals here.

While the Darwins were packing on Gower Street in September, Hooker was sailing for Cape Horn. He saw it on the 19th (when the Darwins had lived five days at Downe) and was told as the *Erebus* skirted it, that the *Beagle's* crew had left a cairn of stones on it. The *Erebus* anchored under the same black precipice where Darwin had been with Lyell's second volume ten years before: "A more extraordinary anchorage for wildness and sublimity we never lay at. . . . Indeed all Darwin's remarks are so true and so graphic wherever we go that Mr. Lyell's kind present is not only indispensable but a delightful companion and guide."

Early in the third trip which the *Erebus* made into the pack-ice Ross was all but driven ashore; and the name of the place—of all the names in the atlas—was Darwin Islet. Later the vessels were almost frozen in and were often in danger of being wrecked. By the time they were safe at the Cape of Good Hope in April there were only two men aboard who were not thoroughly sick of exploring—Ross and Hooker. "It is nothing to me," Hooker wrote, "if they keep us out six years, except the want of seeing my friends; for I am always improving myself, and it will give me a greater claim on the scientific world." But there was one other drawback to remaining longer at sea: "On board this ship I want music more than anything."

Hooker went ashore at Woolwich on the day when Darwin had completed fifty-one weeks of residence at Downe. Darwin had followed his voyage by means of the letters that Hooker had written home and that Lyell passed on. There were several reasons why Darwin should feel a special interest in the young botanist: (1) the similarity of their voyages, (2) the high estimate that Lyell had of Hooker, (3) the affection that Henslow had for him, (4) the esteem that Hooker had expressed for Darwin. A stronger and more practical reason was that Darwin, who had the world's best geologist for an adviser, wanted the world's best botanist for another adviser; and there were signs that Joseph Hooker was fast climbing to that pre-eminence. He was laying a broader foundation than his father had; his intellect was not, like the great Bentham's, imperiled by its love of logic and philosophy; he was not freakish like the *facile princeps* Brown.

3. The Sketch of 1844

Darwin's most urgent reason for seeking an alliance was that in 1843 he harbored a dreadful secret in his bosom. He needed to confide it to some one. We are told that every murderer feels an irresistible impulse to speak about his crime, that the knowledge of the deed is unbearable until it is told. Darwin was in such case. He had committed scientific treason of the most horrible kind, and he needed to confess it. Hooker was a genial and sympathetic soul; what was more, Hooker's letters showed that he was both hard-headed and open to new ideas. It is not possible for a historian, looking back at 1843, to name any man in England who would have been a better confidant.

I dwell upon this choice of Hooker because it is an example of Darwin's strategy throughout his life—his skill in picking men. When he opened a book by an unknown author his foremost query was "What sort of fellow are you?" I think Darwin would have enjoyed being compared to a dog that stands with quivering nostrils, testing the air of a new place. The great geologist Geikie has spoken of "the unerring instinct with which Darwin fastened on principles that would stand the test of time." Darwin had some instinct, independent of mere printed sentences or academic record, which revealed to him whether a man was erratic or dependable. It told him that Hooker was a man on whom he could build an absolute trust.

For some unrecorded reason Darwin did not communicate with Hooker till December. Then he wrote in warm and friendly fashion. The letter was very long and put many searching questions about distribution.

The murder was not confessed till a month later. It was a deed that Darwin had plotted ever since his return from the *Beagle* voyage. Before the end of 1837 he had decided that fixity of species must die. He had been jotting down all sorts of thoughts on the subject, just as they happened into his mind:

The tree of life should perhaps be called the coral of life—base of branches dead, so that passage can not be seen.

Opponents will say, "Show me intermediate forms." I will answer, "Yes, if you will show me every step between bulldog and greyhound."

We can easily see that variety of ostrich may not be well adapted, and thus perish.

Prove animals like plants—trace gradation between animals—and the story will be complete.

Will Mr. Lyell say that some circumstances killed it?

Darwin's thoughts were then, as later, directed toward Lyell as the critic who must be persuaded.

The speculation about why the ostrich perished had prepared Darwin's mind for a striking suggestion that came from reading Malthus's *Essay on the Principle of Population* in October, 1838. The principle was briefly this:

The human race tends to increase by a geometrical ratio—with immensely greater rapidity than its food supply; there is therefore a constant check on population; "the races of plants and animals shrink under this great restrictive law; the effects of the law are waste of seed, sickness, and premature death."

The reasoning was so clear and cogent that the *Essay* made a great impression in its day and has remained a classic in social study. It revealed to Darwin how far his observation about the ostrich might reach. "It at once struck me," he says, "that favorable variations would tend to be preserved, and unfavorable ones to be destroyed." This was, already, a well-developed embryo of an evolution theory.

But Darwin would not hurry the growth of this embryo. He let it incubate very slowly, for he dreaded speculation. One of his 1837 jottings had been: "If we choose to let conjecture run wild, then animals . . . may partake our origin in one common ancestor—we may be all melted together." He would keep such conjecture tied fast: "We are led to endeavor to discover *causes* of change." He would keep searching for facts. Not till 1842 would he allow himself the pleasure of writing an outline of a supposed way in which evolution might operate.

But the theory kept developing itself. By the beginning of 1844 it was ready to hatch. On January 11 Darwin could keep it in the shell no longer. He wrote to Hooker:

Besides a general interest about the southern lands, I have ever since my return engaged in a very presumptuous work, and I know no one individual who would not say a very foolish one. I was so struck with the distribution of the Galapagos organisms, etc., etc., that I determined to collect blindly every sort of fact which could bear any way on what are species. I have read heaps of agricultural and horticultural books, and have never ceased collecting facts. At last gleams of light have come, and I am almost convinced (quite contrary to the opinion I started with) that species are not (it is like confessing a murder) immutable. Heaven forfend me from Lamarck nonsense of a "tendency to progression," "adaptations from the slow willing of animals," etc.! But the conclusions I am led to are not widely different from his; though the means of change are wholly so. I think I have found out (here's presumption!) the simple way by which species become exquisitely adapted to various ends. You will now groan, and think to yourself, "On what a man have I been wasting my time and writing to." I should, five years ago, have thought so.

Darwin had casually encountered an unknown Hooker in 1839. Now he arranged a real meeting by inviting a well-known Hooker to breakfast with him at Erasmus Darwin's London house in Park Street.

Hooker was a brawny tar, with a handshake like a taut sheet and a laugh like a favoring gale. An odd figure he was. The head was prone to be cocked at a sort of owlish angle for careful inspection of whatever came into view. The eyes were somewhat searching and formidable, but there was always a smile in them—kindly for a friend and contemptuous for a foe. Darwin could tell instantly that this man Hooker would perceive falsity as well as a condor could find a carcass, and would mince no words before he pounced on it. Hooker never would permit a conversation to be gravely proper: he joked and used slang. In the hundreds of letters that these two exchanged during the next forty years there was constant chaffing of each other.

When Hooker was, soon after this breakfast, invited to Downe he proved the most sympathetic and adjustable of guests. As he continued his visits while the Darwin children grew up, he got on all fours for them and was a roaring bear. The Darwin household was happy whenever Dr. Hooker was being entertained.

Darwin must have been encouraged by this new friend to go on with his murder of fixity of species; for in July, 1844, he explained to his wife how seriously he regarded the "Sketch" of the theory. He had had this copied out in a fair, clerkly hand on two hundred and thirty-one large pages. Sir Francis Darwin vouches that it is "a surprisingly complete presentation of the argument afterwards familiar to us in *The Origin of Species.*" Darwin took steps to have it cared for in case of his death. The quotation that follows is from a letter to his wife, dated July 5.

I have just finished my sketch of my species theory. If, as I believe, my theory in time be accepted even by one competent judge, it will be a considerable step in science. . . .

I therefore write this in case of my sudden death, as my most solemn and last request, which I am sure you will consider the same as if legally entered in my will, that you will devote £400 to its publication, and further will yourself, or through Hensleigh, take trouble in promoting it. I wish that my sketch be given to some competent person, with this sum to induce him to take trouble in its improvement and enlargement. I give to him all my books on Natural History, which are either scored or have references at the end to the pages, begging him carefully to look over and consider such passages as actually bearing, or by possibility bearing, on this subject. . . . With respect to editors, Mr. Lyell would be the best if he would undertake it. . . . The next best editor would be Professor Forbes of London. The next best (and quite best in many respects) would be Professor Henslow. Dr. Hooker would be *very* good. . . . Lyell, especially with the aid of Hooker (and of any good zoological aid), would be best of all.

It would appear that Darwin's instinct preferred Hooker (he was *very* good), but that reason told him not to choose so young and unknown a man for the chief editor. When he looked over this document ten years later he penciled on it: "Hooker by far best man to edit my species volume."

During the next three years Hooker was often a guest at Downe House. He has given a description of these times.

A more hospitable and more attractive home under every point of view could not be imagined. Of society there were most often Dr. Falconer, Edward Forbes, Professor Bell, and Mr. Waterhouse. There were long walks, romps with the children, music that haunts me still. . . . Latterly, as his health became more seriously affected, I was for days and weeks the only visitor, bringing my work with me and enjoying his society as opportunity offered. It was an established rule that he every day pumped me, as he called it, for half an hour or so after breakfast in his study, when he first brought out a heap of slips with questions botanical, geographical, etc., for me to answer, and concluded by telling me of the progress he had made in his own work, asking my opinion on various points. I saw no more of him till about noon, when I heard his mellow, ringing voice calling my name under my window—this was to join him in his daily forenoon walk round the sand-walk.

4. Vestiges of Creation

How perilous a business Darwin's Sketch was may be judged by the fact that he confided his views to only one friend besides Hooker—Leonard Jenyns, the man who might have been naturalist on the *Beagle*.

The danger may be better judged by the fate of a little book, famous in its day, called *Vestiges of Creation*. The author, Robert Chambers, was a logical, careful, well-read Edinburgh publisher who had gained local celebrity with his *Traditions of Edinburgh* the year before Darwin began to study medicine. The book was so creditable that Sir Walter Scott sought out the author and made a friend of him. Chambers edited a biographical dictionary, founded *Chambers' Journal*, edited *Chambers' Encyclopedia*, and wrote numerous books. The workmanship of this extraordinary miscellany was all sound and worthy. When Chambers prepared to make a book on the species question he took time to inform himself; his writing was done with painstaking care. The book was closely reasoned and the style well suited to so difficult a task. The two small volumes appeared in 1843 and 1845.

This book, the only work of his that lives in history, was brought out anonymously, by a Manchester publisher, and the secret of its authorship was not disclosed for forty years. Chambers had a strong reason for keeping his authorship secret. An argument that the wonderful adaptations of animals had been brought about by natural causes was supposed to be a denial of God's design in His creation, and so to be atheistic. Worse still, an argument for the development of one species out of another was sure to indicate that human beings are not a special creation; it was degrading and atheistical. The odium attaching to such an argument would be greater in proportion as the argument was convincing.

Theologians could afford to laugh at the vagaries of a Monboddo or an Erasmus Darwin, but they would fight against any reasoning that looked like a proof. Chambers dared not endanger a flourishing business by incurring such wrath.

Darwin's fear was of a different sort. He dreaded the ridicule of scientists. You may see him shrinking from it in the letters to Hooker of 1844.

In my most sanguine moments all I expect is that I shall be able to show even to sound naturalists that there are two sides to the question of the immutability of species. . . . With respect to books on this subject, I do not know of any systematical ones except Lamarck's, which is veritable rubbish. . . . The other common (specially Germanic) notion is hardly less absurd, viz. that climate, food, etc., should make a *Pediculus* formed to climb hair, or wood-pecker to climb trees. I believe all these absurd views arise from no one having, as far as I know, approached the subject on the side of variation under domestication. . . .
You will be ten times hereafter more horrified at me than at H. Watson.

Through the following years he frequently condoles with himself about the horror which scientists will feel at his theory. He spoke of it to Jenyns late in 1845: "I know how much I open myself to reproach for such a conclusion, but I have at least honestly and deliberately come to it. I shall not publish on this subject for several years."

Lamarck had been ridiculed for such a conclusion; every scientist that Darwin respected agreed that Lamarck's conclusion was rubbish. Even Chambers, who had now arrived at the same belief, contemptuously disclaimed the Lamarck nonsense:

M. Lamarck suggested an hypothesis of organic progress which deservedly incurred much ridicule, although it contained a glimmer of the truth. . . . His whole notion is obviously so inadequate to account for the rise of organic kingdoms that we can only place it with pity among the follies of the wise.

But the hypothesis of the *Vestiges* was voted a folly by every competent naturalist. There seemed to be some curse on this species question, which destroyed the reason of every one who struggled with it. Even the mind of Lyell, so canny everywhere else, had made assumptions about species that were unworthy of a medieval schoolman. The mind of Chambers—steady and safe as a pile-driver for one hundred and twenty-two pages about geology and anthropomorphism—suddenly behaved like a waltzing mouse when it touched species. This sober and precise Scot argued that mushrooms spring, not from any sort of seed, but from the potency of the mixture of horse dung and cow dung; he seriously proposed that *"development* was a *principle* which has peopled the globe"; he recorded as a fact that "whenever oats are kept cropped and allowed to remain over the winter, a thin crop of rye is the harvest." On such "facts" he founded a theory of the mutability of species. And the theory seemed to him an important pioneer work.

The book, as far as I am aware, is the first attempt to connect the natural sciences into a history of creation.

So we can imagine how Darwin was low in his mind when he foresaw himself as the third in the absurd series of species speculators. For his grand hope was the very one Chambers had had—to bring geology and zoology and botany and heredity into an orderly whole as parts of a unified theory of how species originate.

My only comfort is that I have dabbled in several branches of natural history and know something of geology (an indispensable union); and though I shall get more kicks than half-pennies, I will, life serving, attempt my work. Lamarck is the only exception, that I can think of, of an accurate describer of species, at least in the invertebrate kingdom, who has disbelieved in permanent species, but he in his absurd though clever work has done the subject harm, as has Mr. Vestiges, and as (some future loose naturalist attempting the same speculations will perhaps say) has Mr. D.

Mr. D. humbled himself and became wary. He would hope for no grand, overwhelming demonstration. "In my wildest day-dreams," he averred to Jenyns, "I never expect more than to be able to show that there are two sides to the question—that is, whether species are *directly* created or by intermediate laws." Perhaps he did not dare to feel sure of more success than this, but he certainly had a hope of more.

In the autumn of 1845 he wrote:

Sedgwick's review is a grand piece of argument against mutability of species, and I read it with fear and trembling.

As the years passed after 1845 and every good judge laughed at the *Vestiges,* Darwin resolved to be more slow and painstaking with his evidence, to establish a reputation as a thorough student, to seek out alliances with the best of the younger scholars, to have all his observations and reasoning checked by unsparing critics.

CHAPTER X

EIGHT YEARS OF BARNACLES: 1846-1854

1. Thomas Henry Huxley; 2. Hooker in India; 3. Darwin's Poor Health; 4. The Death of Annie; 5. Darwin Stood All Alone.

IN 1846, when *Geological Observations* was published, Darwin reckoned that during the past ten years he had spent the equivalent of four and a half years on his three geological books. These were so thoroughly done and so influential that they would have kept his name alive in the history of science if he had died when they were completed. So competent an authority as Sir Archibald Geikie says of *Coral-Reefs*: "This treatise has become one of the classics of geological literature. No more admirable example of scientific method was ever given to the world, and even if he had written nothing else, the treatise alone would have placed Darwin in the very front rank of investigators of nature."

In other departments of geology Darwin disclosed new truths about such highly technical matters as cleavage and the behavior of acids and bases in granite; "his account of the bombs and trachytes and obsidians of the island of Ascension has long taken its place as one of the classic descriptions of modern petrography."

Just as Darwin's observation of coral polyps enabled him to prove a great generalization about the rising and sinking of continents, so his four-page study of earthworms (little recognized when first published) brought in time a revelation of the whole vast process of the formation of soil; the pettiest of subjects became "the most original and important of his geological papers." Geologists had been unduly impressed by the power of the mighty oceans to cause changes in land areas; Darwin pointed out to them that rivers were vastly more potent in wearing down continents.

Of the geological chapters in *The Origin of Species* Geikie speaks with highest admiration: "Until these chapters revealed the incompleteness of the geological record I do not believe that any of us [i. e., geologists] had the remotest conception that the extent of its imperfection was so infinitely greater than we had even imagined. . . . Into the department of stratigraphy he threw a flood of new light. . . . His views mark a notable epoch in modern geology. . . . I am glad to be privileged with this public opportunity of acknowledging the deep debt which the science of geology, in many of its departments and in the whole spirit by which it is now informed, owes to the lifelong labor of the author of *The Origin of Species*.

No sooner were the last geological proof sheets off his hands than he plunged into a bit of an anatomical puzzle with which he expected to entertain himself a few weeks. He wanted to understand the structure and relationship of a peculiar barnacle. Most barnacles (their technical name is "cirripedes") attach themselves to objects and live as unadventurously as kelp, but this strange *peruviana* lived by boring through the thick, ribbed, conical shell of a mollusc that was common on the rocks of the coast of Chile. It was a peculiar mollusc, for it was the only species of its genus. Hence the very unusual barnacle was adapted in a special way to prey upon a special animal. Darwin wished to know how it worked, how its structure might have developed, and what its life history was.

To understand the structure of my new cirripede I had to examine and dissect many of the common forms; and this gradually led me on to take up the whole group.

The more he studied the more he grew amazed at the ignorance which all previous classifiers showed. He had to respect the pioneer efforts of Lamarck, and he could excuse blunders in so perplexing a field—indeed he confessed of his own work, "I blundered dreadfully about the cement glands." What he could not excuse was the slipshod way in which specialists had accepted second-hand misinformation, without even taking time to use their own eyes. One high authority declared that the body of cirripedes is not ringed. "But," is Darwin's comment, "if *any* cirripede be well cleaned it will be seen to be most distinctly articulated." It was agreed by the authorities that cirripedes have salivary glands; Darwin proved that the glands were ovaries. High authority, undisputed, said that cirripedes did not have a head; Darwin's examination showed that "the whole of the cirripede externally visible consists exclusively of three segments of the head."

Early in 1849 he described the jungle of ignorance that he was trying to thread.

I am in a perfect maze of doubt on nomenclature. In not one large genus of Cirripedia has *any one* species been correctly defined; it is pure guess-work to recognize any species. . . . Not one naturalist has ever taken the trouble to open the shell of any species to describe it scientifically, and yet all the genera have half a dozen synonyms. . . . I use Agassiz's nomenclator; at least two-thirds of the dates in the Cirripedia are grossly wrong.

A labor of eight years on barnacles is so remote from our experience, so drearily impossible to imagine, that it can easily be made to seem comical. Darwin was quite well aware of how easy a mark he was for caricature.

I do not doubt that Sir E. Lytton Bulwer had me in his mind when he introduced in one of his novels a Professor Long, who had written two huge volumes on limpets.

Darwin's perception of the humor of his occupation was quite as keen as Bulwer Lytton's.

He could never have survived the eight years if he had not been sustained by the enthusiasm of gaining an insight into the nature of a species.

I suspect the pleasure is rather derived from comparisons forming in one's mind with *allied structures*.

The sights that Darwin saw on this long journey in the maze of barnacles were more precious, sometimes more exciting, than the views in the Andes. For he was hacking his way toward the mystery of mysteries, the secret of how life adapts itself by altering its structure to compete in the struggle for existence.

There was always a satisfaction of another sort to cheer Darwin on while he ploughed through the monographs and moistened the thousands of dry specimens for dissection. He was becoming a specialist who could not be snubbed by the Owens and Mivarts who would assail his evolution theory. When he returned from the *Beagle* voyage he was an amateur in every biological field.

Mr. Don remarked on the beautiful appearance of some plant with an astounding long name. Some one else seemed quite surprised that I knew nothing about

a *Carex* from I do not know where. I was at last forced
to plead most entire innocence and that I knew no more
about the plants which I had collected than the man in
the moon.

His zoological specimens had to be parceled out among
scholars in the different fields, because he had no expert
knowledge of any class of animals, living or extinct.
The superiority felt by specialists who criticize an amateur is such as only the humiliated amateur can conceive.
Darwin's work with barnacles was elevating him to the
priesthood of specialists. No amount of general knowledge and wisdom can qualify a man for this sacred band.
But if he has detailed knowledge of all the minutiæ of,
say, Coptic ritual, he will be received as a peer by all
the specialists in glaciers or ornithology. Darwin was
earning membership in the Sanhedrin of science.

It will not do to make fun of this reverence for detailed scholarship. Though it often enthrones poor
minds in the sanctuary of the intellect, it holds in check
the speculations of lazy and empty minds. Until a man
has shown the ability to drudge and sweat for long years
he is an untrustworthy theorizer. He had better be
kept among the rabble that science can not respect.

I know that very few readers would enjoy an account
of eight years among barnacles, which produced two big
volumes on the living species and two thin ones on the
extinct species. Yet I will not bury the record of those
rich years in the Appendix, for the reader who has not
seen something of it will never understand Darwin or his
theory. I will compromise. I will put into this chapter
only a few glimpses of the eight years of patient industry. And I will relieve the tedium of even this slight
view by interspersing some numbered sections that tell
of the mere human life of Darwin while he was becoming
a prophet of species. Read the four sets of excerpts

from Volumes I and II of *Cirripedia*. If you bear in mind that each set represents twenty-four months of baffling investigation, carried on against the odds of illness and weariness, you will not drowse. Put yourself in Darwin's study, which smells of ancient barnacles and alcohol. Imagine that you are searching for an idea which will make you known to every newspaper-reader in Christendom for centuries to come.

Try to realize that each line of this first set of quotations represents two weeks of labor. The numbers refer to pages.

51. In all the genera the double eye is seated deep within the body.

55. Certain parasitic males, which, from their not pairing, as in all hitherto known cases, with females, but with hermaphrodites, I have designated *Complemental Males*.

72. The first five species form a most natural genus; they are often sufficiently difficult to be distinguished, owing to their great variability.

76. From the foregoing description it will be seen how extremely variable almost every part of this species is. I find, in the British Museum, ten distinct specific names given by Dr. Leach to different varieties, or rather to different specimens, for some of them are undistinguishable.

80. This species is almost universally confounded with *anatifera*. Quoy and Gaimard, however, appear to have distinguished it, under the name of *tricolor*, from its colors. Leach named it accidentally, for he specifies not one distinctive character, and besides his two published names, he has appended two other names to specimens in the British Museum.

84. This species has caused me much trouble: I have examined vast numbers of specimens, from a tenth to half an inch in length. [He then describes five ways in which it is distinguished.] Lately, however, in carefully going over a great suite of specimens, all the above

distinctive characters broke down and insensibly graduated away; and I am convinced that this form is only
a variety of *anserifera*.

87.   This at first led me to think that the *P. spirulae*
of Leach was a distinct species; but there are so many
intermediate forms that the idea must be given up.

90.   Until I had carefully examined a perfect series,
showing the gradual changes in this part, I did not
doubt that the young specimens formed a distinct species, and named it accordingly.

97.   As this species grows into an unusually bulky
animal, we see here a beautiful and unique contrivance,
in the cement forming a vesicular membranous mass,
serving as a buoy to float the individuals.

98.   The extreme variability of this species is remarkable.

105.   This species so closely resembles *P. Kaempferi*
that it is superfluous to describe it in detail.

115.   I was at first unwilling to sacrifice Mr. Hind's
genus, *Trilasmis*, which is so neatly characterized by its
three valves.

128.   Notwithstanding these differences, I should not
be much surprised if the present form were to turn out
to be a mere variety.

140.   As the majority of authors have ranked the two
common species under two distinct genera, I may observe that there is no good ground for this separation.

1.   Thomas Henry Huxley

Now, as a little recess before you read of the next two
years of barnacles, you may travel round the world with
a young man who is preparing himself to be a champion
of evolution.

When Darwin set out for Edinburgh in the autumn of
1825, Tom Huxley was a babe five months old.   His
father was the senior assistant master of a school in the
London suburb of Ealing.   Tom was the seventh and
last child—in fact he was the seventh child of a seventh

child, and had quite as miraculous a mind as this birth would indicate.

Of his boyhood in school he gives us this report:

Though my way of life has made me acquainted with all sorts and conditions of men, from the highest to the lowest, I deliberately affirm that the society I fell into at school was the worst I have ever known. . . . We were left to the operation of the struggle for existence among ourselves; bullying was the least of the ill practices current among us. Almost the only cheerful reminiscence in connection with the place which arises in my mind is that of a battle I had with one of my classmates, who had bullied me until I could stand it no longer. I was a very slight lad, but there was a wildcat element in me which, when roused, made up for lack of weight, and I licked my adversary effectually.

It was this wildcat element that made Huxley the most picturesque of the warriors who rallied to support Darwin.

His youth was a great contrast to the gentle breeding of Lyell and Darwin and Hooker; for the father, when the school failed, had become manager of a savings bank, and the sisters had to teach school. At the age of sixteen he began to assist a physician in work among the poor people of the East End. He was apprenticed to learn pharmacy and attended medical lectures in the hope of entering London University.

His instincts were different from those of Darwin and Hooker, for he did not care to collect and was not interested in species. He liked metaphysics and logic. At the age of sixteen he was puckering his brow over this question: What would become of things if their qualities were taken away? He maintained, in a disputation with a man ten years his senior, this thesis: It can not be proved that matter is essentially different from

soul. He debated with himself this question: Is moral-
ity objective or subjective? At the age of sixteen he put
both sides of the argument fairly and acutely, and was
able *to remain in doubt* as to the decision. He could suspend judgment about perpetual motion. He rather felt
that his scheme was based on correct principles, and
went with palpitating heart to ask the great Faraday
about it. Though he detected the vague and wrong logic
with which Faraday objected to his scheme, he realized
that Faraday's mind worked by a higher and safer kind
of logic. He allowed the great physicist to "exorcise
the devil" of perpetual motion.

Huxley was early attracted to Carlyle, whose books
taught him to despise shams of every sort. Carlyle fired
him with a zeal to study German, at a time when only a
few English scientists could read it. Huxley also made
himself proficient in French. In this linguistic ability,
and in the ease with which he could follow subtleties of
metaphysics, his mind was of a different order from
Darwin's.

Darwin never learned to pronounce German; and
when he was urged to be secretary of the Geological
Society pleaded "my ignorance of all languages, and
not knowing how to pronounce a single word of French."
Darwin always felt that Herbert Spencer lived in a
superior and unapproachable world of thought, but Huxley criticized Spencer with easy assurance.

Huxley was hungry for all knowledge. He sat up
late at night to read Hutton's *Geology*. He was seen so
regularly, after the lectures at Charing Cross Hospital,
bending over a microscope at a window that he was
called "The Sign of the Head and Microscope." His
philosophical bent was corrected by an "intense curiosity"; he felt no satisfaction in "mere opinion"; his
proneness to speculate was always checked by observa-

tion of the ugliest facts in London slums and by observation of the sights revealed through lenses. It became the passion of his life to "strip away make-believe."

From the day when he first began to study anatomy and physiology he showed that he was an acute and original observer. At the age of seventeen he won a medal for taking second place in a competitive examination in botany. At eighteen he won a chemistry prize for "extraordinary diligence and success," and a prize in anatomy and physiology. When he was nineteen he discovered a membrane at the base of human hairs, which is still called "Huxley's layer" in textbooks. In his examination for his medical degree, at the age of twenty, he won a gold medal. Two years later he read a paper before the British Association, demonstrating the strange fact that the blood of the lowest kind of vertebrate animal was similar to the blood of invertebrates.

Huxley now felt the spur of an ambition to win scientific distinction, and he chose the path that Hooker and Darwin had taken before him. After a term of service in the Haslar Hospital, a naval institution at Portsmouth, he received an appointment as assistant surgeon on the frigate *Rattlesnake,* which was to explore and make soundings north of Australia. He left England in December, 1846, and was gone almost four years.

His position on board was less favorable than Darwin's had been, for he had to eat with the middies in the gun-room. He proved to be the sort of man whom middies enjoyed as a comrade. His quarters were poor compared with Darwin's.

My total length, as you are aware, is considerable— 5 feet 11 inches, possibly; but the height of the lower deck of the *Rattlesnake,* which will be my especial location, is at outside 4 feet 10 inches. What I am to do with the superfluous foot I cannot divine. Happily, however, there is a sort of skylight into the berth, so that I shall be able to sit with the body in it and my head out.

Huxley's voyage was very monotonous compared with Darwin's. For the *Rattlesnake* headquartered at Sydney and made cruises northward behind the Great Barrier Reef and out to the Louisiade Archipelago that lies to the east of New Guinea. There were three of these cruises, one of three months and two of nine months each. His letters home and his journal tell us what they were like.

Fancy for five mortal months shifting from patch to patch of white sand in latitude from 17° to 10° south, living on salt pork and beef, and seeing no mortal face but our own sweet countenances considerably obscured by the long beard and moustaches. . . .

I wonder if it is possible for the mind of man to conceive anything more degradingly offensive than the condition of us 150 men, shut up in this wooden box, and being watered with hot water, as we are now. It is no exaggeration to say *hot*, for the temperature is that at which people at home commonly take a hot bath. It rains so hard that we have caught seven tons of water in one day, and it is therefore impossible to go on deck. . . . A *hot* Scotch mist covers the sea and hides the land, so that no surveying can be done; moving about in the slightest degree causes a flood of perspiration to pour out; all energy is completely gone, and if I could help it I would not think even; it's too hot. . . . It's too hot to sleep, and my sole amusement consists in watching the cockroaches, which are in a state of intense excitement and happiness. A sudden unanimous impulse seems to seize the obscene thousands which usually lurk hidden in the corners of my cabin. Out they rush, helter-skelter, and run over me, my table, and my desk. . . . It is these outbreaks alone which rouse us from our lassitude.

Discomfort and monotony never kept Huxley's spirits

low. He was in splendid health the whole time. Captain Stanley was a fine officer, who gave him every encouragement.

He is the son of the Bishop of Norwich, is an exceedingly gentlemanly man, a thorough scientific enthusiast, and shows himself altogether very much disposed to forward my views in every possible way.

The whole poop is to be converted into a large chartroom with bookshelves and tables and plenty of light. There I may read, draw, or microscopize at pleasure, and as to books, I have a *carte blanche* from the Captain to take as many as I please.

The Captain's generosity was further shown by his naming a little island of the Louisiades after Huxley.

Between cruises there were months spent at Sydney. Here Huxley met Miss Heathorn, who had spent two years in Germany—and had other attractions. Huxley at once fell in love with her, and she promised to be his wife. It was five years after he left Australia before he had income enough to send for her. Their love for each other grew stronger through forty years of married life.

In the spring of 1850 Captain Stanley, overworked and weakened by the climate, died. The *Rattlesnake* started home in May, was at the Falklands for two weeks in July, and reached England in October.

Throughout the four years of dissecting marine animals Huxley had been animated by one consistent and daring ambition—to destroy the fundamental theory of Cuvier, the great founder of the science of comparative anatomy and the most illustrious anatomist in the world during Huxley's infancy. Cuvier taught that animals were fashioned according to four original patterns which had no relation to each other, which were "ideas" in the mind of God, and which could therefore not be compared. Within the limits of each "idea" there was the greatest variation of patterns, but there was no sort of gradation from one "ideal type" to another. In short, Cuvier's archetypes were like specially created species: there were varieties within them, but no connection between them.

To Huxley this seemed pure mythology. He was training himself to overthrow it, working as cheerfully at jelly-fish for his purpose as Darwin did at barnacles.

Huxley had Darwin's gift of detecting little matters that others had not seen. He noticed the innocent-looking fact that "a jelly-fish consists of two membranes inclosing a cavity." This simple observation of a structure proved to be momentous. It was an eminent specialist in marine zoology, G. J. Allman, who testified to its importance: "This discovery stands at the very basis of a philosophic zoology and a true conception of the affinities of animals. It is the ground on which Haeckel has founded his famous theory, and without it Kowalesky could never have announced his great discovery by which zoologists had been startled."

When Huxley returned to London he found himself well on the road to fame. Edward Forbes, a leading paleontologist, commended his work: "More important or complete zoological researches have never been conducted during any voyage of discovery in the southern hemisphere." In letters to his sister Huxley could exult at the recognition that was being given him.

I have taken a better position than I could have expected among these grandees, and I find them all immensely civil and ready to help me on, tooth and nail, particularly Prof. Forbes, who is a right good fellow, and has taken a great deal of trouble on my behalf. Owen volunteered to write to the "First Lord" on my behalf, and did so. . . . The other day I dined at the Geological Club and met Lyell, Murchison, de la Beche,

Horner, and a lot more, and last evening I dined with a whole lot of literary and scientific people. Owen was, in my estimation, great, from the fact of his smoking his cigar and singing his song like a brick.

Owen seems to have had a gift for making a favorable first impression. Darwin and Asa Gray and Huxley, each for quite a different reason, exclaimed about the pleasure of the first encounter. When a few years had passed—but that's a later story.

Before Huxley had been in England six months he was made a fellow of the Royal Society. At the age of twenty-six he had achieved a position which many men of ability labored for in vain all their lives. Ambition was spurring him up the heights, as he shows in writing to his sister.

I will leave my mark somewhere, and it shall be clear and distinct ⟨T. H. H., his mark.⟩ and free from the abominable blur of cant, humbug, and self-seeking which surrounds everything in this present world—that is to say, supposing that I am not already unconsciously tainted myself, a result of which I have a morbid dread. I am perhaps overrating myself. You must put me in mind of my better self, as you did in your last letter, when you write.

To Miss Heathorn he wrote in a more warlike strain.

Not like the man who, at the Enchanted Castle, had the courage to blow the horn but not to draw the sword, and was consequently shot forth from the mouth of the cave by which he entered with the most ignominious haste—one must be ready to fight immediately after one's arrival has been announced, or be blown into oblivion.

I have drawn the sword, but whether I am in truth to beat the giants and deliver my princess from the enchanted castle is yet to be seen.

There were giants in Huxley's path—creatures like Owen and Wilberforce and Gladstone and Buckland. They had no reason to suspect that this young anatomist was a combination of wildcat and dialectician and giant-slaying knight. If they could have seen his purposes and powers, they would have known that he was the likeliest man in the world to sling a pebble at Goliath.

When Huxley reached home late in 1850 Darwin was completing the six hundred pages of Volume I of *Cirripedia*. As you now read a few fragments of the result of two years of toil, imagine that you are the father of boys and girls who want you to play with them. William is eleven; Annie is nine, a joy in the household every hour; Henrietta is seven, very nice to romp with; George is five, a delightfully serious person; Elizabeth and Frances and Leonard have arrived within the last three years. All these children are well and happy. They have had to keep quiet at certain hours of the day and to stay out of the study while father does his barnacles.

151. As the varieties here mentioned are very remarkable, and may perhaps turn out to be true species, I think they are worth describing in some detail. I will only further add that we must either make several new species, or consider, as I have done, several forms as mere varieties.

155. I should not be at all surprised at varieties, intermediate between this species and the common form, being hereafter found.

182 and 214. We here first meet with the far more wonderful fact of hermaphrodites, whose masculine efficiency is aided by one or two Complemental Males. . . . wonderful though the fact be that the male should pair with an hermaphrodite already provided with efficient male organs.

203. Seeing the analogous facts in the six differently-constructed species of the allied genus *Scalpellum*, I in-

fer there must be some profounder and more mysterious final cause.

216. Hence no less than eight genera might be made out of twelve recent species of *Scalpellum* and *Pollicipes;* but in my opinion this inordinate multiplication of genera destroys the main advantage of classification. At one time I even thought that it would be best to follow Lamarck, and keep the twelve recent species in one genus.

217. The fact of these genera having existed from a remote epoch, and having given rise during successive periods to many species now extinct, is probably the cause that the few remaining species are so much more distinct from each other than is common in the other genera of Lepadidae.

231. I think it is quite impossible to consider them specifically distinct, for . . . in other specimens I could perceive no difference whatever.

240. I have examined a great number of specimens from various localities, taken at different times of the year.

293. As I am summing up the singularity of the phenomena here presented, I will allude to the marvelous assemblage of beings seen by me within the hermaphrodite sack of an *Ibla quadrivalvis*—namely, an old and young male, both minute and worm-like; secondly, the four or five free, boat-shaped larvæ, with their curious prehensile antennæ; and lastly, several hundreds of the larvæ in their first stage of development, globular, with horn-shaped projections on their carapaces, and only three pair of natatory legs. What diverse beings, with scarcely anything in common, and yet all belonging to the same species!

2. *Hooker in India*

While Huxley was on his first cruise in the steaming rain of the Inshore Passage, Hooker sailed for a four-year trip to India. He had been made an F. R. S. and was now an official botanist for the Geological Survey. A few weeks before Huxley became engaged Hooker had become engaged to a daughter of Professor Henslow at Oxford. Hooker was almost as poor as Huxley, almost as much in need of an appointment, and quite as determined to rescue his princess from the tower of maidenhood.

The journey to India was made in state, for he was taken into the suite of Lord Dalhousie, who was going out as Governor-General.

In India he made three remarkable expeditions. After some preliminary trips—for example, ascending a sacred mountain five thousand feet through a jungle on an elephant—he prepared for the first Himalayan expedition. Three hundred miles due north of Calcutta lies Darjeeling, at the foot of the Himalayas; from here he advanced up river-beds to the west of Mt. Kunchinjinga. This is only a thousand feet lower than Mt. Everest and lies about a hundred miles east of it. His business was to botanize, and he frequently sent back to his base the precious bales of specimens which were forwarded to his father at Kew Gardens.

But he was ever attending to the requests that Darwin had made for information on many points of the eternal species question. Why does the cheetah hunt only one season? How far north does this species of squirrel range? What is the effect of destroying a forest? Hooker, in trying his best to answer the queries, described his state of mind: "I am perfectly bewildered by the facts hourly thrown before me, whose importance I can scarce appreciate from my ignorance of Indian natural history. . . . You are constantly in my thoughts. . . . Love to the children."

There were great difficulties in the way of any reckless botanist who wished to penetrate the passes and reach Tibet. Hooker was coached to meet them by a singular man who had an unrivaled knowledge of Indian zoology and was an accomplished linguist, Brian Hodgson. He had been the English representative at the court of Nepal, had been dismissed unfairly by a former Governor-General, and was now living as a recluse on a mountain slope near Darjeeling. He took Hooker's medical advice, soon came to like him thoroughly, and invited him to be a house-mate.

Another aid to Hooker was the friendship of Dalhousie, which of course was powerful. But it would have availed little if Hooker had not been a shrewd and hardy diplomatist. The trouble was that the Rajah of Sikkim, an unscrupulous and wily blackguard, was in the pay of Chinese merchants who wanted to keep the English out of the territory. The "saucy Rajah," though he owed much to the English Government, at first flatly refused to permit Hooker to climb the mountains. Later, when he dared no longer disobey Dalhousie's order, he earned his Chinese pay by contriving obstacles. For six months he shiftily evaded Dalhousie's command. Not until the British agent for Sikkim had threatened him with wrathful punishment did he finally give a permit—and then he stationed a hundred men in the passes to capture Hooker.

Hooker provided himself with a body-guard of Ghurkas, who despised the Rajah's people and would enjoy an encounter with them. He took no money, but arranged that his escort should be liberally paid when they brought him back safe. He was in high good humor with his warlike caravan—fifty-six men, "immense fellows, stout and brawny, in scarlet jackets, carrying a kookry stuck in the cummerbund and heavy iron sword at their side." There was trouble to be expected from some of the Rajah's men, who had to be taken with his party; but Hooker counted on checking their insolence with ridicule before the Ghurkas. "I will warrant," he prophesied in a letter to his father, "that before two days are over every man jack of them will be collecting for me." He was right.

Such handling of men in a complicated and dangerous situation is good training for the battle at Oxford in 1860.

For ninety days the Hooker expedition worked up streams and across shoulders of mountains, to the west of Kunchinjinga. The region was so broken and precipitous that, on the average, it was necessary to travel three miles in order to advance one. Hooker's sketch of the region was the first map that had ever been made. The map was still unique in 1903, and in 1918 a biographer could affirm that the district had never again been traversed by any European.

Near the end of this first expedition Hooker found himself deified. The lamas of a convent had had his likeness painted on the wall of a temple.

To my amazement, I found myself on the walls, in a flowered coat and pantaloons, hat, spectacles, beard and moustache, drawing in a notebook, an Angel on one side offering me flowers and a devil on the other doing homage! I never laughed so much in my life, and the Lamas' artists were pleased beyond measure that I recognized the likeness.

I will offer from all the wealth of Hooker's botanical observation during the first half of his stay in India only one example.

Along the narrow path I found the two commonest of all British weeds, a grass and the shepherd's purse! . . . I could not but regard these little wanderers from the north with the deepest interest. Such incidents as these give rise to trains of reflection in the minds of the naturalist traveler. . . . At this moment these common weeds more vividly recall to me that wild scene than does

all my journal, and remind me how I went on my way
. . . musing on the ages that may have been occupied in
the march of the shepherd's purse.

Hooker was gaining an incomparable knowledge of the
distribution of plants, and it was all to be at Darwin's
disposal.

The second Himalayan expedition, on which Campbell accompanied Hooker, lasted eight months, from
early May to late December, 1849. At the very beginning Hooker met obstructions from the functionaries of
the Rajah. But by continued application of cheerful
bullying he advanced up a pass in the Himalayas.

Hardships increased with altitude.

Above 15,000 feet I am a "gone coon"; my head rings
with acute headache and feels as if bound in a vice, my
temples throb at every step, and I retch with sea-sickness. . . .

I think the leeches are the worst; my legs are, I assure you, daily clotted with blood, and I pull my stock-
ings off quite full of leeches; they get into the hair and
all over the body. I cannot walk ten yards without having dozens on my legs.

But he conquered. On July 24 he reached the summit
of the pass and beheld "the blue and rainless skies of
Tibet." He had accomplished what Hodgson thought a
great feat, and what his other friends had considered a
visionary undertaking.

I found what I so many years have only dreamed of,
the remarkable change in vegetation that only occurs at
the boundary of the mountains and plains, that preva-
lence of species and paucity of specimens which marks
that curious zone.

Here at the border of Tibet the explorers encountered

a band of the Rajah's agents who had orders to capture Campbell. Hooker dashed away from them, determined to do at least a little botanizing in Tibet, and spent a long day of work in the hostile country. When he returned at night he learned that Campbell had been taken prisoner. The agents of the Rajah dared not murder Campbell; they could not frighten Hooker into making promises or giving information; the English Governor despatched an ultimatum; and after two months of captivity the prisoners reached Darjeeling.

The eight months of experience in using cool contempt upon arrogant people taught Hooker something about dealing with blusterers. The lesson was helpful at Oxford in 1860.

We have no space to tell of his last expedition, nine months long, on which he set out with a band of 110 coolies. He returned to England in March, 1851.

3. Darwin's Poor Health

In that month Darwin had a short vacation from barnacles. He took Annie, aged nine, to Malvern for treatment, had some days of rest, and on his return through London was described as "looking uncommonly well and stout."

The words meant only "uncommonly for Darwin." His illness throughout the eight years of barnacle work was almost constant, as a few dated extracts from letters will indicate.

1845. I believe I have not had one whole day, or rather night, without my stomach having been greatly disordered, during the last three years, and most days great prostration of strength.

1847. I should have written before now, had I not been almost continually unwell, and at present I am suffering from four boils and swellings, one of which hardly allows me the use of my right arm, and has stopped all my work, and damped all my spirits.

March, 1849. On the 13th of November my poor dear father died. . . . I was at the time so unwell that I was unable to travel, which added to my misery. Indeed all this winter I have been bad enough.

October, 1849. I am allowed to work now two and a half hours daily, and I find it as much as I can do; for the cold-water cure, together with three short walks, is curiously exhausting; and I am actually *forced* to go to bed at eight o'clock completely tired. I steadily gain in weight, and eat immensely, and am never oppressed with my food. I have lost the involuntary twitching of the muscle, and all the fainting feelings, etc.—black spots before eyes, etc. Dr. Gully thinks he shall quite cure me in six or nine months more.

March, 1852. I dread going anywhere, on account of my stomach so easily failing under any excitement. . . . My nights are *always* bad, and that stops my becoming vigorous.

October, 1852. The other day I went to London and back, and the fatigue, though so trifling, brought on my bad form of vomiting. . . .Another and the worst of my bugbears is hereditary weakness [i. e., the possibility that his children might inherit his weakness]. . . . I agree most entirely what a blessed discovery is chloroform. . . . The other day I had five grinders out at a sitting under this wonderful substance, and felt hardly anything.

July, 1854. I have had the house full of visitors, and when I talk I can do absolutely nothing else; and since then I have been poorly enough.

4. The Death of Annie

Darwin, we have seen, was looking uncommonly well on the last day of March, 1851. Two weeks later he was recalled to Malvern. A "low and dreadful fever" had settled upon Annie. Mrs. Darwin was approaching a confinement and could not leave home.

Darwin wrote the day after he reached Malvern:
"Oh, my own, it is very bitter indeed. God preserve and
cherish you. We must hope against hope." On the 23d
he had to tell of Annie's death.

I pray God Fanny's note may have prepared you.
She went to her final sleep most tranquilly, most sweet-
ly, at 12 o'clock today. . . . God bless her. We must
be more and more to each other, my dear wife.

And the wife replied:

My feeling of longing after our lost treasure makes
me feel painfully indifferent to the other children, but I
shall get right in my feelings to them before long. You
must remember that you are my prime treasure (and always have been). My only hope of consolation is to
have you safe home and weep together.

A visitor to the Abbey churchyard at Malvern may
read on a tombstone:

I. H. S.
ANNE ELIZABETH DARWIN
Born March 2, 1841
Died April 23, 1851
A dear and good child

The grief of the parents was never appeased. The
mother's grief went so deep that through the remainder
of her life she could seldom mention Annie. The father
committed his feelings to writing, but never afterward
wished to speak of them.

We have lost the joy of the household, and the solace
of our old age. She must have known how we loved her.
Oh, that she could now know how deeply, how tenderly,

we do still and shall ever love her dear joyous face!
Blessings on her!

Twenty-five years later he wrote:

Tears still sometimes come into my eyes when I
think of her sweet ways.

When death comes there is nothing a man can do but
turn to his work—his shop or his field or his desk. Darwin had to examine more cases of barnacles, dissect more
hundreds of specimens, trace the strange variations in
their anatomy.

Three weeks after Annie's death Horace was born.
Now there were seven children in the family. They
wanted the father to play with them.

Whatever my father did with us had a glamor of delight over it unlike anything else.

But father must daily perform his duty with the crus-
taceous mummies. To the children it appeared that
barnacles were part of the ordinary routine of any normal family. One of them, hearing of a neighbor who
was sometimes idle in the forenoon, inquired, "But
when does Mr. Blank do his barnacles?"

Prepare your mind to read the following little excerpts slowly. They are from the first part of Volume
II of *Cirripedia* and represent one hundred and four
weeks of daily grubbing. Guess why these results might
be important to a man who is engrossed with the species
question.

151. It is not easy to overstate the singularity and
complexity of the appearance of the basal membrane of
a *Balanus*: and when we consider the homological nature
of the apparatus, the subject becomes still more curious:

I feel an entire conviction . . . that the cement-glands are continuous with and actually a part of an ovarian tube, in a modified condition; and that the cellular matter which, in one part, goes to the formation of ova or new beings, in the other and modified part goes to the formation of the cementing tissue. To conclude with an hypothesis—those naturalists who believe that all gaps in the chain of nature would be filled up, if the structure of every extinct and existing creature were known, will readily admit that Cirripedes were once separated by scarcely sensible intervals from some other, now unknown, Crustaceans.

155. The discrimination of the species in most of the genera offers very great difficulties. . . . Not only does every external character vary greatly in most of the species, but the internal parts very often vary to a surprising degree.

228. Still more unwilling was I to believe that the variety *nitidus* and the common variety could belong to the same species. Their general aspect is totally unlike.

236. Hence I have been compelled to throw all these forms, originally considered by me as specifically distinct, into one species.

237. A good instance of the amount of variation which seems especially to occur in most of the species which have very extensive ranges.

242. In order to show that it has not been from indolence that I have put so many forms together, I may state that I had already named and fully described in detail eight of the following forms as species, when I became finally convinced that they are only varieties. . . . If a person were to get together only some fifty or sixty specimens from only half a dozen different localities, he would almost certainly come to the same conclusion as I at first did, that several of the varieties are true species; but when he gets several hundred specimens from all quarters of the globe, he will find, to his trouble and vexation, that character after character fails and blends away by insensible degrees, and he will be led, as the more prudent course, to include, as I have done, and I hope rightly, all under one specific name.

243. This latter variety has a very peculiar aspect, and I did not doubt it was specifically distinct, until, in a number of specimens on a ship from the West Indies, I got the most perfect series, and another scarcely less perfect series from the Mediterranean, graduating into common colored varieties.

306. The variability of such beautifully contrived teeth is very surprising.

After six years of encountering variation Darwin can still be surprised at the variability of these teeth. His enthusiasm is still stirred to remark upon how "beautifully" they are "contrived." We can foresee how incredible his theory—based on variability—will seem to readers who have not classified barnacles for eight years. We can understand how readers will shrink from a theory that ascribes these "contrivances" to the mere operation of mechanical laws. What force but Deity could "contrive" adaptations?

Barnacles, you can perceive, were not an end in themselves. They were a revelation of how nature works to bring about contrivances—that is, how she creates between kinds of animals those differences that cause the kinds to be grouped as varieties or species or genera. Darwin was learning how species originate.

5. Darwin Stood All Alone

Lyell would have had no sympathy with what Darwin was doing, for Lyell's views remained quite unchanged through these eight years. Huxley, with whom Darwin had only slight acquaintance during the eight years, would not have sympathized. He thought, on the one hand, that the theory of Lamarck and the *Vestiges* was unfounded rubbish; he thought, on the other hand, that Lyell's creation was no better than theological speculation. "A plague o' both your houses," he said to the theorizers; "let me alone to fight Cuvier's humbug of archetypes." The only sympathy Darwin could have had was from speculators whose judgment he distrusted. Not one leading scientist in the world had any patience with a theory of an evolution of one species from another. August Weismann (born in 1834) describes the state of mind of the learned world while Darwin was writing the *Cirripedia*.

Lamarck alone had attempted to indicate the forces from which the transmutation of species could have resulted. . . . Many champions of the "Naturphilosophie" of the time, especially Oken and Schelling, promulgated mere hypotheses as truths; forsaking the realm of fact almost entirely, they attempted to construct the whole world with a free hand, and lost themselves in worthless phantasy. . . . The theory lost all credence and sank so low in the general estimation that it came to be regarded as hardly fitting for a naturalist to occupy himself with philosophical conceptions. . . . Onward from 1830 . . . an idea so important as that of evolution sank into oblivion again and was expunged from the pages of science so completely that it seemed as if it were forever buried beyond hope of resurrection. . . .

How deep was the oblivion by the middle of the century may be gathered from the fact that in my own student days in the fifties I never heard a theory of descent referred to, and I found no reference to it in any book to which I had access.

In 1854 there was only one good observer on the globe who had faith in a theory of descent with modification. He was Charles Darwin, who lived at the village of Downe in Kent. When I think of him, all alone on the ocean of scientific skepticism and knowing that his single mind was steering a solitary course, I have to borrow Clough's words about Columbus:

How in God's name did this Darwin get over!

If we understand, even faintly, the solitude of the
man, we can appreciate how much he was sustained by
the sympathy of Hooker—even when Hooker was climbing to Tibet. Darwin got small encouragement from this
friend, but could at least speak to him about evolution
without being called demented. I will select and date
some of the remarks that Darwin wrote to Hooker between 1846 and 1854.

October, 1846. I am going to begin some papers on
the lower marine animals, which will last me some
months, perhaps a year, and then I shall begin looking
over my ten-year-long accumulation of notes on species
and varieties, which, with writing, I dare say will take
me five years, and then, when published, I dare say I
shall stand infinitely low in the opinion of all sound naturalists—so this is my prospect for the future.

April, 1847. I shall feel quite lost without you to discuss many points with, and to point out (ill-luck to you)
difficulties and objections to my species hypotheses.
. . . I have read your last five numbers, and . . . I
see you have introduced several sentences against us
Transmutationists.

May, 1847. You have made a savage onslaught, and I
must try to defend myself. . . . Whether this letter
will sink me still lower in your opinion, or put me a little
right, I know not, but hope the latter. Anyhow I have
revenged myself with boring you with a very long
epistle. Farewell and be forgiving.

May, 1848. I have lately got a bisexual cirripede, the
male being microscopically small and parasitic within
the sack of the female. I tell you this to boast of my
species theory. . . . I never should have made this out,
had not my species theory convinced me that an hermaphrodite species must pass into a bisexual species by insensibly small stages. . . . But I can hardly explain
what I mean, and you will perhaps wish my barnacles
and species theory al Diavolo together.

April, 1849. In your letter you wonder what "Ornamental Poultry" has to do with Barnacles; but do not

flatter yourself that I shall not yet live to finish the Barnacles, and then make a fool of myself on the subject of species, under which head Ornamental Poultry are very interesting.

October, 1849. You say that you care more for my species work than for the Barnacles; now this is too bad of you, for I declare your decided approval of my plain Barnacle work over theoretic species work had a very great influence in deciding me to go on with the former, and defer my species paper.

November, 1853. I then opened your letter, and such is the effect of warmth, friendship, and kindness from one that is loved, that the very same fact, told as you told it, made me glow with pleasure till my very heart throbbed.

February, 1854. (to Lyell) Hooker's book is out, and *most beautifully* got up. He has honored me beyond measure by dedicating it to me.

March, 1854. I am particularly obliged to you for sending me Asa Gray's letter. To see his and your caution on the species question ought to overwhelm me in confusion and shame; it does make me feel deuced uncomfortable. . . . How awfully flat I shall feel if, when I get my notes together on species, etc., etc., the whole thing explodes like an empty puff-ball.

The work with barnacles finally grew almost unbearable. In 1852 Darwin had confessed to his cousin Fox: "I hate a barnacle as no man ever did before, not even a sailor in a slow-sailing ship." Cultivate an understanding of Darwin's loathing by making yourself read every word of this last instalment of *Cirripedia*.

307. The species are particularly troublesome to identify, not only from the great variability of the most obvious characters, but from the very close general external resemblance of most of the species.

333. Although Dr. Gould's specimens, in external aspect, are absolutely and entirely different from the common varieties of *T. porosa*, there are so many inter-

mediate forms, and the differences are so little important, that I feel no hesitation in attributing them to variation.

355. I feel no hesitation in including the above several genera in one genus. [Cf. this, of genera, with his usual caution, 362: "I am not sure that I have acted rightly in retaining it, but I think that it is distinct."]

456. Some of the varieties I have no doubt are really varieties, but whether this is the case with some of the forms from the more distant localities is a little more doubtful; but I beg that it may be observed that I have, in the case of every one of the varieties, and of all the specimens from distant localities, cleaned with potash and most carefully examined the disarticulated valves, and likewise dissected the included animal's body.

588. It is really beautiful to see how the homologies of the archetype cirripede, as deduced from the metamorphoses of other cirripedes, are plainly illustrated during the maturity of this degraded creature, and are demonstrated to be identical with those of the archetype Crustacean.

602. I can hardly express the perplexity which I felt when I first examined *Proteolepas,* and when I naturally mistook the mouth for the entire head, for I saw, as I thought, the antennæ in direct connection with the second segment of the body! It was quite as monstrous and incredible an inversion of the laws of nature as those fabulous half-human monsters, with an eye seated in the middle of their stomachs.

605. I fully believe that we here see an articulate animal in which the whole of the three anterior segments of the head have been, during the act of metamorphosis, absolutely aborted, with the exception of a mere rudiment on the ventral surface, . . . and which rudiment has been specially developed as a covering for the two cement-ducts.

Darwin knew how hard it might be for the anatomists to accept this very strange observation which he "fully believed." There was an implication in it that reached back through millions of years of the history of the species. For the life of any one animal is a kind of epitome of the history of its race; and the changes rapidly made during the one life may indicate slow alterations that gradually came about in the long history of the development of the race. Darwin's observation indicated that nature had, in the course of millions of generations, converted a head into something else, adapted it to a new use. Clearly this is not "progress" for a head. That noblest part of the anatomy has been degraded to a mere bit of protecting shell. Nature does not seem concerned with progress, but only with adaptation. In 1854 young Huxley could not have sympathized with Darwin's full belief.

Not till September of 1854 was the long labor of barnacles ended. Darwin wrote to Hooker:

I have been sending ten thousand Barnacles out of the house all over the world. I shall now in a day or two begin to look over my old notes on species. What a deal I shall have to discuss with you.

CHAPTER XI

WRITING THE ORIGIN OF SPECIES: 1855-1859

1. The Preparation for Writing; 2. Asa Gray; 3. Owen's Hostility to Huxley; 4. Alfred Russel Wallace; 5. Completing the Origin.

1. The Preparation for Writing

THE four pages of *Cirripedia* in the previous chapter show what a species is—it is a phantom, a mere opinion of some classifier. Darwin had strongly suspected this in 1844; by 1854 he knew it of a surety. For eight years he had searched every cranny of the mazes of the orders of barnacles, and had found no evidence of a hard-and-fast Lyellian "species"—any more than he could have found a ghost by peering under the arm-chairs in his study when the lamps were lighted.

The unreality of a species can never be credited by one who has not, like Lamarck or Darwin, spent years of his life in trying to find them. In ordinary experience we see kinds of animals that are absolutely distinct: men, dogs, cats, robins, angleworms, clams, toads. Each breeds true within itself and produces offspring identical with the parents. None of these species can be crossed with another or can be converted into another. We see a species as an unmistakable reality. But every man who specializes among lower animals or plants finds that a species is just a convenient territory of life whose boundary can not be determined.

Darwin's task in writing the *Origin* was to show the

probability that every species has originated by growing out of a previous species. He could not *prove* this. Even to-day no demonstration is possible. The method of argument, for Darwin as for us now, is to show the strong *probability* that species evolved from one another and that all life is part of one continuous pattern. Hence an evolution theory is never satisfactory to a rigidly philosophical mind, for it is logically incomplete. This was the first of Darwin's difficulties as he set to work in 1854.

The second difficulty was that the probable truth about species could not be illustrated from any one department of science. If geology alone was appealed to, the evidence could be read one way as well as another. If he confined himself to the little-known laws of embryology, he could not be sure that one interpretation was more certain than its opposite. The method of altering plants and animals by breeding was highly suggestive of the gradual growth of one species out of another; but man had not—and has not yet—produced an undeniable species in this way; the most diverse artificial races may still breed among themselves. The evidence from the study of distribution was obscure; the evidence from comparative anatomy, though picturesque, was far from conclusive.

Darwin had to display each of these fields in turn, as if it were a cabinet full of mysteries, and then to prove that his one simple theory was the master key which unlocked them all. To make such an exposition quite clear and unanswerable would have required superhuman skill. Darwin was not a superman. He did not expect to astound and convince the world at once, but merely to point out a likelihood, a hypothesis that was worth considering until some better one was prepared.

He was eager for the work. No sooner had the ten

thousand barnacles been sent out of the house in September, 1854, than he began to look over the old notes and plan an order of assembling them in a book. He expected to write a large and very thorough book, presenting full data from his piles of notes.

Where should he begin? Obviously the beginning of evolution is in those differences that always exist between a parent and its offspring: no tree was ever precisely like its mother; no child ever had the same fingerprint as its father. Between parent and offspring there is always some variation. Darwin's mind was now full of variations of barnacles, in a state of nature. But the natural beginning of his argument was variation in domesticated plants and animals. The steps would then be as follows.

1. Domestic animals and plants vary from generation to generation.
2. The variations may be inherited.
3. These inherited variations are *selected* by man, are piled up in the direction he desires, and finally accumulated to such an extent that a new variety or race is created.
4. There are the same kinds of variations of plants and animals in a state of nature.
5. All wild plants and animals live in a very severe competition, the "struggle for existence."
6. In this struggle for existence an animal that inherits an unfavorable variation will be less likely to have offspring.
7. An animal that inherits a favorable variation will be more likely to have offspring.
8. Hence the hard conditions of existence act in such a way that they are always killing off the unfavorable variations.
9. Hence (by a sort of parable) nature "selects"

favorable variations and tends to produce new varieties in somewhat the way that breeders produce new varieties by selection.

10. The long-continued operation of this "natural selection" produces, gradually in the course of ages, such increasing divergence as we call species, genera, families, etc. Hence the only difference between a variety and a family is one of degree.

The first step in the argument was the one which Darwin knew least about. He set himself to study domestic animals and plants. In addition to his vast store of facts reported in books and periodicals, he wanted first-hand experience. The animal that exhibits the most striking variations, and that can be bred rapidly, is the pigeon. The first reference to this new work is in 1855.

May, 1855. I have got my fantails and pouters in a grand cage and pigeon-house, and they are a decided amusement to me, and delight to H. [Henrietta, aged 12.]
July, 1855. I have done the black deed and murdered an angelic little fantail and pouter at ten days old.

Not long afterward he wrote to his oldest son, then at Rugby, about joining a club of pigeon-fanciers.

My dear old Gulielmus,
I have been so very sorry for your having been ill this half-year again with the measles: you have been most unlucky. . . . Thank goodness it is not now very long to the holidays.
I am going up to London this evening and I shall start quite late, for I want to attend a meeting of the Columbarian Society, which meets at 7 o'clock near London Bridge. I think I shall belong to this Society, where, I fancy, I shall meet a strange set of odd men. Mr. Brent was a very queer little fish; but I suppose Mamma told you about him; after dinner he handed me a clay

pipe, saying, "Here is your pipe," as if it was a matter of course that I should smoke. Another odd little man (N. B. all pigeon-fanciers are little men I begin to think) showed me a wretched little Polish hen, which he said he would not sell for £50 and hoped to make £200 by her, as she has a black top-knot. I am going to bring a lot more pigeons back with me on Saturday, for it is a noble and majestic pursuit and beats moths and butterflies, whatever you may say to the contrary.

Darwin once described to Huxley, a meeting with the Philoperisteras.

I sat one evening in a gin palace in the Borough amongst a set of pigeon-fanciers, when it was hinted that Mr. Bull had crossed his Pouters with Runts to gain size; and if you had seen the solemn, the mysterious, and awful shakes of the head which all the fanciers gave at this scandalous proceeding you would have recognized how little crossing has had to do with improving breeds.

Can you detect, in this jocose sentence, the depth of the knowledge that Darwin was gaining? From the time of Buffon all philosophical-minded scientists had speculated grandly about hybridity as a basic principle in variation. Darwin went to school to ungentlemanlike persons who called him "Squire" and who taught him, as one of their leaders expressed it, "the solace and pleasure derived from the Almond Tumbler." They taught him that hybridizing was not the way breeders produce races.

Darwin put out lines to all quarters of the globe for information.

How I wish I could get a little wild duck of a week old, but that I know is almost impossible.

Amongst all sorts of odds and ends with which I am amusing myself I am comparing the variations of the seeds of plants. I had formerly some wild cabbage seed.

. . . If it was not thrown away, I should be very glad of a pinch of it.

Should you think it too ridiculous to offer a reward for me for lizards' eggs to the boys in your school; a shilling for every half-dozen, or more if rare? . . . My object is to see whether such eggs will float on sea-water, and whether they will keep alive thus floating for a month or two in my cellar.

I have seeds in salt-water, in a great tank filled with snow.

You are a good man to confess that you expected the cress would be killed in a week, for this gives me a nice little triumph. The children at first were tremendously eager, and asked me often, "whether I should beat Dr. Hooker!" . . . If you knew some of the experiments which I am trying, you would have a good right to sneer, for they are so *absurd* even in *my* opinion that I dare not tell you.

Very many thanks for the capital information on cats; I see I had blundered greatly. . . . My notes are so numerous during nineteen years' collection that it would take me at least a year to go over and classify them.

I have just had pigeons and fowls *alive* from the Gambia! . . . I find most remarkable differences in the skeletons of rabbits.

The hawks have behaved like gentlemen, and have cast up pellets with lots of seeds in them; and I have just had a parcel of partridge's feet well caked with mud!!! Adios. Your insane and perverse friend.

[He is speaking of the only small, remote islands that are not volcanic.] What grand work to explore the Seychelles, which with the Cocos so near, must be a remnant of some older land. . . . St. Paul's and Amsterdam would be glorious, botanically, and geologically.

The Revillagigedo Island off Mexico, I believe, has never been trodden by foot of naturalist.

You have shaved the hair off the Alpine plants pretty effectually.

In a bit of ground, 2 by 3 feet, I have daily marked each seedling weed as it has appeared during March,

April, and May, and 357 have come up, and of these 277 have *already* been killed, chiefly by slugs. . . . What a wondrous problem it is, what a play of forces, determining the kind and proportion of each plant in a square yard of turf!

I believe you are afraid to send me a ripe *Edwardsia* pod, for fear I should float it from New Zealand to Chile!!!

Mouse-colored ponies often have spinal and leg bars. . . . But I have not yet got a case of spinal stripe in chestnut, race-horse, or in quite heavy cart-horse. Any fact of this nature of such stripes in horses would be *most* useful to me.

I should like to know whether the case of Endemic bats in islands struck you; it has me especially; perhaps too strongly.

Most of the above quotations are from the letters to Hooker, whose sympathy with the great species venture, though usually discouraging, was Darwin's chief reliance during the making of the *Origin*. So keenly was Darwin aware of the follies of previous reasoners about species that he suspected he might be a fool himself. Mere sympathy, or even encouragement, would not have reassured him. He needed just what Hooker gave—unsparing objection to every point in which some fallacy might lurk.

Few of my readers would wish me to explain the perplexities that Darwin thrashed out with his advisers. But I will briefly describe two of them, just as examples of the maze in which he was trying to keep his head straight.

In Chapter II of the last edition of the *Origin* there are seven pages (66-73) which run along smoothly and present a rather obvious idea: "The most common species oftenest give rise to varieties." This is what any one nowadays—who is familiar with evolution—would naturally guess to be the case. If, for example, the Falkland wolf-fox is a very uncommon species, we should not expect to find many varieties of it; but if the weed, shepherd's purse, is found in the Falklands and on the Himalayas and in England, we should expect to find many varieties of it in all the varied climates. These surmises were easy to verify in 1856. They were not disputed. Many other similar cases could have been named offhand by any botanist or zoologist. Hence any ordinary reasoner would have felt justified in assuming as self-evident that "the most common species oftenest give rise to varieties."

Darwin visualized this statement, much as he did the chart of coral-reefs before he searched out details. He had a mental picture of rare species as confined, unvarying, dying; but of widely-distributed species as branching out in endless variations, adapting to many conditions, flourishing and increasing. This picture pleased him; it was a grand indication that his theory was probably true.

But he was suspicious of everything pleasant. He could not rest till he *knew*. So he did a heart-breaking lot of work, over several years, compiling lists of large and small genera. He corresponded with Hooker, Gray, and others to get their judgments. And he would not put any leading questions; he did not want these men to know what he was driving at; he could not have them influenced by seeing the point at issue. It is amusing to read these letters and see what contortions he goes through to put the query without revealing the purpose of it. Gray and Hooker were mystified at the form of his questions. Darwin trembled for the outcome. He wrote to Hooker:

When I have seen what the sections of the largest genera say, I must come to some definite conclusion whether or not entirely to give up the ghost.

Gray and Hooker were staggered—since they could not believe in the transmutation of species—at the result of all of Darwin's tabulations. The total of these prodigious researches and questionnaires was boiled down to seven diffident pages of the *Origin*—and now we race through it in seven minutes as a sort of truism that need not be defended so elaborately.

The second perplexity that I will describe was the easy-going way in which naturalists and geologists made continents rise conveniently out of the ocean to form bridges for the migration of species. Even the cautious Hooker made no bones about elevating a few continents for the sake of explaining Tasmanian flora. Even the master uniformitarian, Lyell, permitted continents to come and go with much ease. To Darwin this seemed a scandalous catastrophism. For years he labored with Lyell on this subject. Often he used a bantering tone.

If you do not stop this, if there be a lower region for the punishment of geologists, I believe, my great master, you will go there. Why, your disciples in a slow and creeping manner beat all the old Catastrophists who ever lived. You will live to be the great chief of Catastrophists.

There, I have done myself a great deal of good, and have exploded my passion.

So, my master, forgive me, and believe me, ever yours.

Darwin saw the full humor of his presuming to debate with the master, but he crossed swords with hearty good-will. He described his predicament to Wallace.

You will be glad to hear that neither Lyell nor Hooker thought much of my arguments. Nevertheless, for once in my life, I dared withstand the almost preternatural sagacity of Lyell.

He continued to withstand the master, and nearly the

whole world to boot, as he shows in another letter to Wallace eighteen months later.

I differ wholly from you on the colonization of oceanic islands, but you will have *every one* else on your side. . . . I wish I had given a fuller abstract of my reasons for not believing in Forbes' great continental extensions; but it is too late, for I will alter nothing—I am worn out, and must have rest.

The blows that Darwin dealt Lyell in this controversy are the finest sort of swordsmanship. I find that I have several times written in the margin of one of his arguments "Grand"—and I seldom put exclamations in my books.

At this period Darwin had practically no supporter for his views of the permanence of continents except Dana, the American. And Dana was a man whose notion about the Atlantic Ocean was called "childish" by Lyell. He was a supporter of whom Darwin was not proud. (He had the sort of mind that could argue about species of animals on the basis of the "species" of minerals.) Such was the maelstrom of authority in which Darwin was whirled. Yet he and Dana were right. Dana's knowledge and force were so much respected that he was a powerful ally. Modern geology teaches, as a basic truth, the theory of Dana and Darwin that the continents have always been approximately what they are to-day.

These tournaments among the champions of evolution have put into the history of science a kind of glory that is all too rare in the records of disputation. Huxley once expressed the spirit with which they fought among themselves. Hooker had apologized to him for raising some objections in a field that was Huxley's specialty, and Huxley replied:

I wish you wouldn't be apologetic. I always look upon any criticism as a compliment, not but what the old Adam in T. H. H. *will* arise and fight vigorously against all impugnment, and irrespective of all odds in the way of authority, but that is the way of the beast.

Why I value your and Tyndall's and Darwin's friendship so much is, among other things, that you all pitch into me when necessary. You may depend upon it, however blue I may look when in the wrong, it's wrath with myself and nobody else.

The spirit that feels wrath only at itself was the spirit that animated Darwin's friends as they challenged every step he took, and made sure that he was on the road to truth.

2. *Asa Gray*

Darwin could find only a handful of men who were to be thoroughly trusted as critics. He needed more. Especially he wanted one in America—not simply for his technical help, but as an ally when the theory was published and the war was on. Asa Gray proved to be the right person.

Hooker had known this American botanist for fifteen years and had shown some of his letters to Darwin. Darwin recognized in Gray a keen and trustworthy man. He opened a correspondence with him in 1855, asking for information about American plants that grow above the timber line. The quality of the answer was such that Darwin wrote for help of a much more abstruse kind, saying that the information was wanted for a peculiar purpose. One year later he confessed to Gray the murder that he had confessed to Hooker eleven years before, and asked Gray to keep the matter confidential.

Darwin had chosen this Harvard botanist as the American most likely to detect error in a new theory, most likely to support it if it convinced him, and as the most influential sponsor for the new theory in America. "There is always something in Gray's letters," said Darwin to Hooker, "that shows that he is a very lovable man." It will be in order to have a glimpse of this lovable man who is shortly to be the standard-bearer for Darwinism in America.

He was born nearly two years after Darwin in a pioneer hamlet of New York, ten miles south of Utica. The father, an emigrant from Massachusetts, was a tanner, and had had only six weeks of schooling in his life. The mother, brought to the wilds from Connecticut when only four years old, had a father who "was of a very lovable disposition." The uncle for whom he was named was "of a singularly sweet and gentle character." When Asa was born the parents lived on the Methodist side of the creek, but they later moved to the Presbyterian side.

At the age of seven he was—quite unlike Darwin—a champion speller. In the month when Darwin set out for Edinburgh Asa Gray went to study at the academy at Fairfield, a village ten miles beyond the Mohawk River. Next year he gave up the idea of going to college and entered the medical school at Fairfield. In 1830 he was made M. D.

But botany had claimed him for her own. In 1830 he earned forty dollars by giving a summer course in botany at the academy. The next year John Torrey, author of a botanical textbook, invited this extraordinary amateur collector to correspond with him, and later employed him to collect. In 1834 Gray published *North American Gramineæ and Cyperaceæ.* He entered into correspondence with European botanists and began to climb the ladder of fame. In the summer when Darwin was coming home through the Atlantic, Gray was appointed botanist of a South Pacific exploring expedition under Wilkes; but he resigned to accept an appointment as professor in the newly-chartered University of Michigan. The University, since it had not yet any buildings in which to open classes, gave Gray a year's leave of absence on full salary, so that he might visit European botanical collections and help in purchasing a library.

On December 1, 1838, he reached England. On December 2 he went twice to divine service and recorded in his journal that he was anxious to get to Glasgow. Of course he was. Sir William Hooker and his son Joseph lived in Glasgow. Gray told his doings in long letters to Torrey.

Glasgow, Dec. 12. I have been for almost a week, if not at home, yet the next thing to it, in the truly hospitable mansion of our good friends here, where I was received with cordial kindness. Indeed I owe it chiefly to you, who I assure you are not forgotten here. Ecce signum. Both Sir William and Lady Hooker call me, oftener than anything else, by the name of Dr. Torrey. I have been out of the house but twice (except to church on Sunday). I am anxious to improve every moment here. . . . I shall be kept here ten days longer, I think; no one else abroad is so rich in North American botany or takes so much interest in it. I am requested to study all his Sandwich Island plants. . . . I sit over against your portrait at dinner. It is very like you.

London, Jan. 17. This is dated at this modern Babylon, where I arrived about nine o'clock last evening. . . . Brown invited Hooker [i. e., Sir William] and me to breakfast with him on Saturday morning; went out with Hooker; first to the Linnæan Society. . . . We went next to the Horticultural Society's rooms in hopes to find Mr. Bentham; but instead we met Lindley [eminent botanist]. . . . Hooker seems anxious to serve me. He is the most noble man I ever knew.

Jan. 22. This morning we went to the College of Surgeons, by appointment Hooker had made, to see

Professor Owen. . . . We there met Mr. Darwin, the naturalist who accompanied Captain King in the *Beagle*. I was glad to form the acquaintance of such a profound scientific scholar as Professor Owen—the best comparative anatomist living, still young, and one of the most mild, gentle, childlike men I ever saw. He gave us a great deal of most interesting information and showed us personally the whole museum.

Montpellier, April 20. There are many Protestants here, but I fancy that they are chiefly not very pious, and as I should not understand the language well enough to be benefited, I thought it better to spend the Sabbath by myself. This was my first Sabbath on land in which I have not attended divine worship conducted in the English language.

It was this very pious Asa Gray whom Darwin chose for his lieutenant in America. Gray was hungry for knowledge, as much exhilarated by travel to new scenes as Darwin and Hooker and Huxley were when they sailed for the antipodes. The list of scholars visited by Gray in 1839 is almost a complete roster of the noted botanists of Europe. When he left London he had letters of introduction from Bentham to fourteen notables on the Continent; he had many other letters "from Hooker, Arnott, Greville, Boott, etc., with a few that I expect at Paris." In his tour he conferred with the leading botanist and inspected the herbarium at Paris, Lyons, Montpellier, Marseilles, Pisa, Munich, Geneva, Berlin, and Hamburg. He learned about the best microscopes and apparatus, the specialties of technique. He inquired about the latest inside information among scholars. He heard of the unpublished work of the great student of cells, Schleiden: "There is much very curious matter afloat about the process of impregnation and the early development of the embryo, which I am accumulating for future use. . . . Webb says Spach is now falling into the opposite extreme as to species and will hardly admit anything to be distinct.''

When this tireless, pious, keen, lovable young botanist returned to America he was captured by Harvard and made a professor. There he taught with a freshness of zeal and a wisdom which made him famous. His classes became a fountain from which teachers of botany flowed.

In 1846 Louis Agassiz came to Boston to give the Lowell lectures. The relation between Agassiz and Gray during the next quarter of a century was the most important chapter of the history of Darwinism in America. It was a strong reason for Darwin's choice of Gray as a confidant. There is matter enough in it for an interesting book, but I must content myself with a paragraph in which I point out the contrasts between Agassiz and Gray.

(1) Agassiz took his M. D. at Munich and his Ph. D. at Erlangen, after studying at Zürich and Heidelberg. To him Asa Gray's course in the Fairfield Medical School was a laughable curiosity. (2) Agassiz had European fame for his unrivaled knowledge of fishes, and he had recently taught the astonished world of geology about glacial action—he had shown the keenest eyes in Europe how blind they had been. (3) He was an even more ardent and inspiring teacher than Gray; he gathered more money for his department, brought more fame to Harvard, was more influential upon American opinion. Indeed the canny Lyell guessed that no scientific opinion could stand in America against Agassiz's opposition. (4) In all his judgments he was oracular and self-assured, speaking with a brilliance and a power of authority that carried all before it. Whereas Gray was quiet and judicial and rather inconspicuous. (5) Agassiz believed ardently in ''ideals'' of the four types of anatomy; he was allied with Owen in upholding the doctrine which

Huxley and Darwin considered nonsensical. (6) Agassiz had no religious faith.

How, then, do you suppose he contrived in his first Lowell lecture to give the impression that he considered Genesis an authoritative book on geology? Somehow he did so contrive. Gray wrote as follows to his very pious friend John Torrey at Princeton:

Agassiz has finished his lectures with great éclat. . . . They have been good lectures on natural theology. The whole spirit was vastly above that of any geological course I ever heard, his refutation of Lamarckism or "Vestige" views was pointed and repeated. The whole course was planned on a very high ground, and his references to the Creator were so natural and unconstrained as to show that they were never brought in for effect. . . . He believes there is not one such Tertiary species, but that there was an entirely new creation at the commencement of the historic era, which is all we want to harmonize geology with Genesis. . . . We should not receive his general view, rejecting it on other than scientific grounds, of which he does not feel the force as we do. . . . But so far from bringing this against the Bible, he brings the Bible to sustain his views, thus appealing to its authority instead of trying to overthrow it. . . . We may reject his conclusions, but we cannot find fault with his spirit, and I shall be glad to know that Dr. I. A. Smith, in the whole course of his public teaching has displayed a reverence for the Bible equal to that of Agassiz. I have been on the most intimate terms with him: I never heard him express an opinion or a word adverse to the claims of revealed religion.

Yet the fact was that Agassiz had no respect for revealed religion in a scientific discussion,* that his refer-

---

* Edwin Tenney Brewster, who has delved into this question, went so far as to say in the *Truth Seeker* of March 26, 1927: "Agassiz shows nowhere in his writings, it appears nowhere in his biographies, that Agassiz ever looked inside a Bible. Apparently he never went to church. . . . He did not at all 'believe the Bible,' and never paid the least attention to its teaching on matters of science."

ences to the Creator were made for effect, and that his
appeal to the Bible's authority was merely a device to
reduce the friction with orthodoxy. It was a highly successful device, as is proved by the effect on Gray. But it
must have become tarnished and an object of suspicion
by 1857. It was one of many reasons why Gray would
exult in a chance to show that Agassiz was on the wrong
side of a great scientific question. To Darwin it was obvious that Agassiz would oppose an evolution theory,
and his adverse judgment would be all-powerful in
America unless some champion were ready to take the
field against him. Gray was picked to be the champion.
Darwin detected in him a force and skill for the enterprise that others had not seen in this lovable man.

3. Owen's Hostility to Huxley

So the antagonists were being matched for the fray.
Huxley described to his sister in 1852 how warlike the
situation was among the zoologists of London and who
his own special opponent was.

You have no notion of the intrigues that go on in this
blessed world of science. Science is, I fear, no purer than
any other region of human activity; though it should be.
Merit alone is very little good; it must be backed by tact
and knowledge of the world to do very much.

For instance, I know that the paper I have just sent
in is very original and of some importance, and I am
equally sure that if it is referred to the judgment of my
"particular friend"—that it will not be published. He
won't be able to say a word against it, but he will pooh-
pooh it to a dead certainty.

You will ask with some wonderment, Why? Because
for the last twenty years —— has been regarded as the
great authority on these matters, and has had no one to
tread on his heels, until at last, I think, he has come to
look upon the Natural World as his special preserve, and

"no poachers allowed." So I must maneuver a little to get my poor memoir kept out of his hands.

The necessity for these little stratagems utterly disgusts me. . . . I have a certain pleasure in overcoming these obstacles, and fighting these folks with their own weapons. . . . But ——, I see, is determined not to let either me or anyone else rise if he can help it. Let him beware. On my own subject I am his master, and am quite ready to fight half a dozen dragons.

The particular friend whose name the editor left blank was Owen. It was Owen's hostility that obliged Huxley to maneuver for a fight. Huxley labored with unceasing energy in his profession; his carefulness and bold originality were recognized on all hands. In 1852 he received the Royal Society's medal, the worth of which he estimated thus when writing to Miss Heathorn:

I must look upon the award of this medal as the turning-point of my life, as the finger-post teaching me as clearly as anything can what is the true career that lies open before me.

When the Earl of Rosse conferred the medal he recognized "a new spirit of anatomical inquiry." For Huxley had defied the mysticism of Owen and was facing his problems in the spirit of physics.

By 1854 Huxley had three appointments to important lectureships, and had been made naturalist of the Coast Survey. He could thank God that he had "weathered the Cape Horn of his life" and that a career lay fair before him. By the end of 1858 he was a fellow of the Linnæan Society and a member of the Athenæum Club. Early in 1859 he was elected secretary of the Geological Society.

4. Alfred Russel Wallace

As early as 1856 Lyell and Hooker had urged Darwin not to delay the publication of his theory by taking time to amass all the evidence. Rumors of his purpose were going round; opinions about the variation of species were in the air; hence some one might forestall him by printing an essay that would have to rank in history as the source of his views. But Darwin was loath to present his theory in such a brief, unscientific form. He set himself to long years of preparing the great work.

A few quotations will show the occasional panic and the steady conviction with which he worked till the summer of 1858.

July, 1857, to Hooker. Lubbock has pointed out to me the grossest blunder. . . . I am the most miserable, bemuddled, stupid dog in all England, and am ready to cry with vexation at my blindness and presumption.

September, 1857, to Gray. I did not feel in the least sure that, when you knew whither I was tending, you might not think me so wild and foolish in my views that you would think me worth no more notice and assistance.

February, 1858, to Hooker. I have partly written this note to drive bee's cells out of my head; for I am half mad on the subject, to try to make out some simple steps from which all the wondrous angles may result. . . . Forgive your intolerable but affectionate friend.

April, 1858, to Mrs. Darwin. At last I fell fast asleep on the grass, and awoke with a chorus of birds singing around me, and squirrels running up the trees, and some woodpeckers laughing, and it was as pleasant and rural a scene as ever I saw, and I did not care one penny how any of the beasts or birds had been formed.

June, 1858, to Hooker. I am confined to the sofa with boils, so you must let me write in pencil. You would laugh if you could know how much your note pleased me. I had the firmest conviction that you would say all my MS. was bosh, and, thank God, you are one of the few men who dare speak the truth. . . . I have been forced to confess to myself that . . . if you condemned that you would condemn all my life's work, and that, I confess, made me a little low; but I could have borne it, for I have the conviction that I have honestly done my best.

Ten days after being so pleased with Hooker's note Darwin was struck by the strangest thunderbolt that ever hit a scientist. It had been forged by a modest and harmless young man who was collecting birds in the East Indies, Alfred Russel Wallace. It was sailing slowly across the Indian Ocean on the day when Darwin watched the squirrels. It exploded in the study at Downe on June 18.

My dear Lyell:

Your words have come true with a vengeance—that I should be forestalled. You said this when I explained to you here very briefly my views of "Natural Selection" depending on the struggle for existence. I never saw a more striking coincidence; if Wallace had had my MS. sketch written out in 1842, he could not have made a better short abstract! Even his terms now stand as heads of my chapters. Please return me the MS., which he does not say he wishes me to publish, but I shall of course at once write and offer to send to any journal. So all my originality, whatever it may amount to, will be smashed. . . . I hope you will approve of Wallace's sketch, that I may tell him what you say.

In the bitter and bewildering hour when his fame seemed broken to flinders his first thought was to secure some recognition for the obscure naturalist who had sent the bomb. Darwin knew how Wallace would rejoice in a word of praise from the great Sir Charles.

What torture he suffered after sending the news to Lyell is not recorded. He was ashamed of feeling hard-hit and tried to compose himself. A week later he closed a letter to Lyell thus:

This letter is miserably written, and I write it now, that I may for a time banish the whole subject; and I am

worn out with musing. . . . My good dear friend, forgive me. This is a trumpery letter, influenced by trumpery feelings. I will never trouble you or Hooker on the
subject again.

He took it for granted that he could not now publish
his book on species, that his labor of twenty years had
been done in vain. The day after apologizing to Lyell
for his trumpery feelings he wrote again, calling his note
"a P. S. to make the case as strong as possible against
myself":

It seems hard on me that I should be thus compelled
to lose my priority of many years' standing, but I cannot feel at all sure that this alters the justice of the case.
First impressions are generally right, and I at first
thought it would be dishonorable in me now to publish.

While Lyell and Hooker are consulting about this
quixotic notion we may look for a few minutes at the
career of the bird-collector who has brought Darwin to
despair.

Wallace was born in Usk, near the Bristol Channel,
seventy-five miles south of Shrewsbury, in the neighborhood of the romantic ruins of Tintern and Raglan.
When Darwin became acquainted with Dr. Grant in
Edinburgh, Wallace was nearly three years old. He
lived in poverty; for his father, though he had a gift for
living genteelly, could do no more for the support of a
family than to keep a neat vegetable-garden.

At the age of fourteen he began to earn his living by
surveying. When he was eighteen he bought for a shilling a book on botany, which proved a revelation to his
uneducated mind. He studied passionately whenever he
was out of a job. For a time he was a school-teacher.
He read Malthus's *Population,* which had the same effect on him that it had on Darwin. While Darwin was

slaving through his second year of barnacles, Wallace read the *Vestiges* and considered it an ingenious hypothesis. From that time on his mind dwelt much on the origin of species, and he was "taking note of everything bearing upon it that came in my way."

He wrote to his chum Bates: "Darwin is an able supporter of Mr. Lyell's views. His style of writing in the *Journal* I very much admire—so free from all labor, affectation, or egotism." The *Journal* and Humboldt's *Personal Narrative* inspired him with a wish to see the tropics. In 1848 he went with Bates to Brazil, where he collected for four years. Collecting was Wallace's way of earning a living: there was a market in London for strange butterflies and birds. Wallace shipped his specimens to an agent who sold on commission and provided expenses. But the ambition for scientific distinction was a deeper motive than earning money. He disclosed his purpose to Bates: "I should like to take some one family to study thoroughly, principally with a view to the theory of the origin of species." He adds when he quotes this in *My Life:* "I firmly believed that a full and careful study of the facts of nature would ultimately lead to a solution of the mystery."

He made a bid for fame by going with a retinue of ten natives farther up the Amazon Valley than any other Englishman penetrated in the nineteenth century—following the branch called Rio Negro, and then the branch of that called Uaupes (or Waupes) far into Colombia.

He had Darwin's experience of seeing utter savages: "The most unexpected sensation of surprise and delight was my first meeting with and living with man in a state of nature. The surprise of it was that I did not in the least expect to be surprised."

There is much meaning in those words. Students who remain among the familiar people and animals can not realize that they would be surprised into new understanding if they could see what nature does elsewhere.

When Wallace embarked for the return to England he had with him a collection of specimens which he expected to sell for five hundreds pounds sterling, and another collection that he planned to keep and that he thought would be the finest exhibition of American species in Europe. The ship caught fire; the crew took to the boats and watched her burn; they began to row toward Bermuda, nine hundred miles away. They had covered seven hundred miles before they were picked up. And the vessel which took them aboard was so slow and unseaworthy and short of provisions that the rescued captain said he should have felt safer in the open boats. But she finally conveyed the ruined Wallace to England.

Perhaps you think that recounting these tales is a poor way to use space while Darwin's fate hangs in the balance. I hope it is not. Wallace's name is inseparably linked with Darwin's, so that his life is of some interest. My real purpose is to show once more the stuff of which Darwin's phalanx was composed. These men were not mere intellectuals. They adventured through all the perils that the globe afforded; they were knights-errant in quest of knowledge; and they gained a rugged strength and fearlessness. When they went into action against philosophical carpet-knights they knew their own prowess. They could no more be damaged by dialectic than a hardened sailor could be injured by a blast from a pair of bellows. They were armed with facts and trained in the stern tournaments of nature.

Wallace had no thought of surrendering to an unkind providence. He fought his way to fame by spending eight years collecting in the East Indies. The chronicle of his perilous trips there would be incredible if it were a romance.

While Darwin was spending his last five months on barnacles Wallace was lodging with Catholic missionaries at Singapore and Malacca, making sallies into the jungle to capture beetles. Then he was in Borneo fifteen months. During the first two years he collected six thousand species of insects—thirty thousand specimens.

Early in his stay on Borneo he wrote an article on the distribution of animals as an indication of "the way in which species have come into existence." He sent this to a natural history magazine in London, where it appeared in September, 1855.* He was grieved that no notice seemed to be taken of his very original paper, and wrote to Darwin to inquire about its fate. Darwin replied that Lyell had spoken of it and praised it. So Wallace was heartened to continue his theorizing.

By carefully charting his observations of species he determined a remarkable boundary-line that runs through the East Indies, separating two very distinct regions of life. It is still called "Wallace's Line."

After three more years of visiting unexplored islands in native praus, living with natives in huts, waiting through dreary weeks for a chance trading-vessel to take him to new hunting-grounds, he was at the little island of Amboyna, midway between Borneo and New Guinea. From here he wrote to Bates, January 4, 1858:

I have been much gratified by a letter from Darwin, in which he says that he agrees with "almost every word" of my paper. He is now preparing his great work on "Species and Varieties," for which he has been collecting material twenty years. He may save me the trouble of writing more on my hypothesis, by proving that there is no difference in nature between the origin of

---

*It is printed as Chapter I of Wallace's *Natural Selection and Tropical Nature*.

species and of varieties; or he may give me trouble by arriving at another conclusion; but at all events, his facts will be given for me to work upon.

On January 25 Wallace reached Ternate, a small island three hundred miles north of Amboyna. Here he was taken with a fever. He describes the thoughts he busied himself with.

For the preceding eight or nine years the great problem of the origin of species had been continually pondered over. . . . My paper written at Sarawak rendered it certain to my mind that the change had taken place by natural succession and descent—one species becoming changed either slowly or rapidly into another. But the exact process of the change and the causes which led to it were absolutely unknown and appeared almost inconceivable. . .

Every day during the cold and succeeding hot fits of fever I had to lie down for several hours, during which time I had nothing to do but to think over any subjects then particularly interesting me. One day something brought to my recollection Malthus's *Principle of Population,* which I had read about twelve years before. I thought of his clear exposition of "the positive checks to increase"—disease, accidents, war, and famine. . . . It then occurred to me that these causes or their equivalents are continually acting in the case of animals also. . . .

Vaguely thinking over the enormous and constant destruction which this implied, it occurred to me to ask the question, "Why do some die and some live?" And the answer was clearly that on the whole the best fitted live. . . . Then suddenly it flashed upon me that this self-acting process would necessarily *improve the race,* because in every generation the inferior would inevitably be killed off and the superior would remain—that is, *the fittest would survive.*

The more I thought over it the more I became convinced that I had at length found the long-sought-for law of nature that solved the problem of the origin of species. For the next hour I thought of the deficiencies in the theories of Lamarck and of the author of the *Vestiges,* and I saw that my new theory supplemented these views and obviated every important difficulty. I waited anxiously for the termination of my fit so that I might at once make notes for a paper on the subject. The same evening I did this pretty fully, and on the two succeeding evenings wrote it out carefully in order to send it to Darwin by the next post, which would leave in a day or two.

I wrote a letter to him in which I said that I hoped the idea would be as new to him as it was to me, and that it would supply the missing factor to explain the origin of species. I asked him if he thought it sufficiently important to show to Sir Charles Lyell, who had thought so highly of my former papers.

"Sufficiently important!" The innocent collector had shaken the pillars of British science. Lyell and Hooker held a very troubled conference over this disastrous letter from Ternate.

And while they were arranging a course of action there was scarlet fever in Downe. It came into the Darwin home and on June 28 killed the youngest child, eighteen months old, Charles Waring. The death was not a deep grief, because the boy had been born defective and it was better that he should die. But a daughter and a nurse had the fever; it was a time of distress.

So Darwin was excusable for writing to Hooker on the 29th: "I cannot think now on the subject. . . . I am quite prostrated, and can do nothing, but I send Wallace and the abstract of my letter to Gray. . . . I dare say all is too late. I hardly care about it. But you are too generous to sacrifice so much time and kindness. . . . I send my sketch of 1844 solely that you may see by your own handwriting that you did read it. I really cannot bear to look at it. Do not waste much time. It is miserable in me to care at all about priority. . . . I will do anything. God bless you, my dear kind friend."

Darwin hunted out these documents and sent them by a servant to Kew Gardens because Hooker had urged him to do so at once. Left to himself, while death was in his house, he would have consigned his twenty years of labor to the same grave in which he was to bury the child. But he had put his case into the hands of Lyell and Hooker as trusty attorneys to take the right action. They had decided to submit Wallace's essay, together with a section of Darwin's sketch of 1844 and his letter to Gray of 1857, to the Linnæan Society as a joint paper. This plan was, as Wallace agreed, more than fair to him; for Darwin's real priority was unquestioned. The plan left Darwin free to continue with his work and publish it.

On the evening of July 1, 1858, the joint paper was read. Lyell and Hooker spoke briefly, in order that the members should understand the importance of what they heard. Hooker described the affair.

The interest excited was intense, but the subject was too novel and too ominous for the old school to enter the lists, before armoring. After the meeting it was talked over with bated breath: Lyell's approval, and perhaps in a small way mine, as his lieutenant in the affair, rather overawed the Fellows, who would otherwise have flown out against the doctrine.

Certain of the members occupied themselves diligently during the next two years in furbishing and sharpening their arms against the next occasion when this Evolution Theory should venture into the arena.

Hooker wrote a letter to Wallace explaining what had been done at the Linnæan meeting, and sent it to Darwin, who was to read it and send it on to Wallace. Darwin wrote to Hooker about this letter on July 13.

Your letter to Wallace seems to me perfect, quite clear and most courteous. I do not think it could possibly be improved, and I have today forwarded it with a letter of my own. I always thought it very possible that I might be forestalled, but I fancied that I had a grand enough soul not to care; but I found myself mistaken and punished; I had, however, quite resigned myself, and had written half a letter to Wallace to give up all priority to him, and should certainly not have changed had it not been for Lyell's and your quite extraordinary kindness.

5. Completing the Origin

Darwin now began to prepare an abridgment of his species work, to be published as early as possible. This seemed to him a mere preliminary outline of the real book, and he referred to it as the "abstract." He supposed at first that it would be a pamphlet issued by the Linnæan Society; he thought of a thin book of some sort. But within a couple of months it was evident that he would have to make a thick volume.

He had an outing on the Isle of Wight, and there, on July 20, began the fourteen months of writing. A few quotations from his letters of this period will indicate the ups and downs of his spirit.

August, 1858, to Gray. All this will appear very rash to you, and rash it may be; but I am sure not so rash as it will at first appear to you: Hooker could not stomach it at all at first, but has become largely a convert.

October, 1858, to Hooker. I have so accustomed myself to expect opposition and even contempt that I forgot for the moment that you are the one living soul from whom I have constantly received sympathy.

January, 1859, to Wallace. You ask about Lyell's frame of mind. I think he is somewhat staggered, but does not give in, and speaks with horror, often to me, of what a thing it would be, and what a job it would be for the next edition of the *Principles,* if he were "perverted." But he is most candid and honest, and I think will end by being perverted.

March 28, 1859, to Lyell. Would you advise me to tell Murray that my book is not more unorthodox than the subject makes inevitable? That I do not discuss the origin of man. That I do not bring in any discussion about Genesis, etc., etc., and only give facts, and such conclusions from them as seem to me fair.

April 2, 1859, to Hooker. This morning I received from Murray a letter offering me handsome terms, and agreeing to publish without seeing the MS.! So he is eager enough. . . . Please to send my Geographical MS., that I may send it with more to Murray; and God help him if he tries to read it. . . . I know that Lyell has been *infinitely* kind about my affair, but your "induce" gives the idea that Lyell had unfairly urged Murray.

Murray needed inducement—as well as divine help. When he had read the MS. he remarked, "The theory is as absurd as though one should contemplate a fruitful union between a poker and a rabbit." (See Leonard Huxley's *Darwin,* page 57.)

May 11, 1859, to Hooker. Thank you for telling me about obscurity of style. But on my life no nigger with lash over him could have worked harder at clearness than I have done.

May 18, 1859, to Hooker. My health has quite failed. I am off tomorrow for a week of hydropathy.

September 2, 1859, to Lyell. I am very glad you wish to see my clean sheets. . . . Remember that your verdict will probably have more influence than my book in deciding whether such views as I hold will be admitted or rejected at present; in the future I cannot doubt about their admittance.

October 15, 1859, to Huxley, from Otley, Yorkshire. I am here hydropathizing and coming to life again, after having finished my accursed book. . . .

I need not say that I will send, of course, a copy to you, in the first week of November. I shall be *intensely* curious to hear what effect the book produces on you.

October 23, 1859, to Hooker, from Otley. What you say about Lyell pleases me exceedingly; I had not at all inferred from his letters that he had come so much round. I remember thinking, above a year ago, that if ever I lived to see Lyell, yourself, and Huxley come round . . . I should feel that the subject is safe, and all the world might rail, but ultimately the theory of Natural Selection would prevail.

On November 24 the *Origin* was released for sale. By what art the dealers had been so keyed up for its appearance we do not know, but the fact is that they bought the whole edition, 1250 copies, on the first day.

CHAPTER XII

The Reception of the Origin: 1859-1870

On November 11, 1859, Darwin had ordered a number of advance copies of the *Origin* sent to scientific men of note—Gray, Agassiz, Henslow, Sedgwick, etc. To each of them he wrote a diffident but skilfully-phrased note. To Agassiz he said, "You might think that I had sent it to you in a spirit of defiance or bravado, but I assure you that I act under a wholly different frame of mind." To the peculiar and irascible Falconer he wrote: "Lord, how savage you will be if you read it, and how you will long to crucify me alive! . . . If it should stagger you in ever so slight a degree, I am fully convinced that you will become, year after year, less fixed in your belief in the immutability of species." In these various notes Darwin took pains to drop a hint that his new theory had some support from great minds—for example, to Gray: "Lyell is nearly a convert to my views." Lyell had made two tours of the United States, had ingratiated himself everywhere, had lectured with great success in Boston, and was in the highest repute as a safe man of profound learning. The reference to Lyell would not be lost on Gray. Henslow received an affectionate word: "I have told Murray to send a copy of my book on species to you, my dear old master in natural history. . . . If you would take the trouble to point out what parts seem weakest to you and what best, it would be a most material aid to me in writing my bigger book."

On the 12th* Darwin went to Yorkshire for a rest. But even there he kept up the barrage of propaganda. To Wallace: "No one has read it except Lyell. Hooker thinks him a complete convert, but he does not seem so in his letters to me."

On the 16th Darwin described his affliction to his cousin W. D. Fox: "I have had a series of calamities; first a sprained ankle, and then a badly swollen whole leg and face, much rash, and a frightful succession of boils—four or five at once. . . . Judging from Lyell's letters to me he is deeply staggered."

What Lyell thought of the *Origin* was of more concern than boils and swelling and rash. On the 18th he thanked Carpenter, an eminent physiologist who, after reading only the last chapter, had volunteered to review and defend the book. The next day he wrote again to Carpenter, asking for his general impression as soon as he had finished reading: "I feel sometimes a little frightened, whether I may not be one of those monomaniacs."

At this time he told Hooker of his mental state: "Out of seven weeks I have been confined for five to the house. This has been bad for me, as I have not been able to help thinking to a foolish extent about my book. If some four or five *good* men come round nearly to our view, I shall not fear ultimate success."

On November 21 a well-known botanist, Watson, from whom Darwin had expected no approval, wrote: "Your leading idea will assuredly become recognized as an established truth in science—that is, Natural Selection." And on the same day Hooker reported, "Lyell, with whom we are staying, is perfectly enchanted, and is ab-

---

*The chronology in *More Letters* gives October 2 as the date of departure for Ilkley, but Darwin's letters of early November are dated from Downe.

solutely gloating over it." Thereupon Darwin poured
out his gladness to Lyell: "I rejoice profoundly; for,
thinking of so many cases of men pursuing an illusion
for years. . . . I have asked myself whether I may
not have devoted my life to a phantasy."

The rejoicing was premature. However enchanted
Lyell may have been in private, he cautiously refrained
from any public gloating.

On November 25 Darwin received glad tidings from
Huxley.

Since I read Von Bär's essays, nine years ago, no
work on natural history science I have met with has made
so great an impression upon me, and I do most heartily
thank you for the great store of new views you have
given me. . . .

I am prepared to go to the stake, if requisite, in support of Chapter IX and most parts of Chapters X, XI,
XII, and Chapter XIII contains much that is most admirable. . . . As to the first four chapters, I agree
thoroughly and fully with all the principles laid down in
them. . . . But I feel that I have not yet by any means
fully realized the bearings of those most remarkable and
original Chapters—III, IV, and V—and I will write no
more about them just now. . . .

Depend upon it, you have earned the lasting gratitude
of all thoughtful men. And as to the curs which will
bark and yelp, you must recollect that some of your
friends are endowed with an amount of combativeness
which may stand you in good stead.

I am sharpening up my claws and beak in readiness.

Darwin replied: "Like a good Catholic who has received extreme unction, I can now sing 'nunc dimittis.'
Fifteen months ago I had awful misgivings; and thought
perhaps I had deluded myself, like so many have done.
. . . I am now contented."

The next day, while still exhilarated, he exclaimed to

Lyell: "I sometimes fancied that my book would be successful, but I never even built a castle in the air of such success as it has met with. . . . The whole has infinitely exceeded my wildest hopes."

By December 3 he felt that his adherents would stand fast and be irresistible: "We are now a good and compact body of really good men, and mostly not old men. In the long run we shall conquer."

On December 12 he met a reverse: "Herschel says my book is 'the law of higgledy-piggledy.' What this exactly means I do not know, but it is evidently very contemptuous. If true, this is a great blow and discouragement."

But two weeks later the world was rosy again, for Huxley's favorable review appeared in the London *Times*. We can not realize the boldness of this unless we know how new the argument of the *Origin* was. For in our day we hear much vague talk about Darwin as one of a flock of evolutionists, and we may fail to realize that Huxley was espousing an utterly strange and novel cause.

He has said that he was a complete agnostic about evolution theories before the appearance of the *Origin*. If creationists asked him to approve one of their theories, he answered, "Show me some particle of evidence."

I had exactly the same answer to give to the evolutionists of 1851-8. Within the ranks of the biologists, at that time, I met with nobody, except Dr. Grant, of University College, who had a word to say for Evolution— and his advocacy was not calculated to advance the cause. Outside these ranks, the only person known to me whose knowledge and capacity compelled respect, and who was, at the same time, a thorough-going evolutionist, was Mr. Herbert Spencer, whose acquaintance I made, I think, in 1852. . . . Many and prolonged were the battles we fought on this topic. But even my friend's rare dialectic skill and copiousness of apt illustration could not drive me from my agnostic position. . . .

I had studied Lamarck attentively and I had read the *Vestiges* with due care; but neither of them afforded me any good ground for changing my negative and critical attitude. . . .

The suggestion that new species may result from the selective action of external conditions upon the variations . . . is as wholly unknown to the historian of scientific ideas as it was to biological specialists before 1858. But that suggestion is the central idea of *The Origin of Species.* . . .

I remember, in the course of my first interview with Mr. Darwin, expressing my belief in the sharpness of the lines of demarcation between natural groups and in the absence of transitional forms, with all the confidence of youth and imperfect knowledge. I was not aware, at that time, that he had then been many years brooding over the species question; and the humorous smile which accompanied his gentle answer, that such was not altogether his view, long haunted and puzzled me. . . .

I imagine that most of those of my contemporaries who thought seriously about the matter were very much in my own state of mind. . . . And I may further suppose that the publication of the Darwin and Wallace papers in 1858, and still more that of the *Origin* in 1859, had the effect upon them of the flash of light, which to a man who has lost himself in a dark night, suddenly reveals a road which, whether it takes him straight home or not, certainly goes his way. That which we were looking for, and could not find, was a hypothesis respecting the origin of known organic forms, which assumed the operation of no causes but such as could be proved to be actually at work. We wanted, not to pin our faith to that or any other speculation, but to get hold of clear and definite conceptions which could be brought face to face with facts and have their validity tested. The *Origin* provided us with the working hypothesis we sought. . . . Darwin and Wallace dispelled the darkness, and the beacon-fire of the *Origin* guided the benighted. . . .

I venture to affirm that, so far as my knowledge goes, all the ingenuity and all the learning of hostile critics have not enabled them to adduce a solitary fact of which it can be said, "This is irreconcilable with the Darwinian theory."

Huxley's support of the new theory was qualified in only one way: he felt that there was a logical gap because domestication had not produced a well-defined new species, one which could not breed with the species from which it had descended. He took such pains to emphasize this that he rather nettled Darwin. But otherwise Huxley was an unsparing swordsman for the new cause.

He was, however, a discreet soldier. He knew that while the cause was so novel, while science was gaping in wonder at it, the best policy was to show that he was temperate and discriminating. When a singular good fortune caused a *Times* editor to apply to him for a review of the strange book by a Mr. Darwin, he did not write as an enthusiastic convert and advocate. He said that the book deserved a respectful hearing, that its most ingenious and promising thesis should be regarded with due skepticism for the present. In closing he warned the *Times* readers thus:

Mr. Darwin is as greedy of cases as any constitutional lawyer. . . . The path he bids us follow professes to be . . . a solid and broad bridge of facts. If it be so, it will carry us safely over many a chasm of our knowledge.

Huxley spoke his praise with an *if*. This was wise policy.

We who review the battle seventy years afterwards can not realize how dangerous it was for Darwin's four lieutenants. Hooker had to be intimately acquainted with the ins and outs of the arguments for fifteen years before he dared credit it. Surely, then, it was marvelous hardihood for Huxley to accept it provisionally as soon as he had read it. He well knew that he might fail to see some fallacy lurking in the complicated exposition; if he missed it, he would be a laughing-stock to Owen for years.

Consider what Lyell had to lose by adopting the new theory. A vital part of his *Principles,* the most authoritative text during thirty years, would have to be recanted and destroyed. There would be a far more serious loss. For thirty years Lyell had loathed the thought of being descended from apes: to accept the *Origin* was to lose faith in his gentlemanlike superiority to beasts. Of course that may be a despicable influence in a scientist's brain, and no doubt Lyell hated to admit it; but it appears clearly in his letters. He declared it plainly to Darwin as soon as he had read the proofs in October: "It is this which has made me so long hesitate, always feeling that the case of Man and his races, and of other animals and that of plants, is one and the same . . . and that if a 'vera causa' be admitted for one . . . all the consequences must follow."

It was the deliberate judgment of Huxley, who was closely associated with Lyell in gathering data about the skulls of apes, that Lyell would have adopted Darwinism much sooner if he had not dreaded all the consequences that must follow—the simian ancestry.

But Lyell, even though a laggard, was useful to the champions. Perhaps if he had rushed into warm advocacy, he might have antagonized many wavering scientists and driven them into the philistine camp. Most scientists had to waver for a time—the theory was so immense, so astonishing in its wide ramifications. Thoughtful men needed time—time to confer, to compare notes, to learn whether fallacies were being discovered by their friends. Lyell's example was a powerful influence in persuading men to do just what Huxley advised, to give the book a respectful hearing.

Of course Darwin was somewhat restive when he saw Lyell holding off and Huxley demurring about incomplete logic. But he also knew how to play the waiting game. In the dozens of letters that he wrote to friends during the first six months after the publication of the *Origin* his regular injunction was to take time, to give the new views a fair chance. "If you come round ever so little" or "if you are in the least staggered" were formulas that he employed for all doubters.

Asa Gray pursued the same policy in America. The reviews that he wrote in 1860 took this tack: "Of those who agree with us in thinking that Darwin has not established his theory many will admit with us that he has rendered a theory of derivation much less improbable than before; that such a theory chimes in with the established doctrines of physical science and is not unlikely to be largely accepted long before it can be proved." When an ignorant reviewer attacked the *Origin*, Gray exposed the ignorance. When theological and philosophical curses were hurled at the *Origin*, Gray replied suavely and convincingly that the *Origin* did not contain any atheistical or unphilosophical dogma.

In short, the strategy of Darwin's champions was to show up the folly of those who criticized adversely. The champions were united on one plain reason: This theory can only be disproved by adverse facts; what facts do you offer? The philistines could not unite on any argument. The nearest they could come to a combined attack was to assault the *Origin* as irreligious. But men like Agassiz and Owen had no interest in the religious appeal; and even Gray smilingly assured the New England divines that there was nothing irreligious in Darwin's reasoning.

Agassiz defiantly announced that Darwin's book failed miserably because there was no such thing in nature as a real variety. But Agassiz was almost alone in this queer onslaught. Gray entertained the *Atlantic* readers with this retort: "We cannot sit gravely down to prove that wild varieties abound. We should think it just as necessary to prove that snow falls in winter." Agassiz had rushed against the biggest and hardest fact that all botanists know; his shining spear was splintered on the rock of fact; and every botanist who saw the spectacle was amused.

Most philosophical minds could unite on the charge that Darwin, when he ascribed all evolution to "chance" variations, was guilty of lese-majesty in metaphysics. To this day there are minds that reiterate the charge against Darwin's horrible use of "chance." But they are minds blindly hurling themselves against a granitic fact. Darwin had frequently explained in the *Origin* that he used *chance* in the most strict and proper scientific sense of "having an unknown cause." An assailant who accused him of being unphilosophical in this particular simply showed ignorance of philosophy and science. He was amusing to the spectators of the tournament.

The variety of the wild attacks upon the *Origin* is laughable. Darwin was accused of "stealing from his master, the author of the *Vestiges*." Some critics, assuming that "progress" is an axiom, charged Darwin with denying the very foundation of right reason. Owen wrote an anonymous and violent attack in the *Quarterly Review*, asserting that Darwin's argument was "We must accept the hypothesis because we lack knowledge." But any reader who cared to check up this accusation would find that it turned Darwin's plain statement upside down. A renowned Frenchman found fault with the *Origin* because it was based on imaginings and speculation—not troubling to explain why Huxley and Lyell had found no speculation in the book. The critic in the *North American Review* rebuked Darwin for "sneering" and "scornfully repudiating." Yet no sneering or scorn is to be found in Darwin's book. Charges of carelessness and ignorance were brought against an author who had obviously been most painstaking in assembling guaranteed data. Darwin, with extraordinary candor, had displayed as impressively as he could all the objections to his theory, all the gaps in his knowledge, all the reasons for distrusting his conclusions. Many reviewers helped themselves to these weapons which Darwin had obligingly prepared for them and turned them against him without any acknowledgment of their source. Scarcely any valid objections were invented by reviewers. For the most part reviews were written by men who had no special knowledge of the subject, who trusted to mere logic and pure reason.

If a quarter part of all this fury had been concentrated on some one *scientific* issue, the fray would have been more equal. But the opponents of Darwin's band were at cross-purposes and, for the most part, philosophical. They were frustrated by a deeper weakness. So far as we can now judge, each of their attacks was animated by a fear of losing prestige. Owen, for example, had long meditated a theory of transmutation of species; if Darwin's theory received support, Owen's would come to naught. If Darwin triumphed, Agassiz's pet catastrophes would be obsolete. Mivart's review of the *Origin* would become archaic mysticism, Sedgwick's defense of Genesis would be absurd, Bishop Wilberforce's ecclesiastical authority would be impaired. Each of the opponents was fighting for his own reputation.

But there was one bond of common purpose among

them: they all wanted to be rid of a proof that "man is descended from monkeys." Lyell confessed in private that he shuddered at the thought of the idea. Gray publicly professed his dislike: "The prospect of the future is encouraging. It is only the backward glance that reveals anything alarming. . . . The very first step backward makes the negro and the Hottentot our blood relations." The rest of the backward steps alarmed Gray. But he did not shrink and cover his eyes as Lyell did. He remarked, like the sane and lovable man that he was, "Not that reason or Scripture objects to that, though pride may." He was using Darwin's very word in the *Origin*—"however revolting to our pride." We can not blame theologians for not following Gray. Most of them felt that the teaching of reason and Scripture made Darwin the enemy of their church. They honestly felt that his horrid doctrine removed the divine soul from man. The fundamentalists of to-day can not resign themselves to having "the blood of the beast" in their veins. And who shall blame them? That man is fortunate who easily overcomes the horror he feels when he first learns that his ancestors were ape-like. Perhaps it is a silly horror. But it is very strong in many of us. We have to sympathize with all priests who could not abide it.

We can honor any man who admits that he is alarmed at the backward glance toward his ancestors. We can excuse the man who cries out, "I *will* not believe this." No one is a philistine for not accepting Darwinism. A philistine is one who deceives himself, who shouts about fossils or pigeons when he is really in agony about his injured pride. We can not excuse the hypocrite.

The hurricane of wrathful hypocrisy that burst upon Darwin in December, 1859, is perhaps the most simian exhibition that the human race ever made of itself. It would be a deplorable chapter in history if it were not so instructive and so funny.

While Huxley was penning his *Times* review, the Rev. Adam Sedgwick was admonishing his old pupil about his silly new book. Shall we call Sedgwick's verdict funny or pathetic?

I have read your book with more pain than pleasure. Parts of it I admired greatly, parts I laughed at till my sides were almost sore; other parts I read with absolute sorrow, because I think them utterly false and grievously mischievous. You have deserted the true method of induction, and started us in machinery as wild, I think, as Bishop Wilkin's locomotive that was to sail with us to the moon. . . .

You write of "natural selection" as if it were done consciously by the selecting agent.

Sedgwick's understanding of natural selection was —and still is—the most common distortion of Darwin's clearly expressed meaning. Darwin specially and forcefully warned his readers that he was using only a convenient metaphor, that there was not in nature any conscious force or any agent.

I should like to know whether Fitz-Roy received a copy of the *Origin* and whether he expressed an opinion on it. There is nothing about him in the published correspondence of this period except one reference. Darwin sent Lyell a clipping from the *Times*, a letter signed "Senex," which he thought was "rich" and which he was sure Fitz-Roy had written. His comment was:

It is a pity he did not add his theory of the extinction of *Mastodon*, etc., from the door of the Ark being too small.

It is a relief to turn from the fears of Fitz-Roy and

Sedgwick to the feeling of the Rev. Charles Kingsley. He had read an advance copy in November and had written promptly from his rectory.

That the naturalist whom, of all naturalists living, I most wish to know and to learn from should have sent a scientist like me his book encourages me at least to observe more carefully, and think more slowly. . . .

All I have seen of it *awes* me; both with the heap of facts and the prestige of your name, and also with the clear intuition that if you be right, I must give up much that I have believed and written. . . .

I have gradually learnt to see that it is just as noble a conception of Deity to believe that he created animal forms capable of self-development into all forms needful . . . as to believe that He required a fresh act of intervention to supply the *lacunas* which He Himself had made. I question whether the former be not the loftier thought.

Kingsley was not worried about his ancestry. He liked the prospect of learning a better conception of God.

It is pleasant to turn from the mental contortions of Owen and Agassiz to the judgment of Francis Galton, expressed as early as December 9.

I have laid it down in the full enjoyment of a feeling that one rarely experiences after boyish days, of having been initiated into an entirely new province of knowledge.

On the same day Darwin reported to Lyell that the geologist Ramsay was probably a convert.

Some quotations from Darwin's correspondence of the first five months of 1860 will show how other converts came in and how the flood of ignorant abuse mounted before the great battle of Oxford was fought the last day of June. Notice how sure it seems that Lyell is a convert: he spoke of himself to Darwin as one of "us."

January 4, to Lyell. I have received rather a good squib, showing that I have proved "might is right," and therefore that Napoleon is right, and every cheating tradesman is also right.

February 15, to Lyell. Henslow is more candid than any opposer I have heard of, for he says, though he *cannot* go so far as I do, yet he can give no good reason why he should not.

February 25, to Lyell. I cannot help wondering at your zeal about my book. I declare to heaven you seem to care as much about my book as I do myself.

March 3, to Hooker. I am astonished and rejoiced at the progress which the subject has made.

April 3, to Gray. Sedgwick has reviewed me savagely and unfairly in the *Spectator*. . . . My dear old friend Sedgwick, with his noble heart, is rabid with indignation.

April 10, to Lyell. There has been a plethora of reviews, and I am really quite sick of myself. . . . I have just read the *Edinburgh* which without doubt is by Owen.* It is extremely malignant, clever, and I fear will be very damaging. He is atrociously severe on Huxley's lecture, and very bitter against Hooker. So we three *enjoyed* it together. Not that I really enjoyed it, for it made me uncomfortable for one night; but I have got quite over it today. It requires much study to appreciate all the bitter spite of many of the remarks against me; indeed I did not discover all myself. It scandalously misrepresents many parts. He misquotes some passages, altering words within inverted commas. . . . It is painful to be hated in the intense degree with which Owen hates me.

May 15, to Hooker. As for the old fogies in Cambridge, it really signifies nothing. It makes me resolve to buckle on my armor. I see plainly that it will be a long uphill fight.

May 18, to Wallace. Agassiz sends me a personal civil message, but incessantly attacks me; but Asa Gray fights like a hero in defense. Lyell keeps as firm as a

---

*The name is deleted in *Life and Letters*, but is supplied in *More Letters*, I, 145.

tower, and this autumn will publish on the "Geological History of Man," and will then declare his conversion, which now is universally known.

May 30, to Hooker. The battle rages furiously in the United States. Gray is fighting splendidly, and there seem to have been many discussions with Agassiz and others at the meetings. Agassiz pities me much as being so deluded. As for the progress of opinion, I clearly see that it will be excessively slow, almost as slow as the change of species. . . . I am getting wearied at the storm of hostile reviews and hardly any useful.

June 1, to Lyell. All these reiterated attacks will tell heavily; there will be no more converts, and probably some will go back. I hope you do not grow disheartened, I am determined to fight to the last.

June 5, to Hooker. This review and Harvey's letter have convinced me that I must be a very bad explainer. Neither really understand what I mean by Natural Selection. I am inclined to give up the attempt as hopeless. Those who do not understand, it seems, cannot be made to understand. . . . I should begin to think myself wholly in the wrong, and that I was an utter fool, but then I cannot yet persuade myself that Lyell, and you and Huxley, Carpenter, Asa Gray, and Watson, etc., are all fools together. Well, time will show, and nothing but time.

The wail about the hopeless attempt to explain was hardly exaggeration or pessimism. To this day it continues true that learned essayists and editors, even if friendly to evolution, most marvelously contrive to misapprehend natural selection. Modern college teachers have to shout and repeat the right idea to students— and then discover that the attempts to explain seem hopeless.*

Even Lyell felt uneasy about natural selection and accused Darwin of "deifying secondary causes." Dar-

---

*I have done my bit of shouting on pages 136-160 of *Evolution for John Doe.*

win must have felt giddy when he discovered that his master in geology was accusing him of interfering with first causes.

He could not expect much but ridicule and misrepresentation at the meeting of the British Association for the Advancement of Science which was to begin its session June 28. Huxley had decided to be absent, because he knew that there was to be a concerted onslaught upon Darwin's theory; he knew that there would not be a scientific discussion, but a fight. For Wilberforce, Bishop of Oxford, had announced that he intended "to smash Darwin." Huxley was not interested in such Right Reverend pugilism. But by chance he encountered Robert Chambers, author of the *Vestiges*, who besought him "not to desert us." Perhaps Huxley was amused at the "us." At any rate, he yielded to Chambers.

Hooker went to Oxford, but did not attend the section meetings. He explained his reasons in a letter to Darwin.

Without you and my wife I am as dull as ditchwater, and crept about the once familiar streets feeling like a fish out of water. I swore I would not go near a Section and did not for two days, but amused myself with the College buildings and attempted sleeps in the sleepy gardens and rejoiced in my indolence. Huxley and Owen had a furious battle over Darwin's absent body, at Section D, before my arrival, of which more anon. H. was triumphant; you and your book forthwith became the topics of the day, and I d——d the days and double d——d the topics too, and like a craven felt bored out of my life by being woke out of my reveries to become referee on Natural Selection, etc., etc., etc.

The furious battle had been waged on the first day of the session, Thursday, in the discussion of a botanical paper. The President called upon Huxley, who declined to speak, giving as his reason:

A general audience, in which sentiment would unduly interfere with intellect, is not the public before which such a discussion should be carried on.

But Owen seemed to relish just that sort of audience. He proposed to approach the subject in the spirit of a philosopher; he softly said, "I am convinced that there are facts by which the public may come to some conclusion as to the truth of Mr. Darwin's theory."

One of the "facts" was a statement about the brain of a gorilla: "It is more different from a man's brain than it is from the brain of the lowest apes." His method of smashing Darwin, you see, was to bring up the disagreeable monkey question. He expected the force of his statement to be smashing because he was the world's greatest anatomist.

It happened that Huxley had for two years been making a special study of the brains of primates. He knew that Owen was wrong. If this error had been the only fault in Owen's speech, Huxley would have kept still and bided his time. But Owen knew that he was talking about a moot point; he knew that Huxley and others had reached the opposite conclusion; and yet, for the sake of smashing Darwin, he had pretended that he spoke the whole truth.

The wildcat in Huxley was roused. He replied to Owen: "I must directly and unequivocally contradict the statement. My procedure is unusual, but seems necessary. I shall justify it elsewhere." Every one in the room knew that such language was an ultimatum and that there would be a fight to the death. Most of the audience must have realized, as Hooker did, that Huxley was already "triumphant."

I am glad that I do not have to describe the greater battle that was fought on Saturday; for if I told about it faithfully, you would suppose I had the instincts of a sports reporter. You shall hear what Hooker wrote to Darwin. Remember that he later became Sir Joseph, Director of Kew Garden, President of the Royal Society for five years, and that a principal reason for his honors was "his cool judgment and knowledge of men."

I will preface Hooker's account with a picture of the room in which the contest was staged. The meeting had been scheduled for the Lecture Room of the Museum, but this had been filled long before the hour by an eager throng that wanted to hear the Bishop smash Darwin. And, mind you, the admission was strictly limited to those who held cards. The audience had to be moved to a much larger room, the Library. Even this was not big enough; ladies were seated on the window-sills all down the west side.

On the east side was the platform. The President, seated in the center, was the Reverend Professor Henslow. On his right sat Wilberforce, who had been Dean of Westminster, had been Bishop of Oxford for fifteen years, had proved himself a skilful executive, and was famous for his oratorical skill. At the Bishop's right sat the American, Dr. Draper, who was to read the paper for which the session was nominally held. At the President's left sat Huxley. Beyond Huxley was Sir Benjamin Brodie,* a noted surgeon and a baronet; beyond Sir Benjamin, a country clergyman named Dingle. In front of Dingle sat Sir John Lubbock (a neighbor of Darwin at Downe, already a convert to his views) and Hooker.

Clerical sympathizers were massed in the center of the room. In one corner, at the back, was a small knot of undergraduates, sympathizers with the new theory, who rallied around a young clergyman.

---

*Leonard Huxley says his father sat near Beale and that Brodie was in the back of the room; Hooker does not mention being on the platform. Perhaps there was shifting of seats during the session; perhaps memories of witnesses were mixed.

Now for Hooker's story.

On Saturday I walked with my old friend of the *Erebus*, Capt. Dayman, to the Sections and swore as usual I would not go in; but getting equally bored of doing nothing, I did. A paper of a Yankee donkey called Draper on "Civilization according to the Darwinian Hypothesis," or some such title, was being read, and it did not mend my temper, for of all the flatulent stuff and all the self-sufficient stuffers, these were the greatest; it was all a pie of Herbert Spencer and Buckle without the seasoning of either; however, hearing that Soapy Sam was to answer, I waited to hear the end. The meeting was so large that they had adjourned to the Library, which was crammed with between 700 and 1000 people, for all the world was there to hear Sam Oxon.

But all the world had to wait a while. As always in the best pugilistic circles, there were some preliminary bouts with the Darwinian Hypothesis. Henslow announced, in opening the discussion from the floor, that the meeting was for scientific purposes and that only valid scientific arguments would be tolerated. The first response to this warning was from a member of the Economics Section, who spoke theologically until he was stopped by the President. Then the Reverend Greswell began in a theological vein, but the audience would not allow him to go on. The Reverend Dingle advanced from his corner of the platform and began, very scientifically, to chart his objection to Darwinism: "Let this point A be a man, and let that point B be the mawnkey"— but the audience shouted "mawnkey, mawnkey," and would none of him. However prejudiced the audience may have been against Darwinism, it would not tolerate such incompetents.

Admiral Fitz-Roy arose—yes, the old Captain of the *Beagle*. He had been governor of New Zealand, was

now a Fellow of the Royal Society, and had for years
devoted himself to the welfare of sailors by making better weather-charts and life-boats. He testified that Mr.
Darwin's book had given him the acutest pain and that he
had often expostulated with his old comrade for entertaining views which were contradictory of the first chapter of Genesis. Those are the last words he will speak
in this book. Five years later, while his vehement spirit
was unbalanced by overwork, he committed suicide.
Probably he never forgave himself for the part he had
played in perverting Darwin's mind.

At last the Bishop stepped forward to speak and was
cheered loudly. Hooker's letter continues:

Well, Sam Oxon got up and spouted for half an hour
with inimitable spirit, ugliness and emptiness and unfairness. I saw he was coached up by Owen and knew
nothing, and he said not a syllable but what was in the
reviews; he ridiculed you badly and Huxley savagely.

Near the close of his speech he turned to Huxley,
smiling as a great man should when he resolves not to be
too hard on an inferior:

I should like to ask Professor Huxley, who is sitting
by me, and is about to tear me to pieces when I have sat
down, as to his belief in being descended from an ape.
Is it on his grandfather's or his grandmother's side that
the ape ancestry comes in?

The room rocked with laughter. While the uproar
was on, Huxley said exultingly to Brodie, "The Lord
hath delivered him into mine hands."

The Bishop, with excellent art, changed suddenly
from his jesting to a grave tone, and concluded by de-
claring with all his episcopal seriousness that the Darwin

theory was contrary to the revelation of God in the Scriptures.

The men cheered; the women waved handkerchiefs. The Bishop's oratory had succeeded.

Now the audience shouted for Huxley. He was in no hurry to respond, but waited until the call for him became loud and insistent. Then with deliberate dignity he rose, and in quiet self-possession waited for the room to grow silent. It was a hostile audience that he faced. It was somewhat distracted from the issue by a curious coincidence: Huxley looked very much like the Bishop!

Huxley briefly discussed certain points in the Bishop's oration and then took up his last question. He spoke slowly.

I asserted—and I repeat—that a man has no reason to be ashamed of having an ape for his grandfather.

He paused. The audience began to realize that the Bishop's crude jibe was to be answered sternly. People wondered and grew still. Something in the manner of Huxley made them conscious of how cheap the Bishop's joke had been, how unworthy of a gentleman. And a British audience likes a gentleman.

If there were an ancestor whom I should feel shame in recalling, it would be a man——

Again Huxley paused, so that the audience might anticipate what was coming.

—a man of restless and versatile intellect, who, not content with success in his own sphere of activity, plunges into scientific questions——

The stone had hit the forehead of Goliath.

The audience was not interested in the rest of the sentence. They had come to see Darwin smashed by a mighty champion, and now the champion was struck between the eyes. Englishmen know what a fair fight is. The audience began to applaud, so that the rest of Huxley's words were almost drowned in the noise.

—questions with which he has no real acquaintance, only to obscure them by an aimless rhetoric, and distract the attention of his hearers from the point at issue by eloquent digressions and skilled appeals to religious prejudice.*

Perhaps this famous retort had sufficient momentum to be deadly. But perhaps not. Lyell's impression, after comparing "several varying versions of this shindy," was:

The Bishop had been much applauded in the section, but before it was over the sections were quite turned the other way, especially by Hooker.

So I should guess that the account of the shindy which Hooker gave Darwin, though it seems to underrate Huxley's effect, is not an overstatement of Hooker's share in the battle. Hooker was not the man to exaggerate his own importance. It was probably his impetus which sank the stone into Goliath's forehead. His long letter to Darwin, from which I have been quoting, ended thus:

Huxley answered admirably and turned the tables, but he could not throw his voice over so large an assembly, nor command the audience; and he did not allude to Sam's weak points nor put the matter in a form or way that carried the audience. The battle waxed hot. Lady

---

*There is no record of Huxley's actual words. This attempt to report them (made by the historian J. R. Green, then twenty-two years old) is too florid to represent Huxley's incisiveness.

Brewster fainted, the excitement increased as others spoke; my blood boiled, I felt myself a dastard; now I saw my advantage; I swore to myself that I would smite that Amalekite, Sam, hip and thigh if my heart jumped out of my mouth, and I handed my name up to the President (Henslow) as ready to throw down the gauntlet. . . . So there I was cocked up with Sam at my right elbow, and there and then I smashed him amid rounds of applause. I hit him in the wind at the first shot in ten words taken from his own ugly mouth; and then proceeded to demonstrate in as few more: (1) that he could never have read your book, and (2) that he was absolutely ignorant of the rudiments of Bot. Science. I said a few more on the subject of my own experience and conversion, and wound up with a very few observations on the relative positions of the old and new hypotheses, and with some words of caution to the audience. Sam was shut up—had not one word to say in reply, and the meeting *was dissolved forthwith,* leaving you master of the field after 4 hours' battle. Huxley, who had borne all the previous brunt of the battle, and who never before (thank God) praised me to my face, told me it was splendid, and that he did not know before what stuff I was made of. I have been congratulated and thanked by the blackest coats and whitest stocks in Oxford.

Do the words sound coarse? There is no record that the Reverend and amiable Henslow ever rebuked his son-in-law for smiting the Amalekite. Henslow and other Oxford clergymen were grateful to Hooker, for they knew that the Bishop was disgracing his church.

If it is discouraging to read of the folly of a bishop, it does the heart good to hear how the clergy congratulated Hooker. He had not attacked the church. He had resented the intrusion of a bishop into science. Bishop Wilberforce was allowed to speak at British Association meetings because he had once taken honors in mathematics, and so had the courtesy title of scientist. But he had abused his privilege. The Vice-Chancellor of Oxford let it be known that he thought the Bishop got no more than he deserved.

After his downfall in a scientific session he was free to speak as a churchman against evolution. He had sense enough—to his honor be it recorded—to be civil to Huxley when they met thereafter. A large body of the clergy continued, as priests, to denounce evolution. That was their right; perhaps it was their duty. But never again in England did a church official attempt to overawe a scientific assembly or to smash a scientific theory with a cheap joke. When the Bishop of Oxford posed as a scientist he was a charlatan and a disgrace to religion. The Goliath of his kind of insolence was beheaded.

It will now be pleasant to escape from the stuffy Library at Oxford to the salt breezes of the East Indies. The place is the island of Waigiu, which is two hundred miles east of Ternate, where Wallace wrote the bombshell letter to Darwin. The time is two months after the Oxford meeting. Wallace is still collecting birds. He has read the *Origin* five or six times and has recorded his opinion in a letter to a friend.

It will live as long as the *Principia* of Newton. Mr. Darwin has given the world a new science, and his name should, in my opinion, stand above that of every philosopher of ancient or modern times.

To another friend he wrote:

I could never have approached the completeness of his book, its vast accumulation of evidence, its overwhelming argument, and its admirable tone and spirit. I really feel thankful that it has not been left to me to give the theory to the world.

As often as the world reads those words of enthusiasm for Darwin and modesty about himself it will be charmed afresh. There was in Wallace's nature a beauty that will shine when the splendor of Agassiz and the greatness of Lyell are dim. He never laid claim to more honor than the Linnæan paper gave him, and so gained a higher kind of fame than scientific discovery can bring.

He was right in giving thanks that fate had not made him the leader of the evolution army. For such a part he lacked every qualification. He had small sagacity for sifting false men from true ones, small endurance of the hardship of long-continued research, small sense of strategy in the polemics of the biological war. He was not even a reliable reasoner: his theory of natural selection was the only case in which he showed acuteness for large principles. His other attempts—not any one of them, but all taken together—will show the untrustworthiness of his mind.

1. In his youth he became a convert to phrenology; he placidly and unwaveringly held to this faith all his life.

2. He was a convert to Robert Owen's "philosophy of human nature."

3. He believed that an almanac-maker, Murphy, had predicted a whole year's weather in advance; he argued that "the larger phases of the weather are to a considerable extent dependent on the relative positions of the sun and moon."

4. He felt that he had a cure for "the all-embracing system of land-robbery" that had been in vogue since the days of Henry VIII.

5. He was "struck amazingly" by Williams's *Fuel of the Sun,* which taught that the sun maintained its heat by coming into contact with a "space-atmosphere." Wallace considered the book "beautifully worked out and quite intelligible."

6. Of Darwin's "Pangenesis" (see page 348) he

judged: "It is sublime in its simplicity, satisfying in the extreme, the most wonderful thing Darwin has given us."

7. He argued against vaccination.

Indeed his advocacy of everything is calm, placid, undisturbed by suspicions of possible error. His contributions to Darwinism—able and potent essays—are curiously untroubled by any such worries as afflicted all others who accepted the theory.

Wallace lived until 1913, famous for his connection with Darwin, his unrivaled knowledge of tropical fauna, and his many books on zoology and social subjects.

As the summer of 1860 passed Darwin felt assured that his theory was well founded. He had been amazed at a review of the *Origin* by the Bishop of Oxford, and wrote to Huxley about it.

The *Quarterly* is uncommonly clever; and I chuckled much at the way my grandfather and self are quizzed. I could here and there see Owen's hand. By the way, how comes it that you were not attacked? Does Owen begin to find it more prudent to leave you alone? I would give five shillings to know what tremendous blunder the Bishop made; for I see that a page has been canceled and a new page gummed in.

I am indeed most thoroughly contented with the progress of opinion. From all that I hear from several quarters, it seems that Oxford did the subject great good. It is of enormous importance the showing the world that a few first-rate men are not afraid of expressing their opinion. I see daily more and more plainly that my unaided book would have done absolutely nothing. Asa Gray is fighting admirably. He is a thorough master of the subject, which cannot be said by any means of such men as even Hopkins.

"Fighting" would have seemed a queer word to American readers of Gray's *Atlantic* articles, for they

did not advocate Darwin's theory. Moreover, they are
so simply and affably expressed that few readers suspected them of being admirable fighting. But Darwin
was right. The lucid mind of Gray never distorted the
plain teachings of the *Origin*: it understood and expounded them with more clarity than Hooker and Lyell
could achieve after years of familiarity with them. Darwin rejoiced in Gray more and more as the months
passed.

No one person understands my views and has defended them so well as A. Gray.

Asa Gray strikes me as one of the best reasoners and
writers I ever read. He knows my book as well as I do
myself.

How generous and unselfish Gray has been in all his
labor! Are you not struck by his metaphors and similes?
I have told him he is a poet and not a lawyer.

The poetical botanist had the most simple and hard-
headed notion of how to regard evolution: Let's see if
it works. More and more as Gray applied evolution in
his classifying he found that it worked. Other botanists
found so. There never has been any other test of Darwin's theory. It does so much work for all the biological
sciences that they can not get on without it.

Gray never could have told when he crossed the line
and became a convert. His progress was gradual and
slow. Even in 1874 his form of speaking was, "The
adequacy of Darwin's causes has not been made out."
But, for the matter of that, their adequacy is still in
doubt. Before 1870 Gray must have been well persuaded
that, however caused, some process of evolution was a
necessary assumption.

Yet, all the while, this admirable and poetic fighter
for evolution kept Darwin uneasy by his worries about
Design—with a capital D. Gray had been comforting

Americans by pointing out how Darwin recognized Divine Purpose. He cited the three quotations that Darwin had posted in the front of the *Origin*—two from theologians and one from Bacon—which emphasized "Divine power," "intelligent agent," "and book of God's word." In the last sentence of the *Origin* Darwin had said, "There is a grandeur in this view of life, with its several powers, having been originally breathed by the Creator into a few forms or into one." So Gray wanted Darwin to speak out clearly his convictions about the Creator's Design. But Darwin could only reply that he had no knowledge of how God managed the universe.

> The theological view of the question is always painful to me. I am bewildered. I own that I cannot see as plainly as others do, and as I should wish to do, evidence of design and beneficence on all sides of us. . . . I feel most deeply that the whole subject is too profound for the human intellect. A dog might as well speculate on the mind of Newton. Let each man believe and hope what he can.

Gray went so far and was so persistent in arguing for Design that in 1867 Darwin, when finishing his great two-volume supplement to the *Origin,* had to disclaim Gray's theology:

> I finish my book by a single paragraph, answering, or rather throwing doubt on, Asa Gray's doctrine that each variation has been specially ordered or led along a beneficial line. It is foolish to touch such subjects, but there have been so many allusions to what I think about the part which God has played in the formation of organic beings that I thought it shabby to evade the question.

If Darwin was impatient because one of his supporters wanted to talk theology, he was depressed by

Lyell's determination to discuss metaphysics. Lyell could not give up creation, especially the separate creation of man. Therefore he could not declare himself openly a convert to natural selection.

Darwin had understood as early as November, 1859, that Lyell was all but persuaded. On the 11th he wrote to Gray, "Lyell is nearly a convert to my views"; and on the 13th to Wallace, "Hooker thinks Lyell a complete convert." On the 23d he poured out gratitude and admiration to Lyell for accepting the new theory of species.

I rejoice profoundly that you intend admitting the doctrine of modification in your new edition. . . . I honor you most sincerely. To have maintained, in the position of a master, one side of a question for thirty years, and then deliberately give it up is a fact to which I much doubt whether the records of science offer a parallel.

But in September there is doubt. He tells Hooker:

I have had a long letter from Lyell, who starts ingenious difficulties opposed to natural selection, because it has not done more than it has.

And he replied to Lyell:

You cut my throat, and your own throat; and I believe will live to be sorry for it.

Lyell was writing *The Antiquity of Man,* and Darwin understood that it was to contain his profession of faith. But when Darwin read it (in February, 1863) he had to break bad news to Hooker:

I am deeply disappointed to find that his timidity prevents him giving any judgment. . . . From all my communications with him I must ever think that he has really entirely lost faith in the immutability of species; and yet one of his strongest sentences is nearly as fol-

lows: "If it should *ever* be rendered highly probable
that species change by variation and natural selection."

Other expressions of Lyell's were: "Mr. Darwin labors
to show," "is believed by the author to throw light."
Darwin explained later in the letter how deeply he was
disappointed.

> The Lyells are coming here on Sunday evening to
> stay till Wednesday. I dread it, but I must say how
> much disappointed I am that he has not spoken out on
> species, still less on man. And the best joke is that he
> thinks he has acted with the courage of a martyr of old.
> . . . Now I must, in common honesty, retract. I wish
> to heaven he had said not a word on the subject.

Two weeks later he wrote to Lyell:

> I have been greatly disappointed that you have not
> given judgment and spoken fairly out what you think
> about the derivation of species. . . . I think the
> *Parthenon* is right, that you will leave the public in a
> fog. . . . I had always thought that your judgment
> would have been an epoch in the subject. All that is
> over with me, and I will only think on the admirable
> skill with which you have selected the striking points.

Lyell replied:

> You ought to be satisfied, as I shall bring hundreds
> towards you who, if I treated the matter more dogmatic-
> ally, would have rebelled.

Darwin could by no means be satisfied. He went as
far as courtesy would permit in suggesting to Lyell that
his treatment of the species question was not honest:
"It is nearly as much for your sake as for my own that
I so much wish that your state of belief could have permitted you to say boldly and distinctly out that species
were not separately created."

Lyell would not commit himself in print. Every opponent of Darwin could cite Lyell's words of 1863 to prove that Lyell still believed in the separate creation of species. Lyell had not even said explicitly that he meant creation by natural law; he still left his readers free to infer that "creation" meant miraculous intervention by God in the operations of natural laws. No wonder that Darwin exploded in a letter to Gray (May 11, 1863): "I have sometimes almost wished that Lyell had pronounced against me."

Lyell's policy of facing both ways was harrowing to Darwin. Why had Lyell not declared plainly in 1859 that he was *not* a convert? He knew that Hooker and Darwin were referring to him as a convert. He had not objected. Thus he brought humiliation on his friends.

Yet Lyell considered himself an ally of Darwin. On November 30, 1864, he spoke at the Royal Society meeting when the Copley medal was awarded to Darwin. In his account of his speech he told Darwin (letter of Jan. 16, 1865): "It was somewhat of a confession of faith as to the *Origin*. . . . I think you would have been satisfied with the length I went." Later in the same letter he gave Darwin still more cheering words, without a qualifying *somewhat*:

At Berlin I had an animated conversation on Darwinism with the Princess Royal, who was very much *au fait* at the *Origin*. . . . She asked me what I had been doing, and I explained that in recasting the *Principles* I had to give up the independent creation of species. She said she understood my difficulty, for after your book "the old opinions had received a shake from which they would never recover."

Yet Lyell in his Copley medal speech had not confessed any faith, and had not published any recantation of his creation theory. Darwin could put no more trust in such private intimations. He had to wait, mystified and despondent. Not till July, 1867, could he permit himself to hope again. Lyell was then making the tenth edition of his *Principles* and had said to his friend Bunbury: "Even if you had been as thoroughly imbued with the transmutation creed as I am beginning to be by writing my second volume." So at last he was *beginning* to be a convert.

He seems to have given Darwin some assurance that he would definitely, in print, announce his new faith. Darwin replied (July 18, 1867), "I rejoice from my heart that you are going to speak out plainly about species."

I have amused myself by playing that I am Darwin opening a copy of the new edition of the *Principles* to see how plainly Lyell has spoken. I use the 11th and last edition (1872) because I wish to see the best that Lyell could do before he died in 1875.

I open to the ten chapters that discuss the species question. The first of these is a reprint of the chapter of 1831 in which he ridiculed Lamarck for "the last grand step by which the orang-outang is made to attain the dignity of man." As I go through the next nine chapters I do not find any denial of the first chapter: Lyell is ridiculing the descent of man now in the identical words that he wrote before I boarded the *Beagle*.

I find in the two hundred and fifty-four pages of the ten chapters many generous compliments paid to the enemies of my theory; also I find my theory mentioned with much respect. But I can not guess what the upshot is to be. The two sides of the question are being carefully and impartially assayed. Now my hope goes up; now it drops far down. I reach the two hundred and fiftieth page without knowing in the least whether the verdict is going for me or against me. Here is strong approval of the Duke of Argyll's argument against my natural selection. There are only four pages more. Surely Lyell will conclude against me.

Not till the two hundred and fifty-second page do I find a brief acknowledgment that Mr. Darwin has made evolution seem highly probable and that the human race can not expect to be exempted from evolution.

Why, then, reprint the ancient ridicule of descent from an orang-outang? Why tuck into one paragraph the very brief admission that I have made my theory "seem probable"? Most readers would not have known by the end of the tenth chapter that Lyell was a convert. I can not be sure myself. I can not refer any one to these two huddled sentences as proof that Lyell is a convert. An opponent of my theory would not admit that Lyell has committed himself.

Lyell's reluctance and Gray's theology kept Darwin somewhat uneasy about the reception of the *Origin* before 1870. Another of his band also caused worry. Early in 1869 Darwin described the cause of it (to Lyell, May 4):

Wallace's calm trust in logic was a source of anxiety I was dreadfully disappointed about Man, it seems to me incredibly strange. . . . Had I not known to the contrary, I would have sworn it had been inserted by some other hand.

Wallace's calm trust in logic was a source of anxiety to Darwin. The previous year Darwin had had to confess to him:

I do not feel that I shall grapple with the sterility argument till my return home; I have tried once or twice, and it has made my stomach feel as if it had been placed in a vice. Your paper has driven three of my children half mad.

Darwin had expressed his anxiety to Lyell:

I agree with Wallace's wonderful cleverness, but he is not cautious enough in my opinion. . . . He is riding that hobby of protection to death.

And Darwin admitted to Wallace a deep difference between them:

I think we start with different fundamental notions on inheritance. . . . I grieve to differ from you, and it actually terrifies me and makes me constantly distrust myself. I fear we shall never quite understand each other.

Yet in spite of these differences among the leaders the world of biology was coming steadily to Darwin's view. The new theory was flourishing in Germany and America. In France it made hardly any progress among the older men, but an anecdote of 1864 shows what its fortune was soon to be with the younger ones. Falconer, who was none too enthusiastic a believer, wrote to Darwin about a visit to the museum at Dijon: "Professor Brullé told me in despair that he could not get his pupils to listen to anything from him except à la Darwin! He, poor man, could not comprehend it, but said that all young Frenchmen would hear or believe nothing else."

The younger men in England were almost solidly in its favor by 1870—at least so far as to agree that there had been an evolution of species and that no other explanation of the process had been offered which could compare with natural selection. Prominent clergymen were "reconciling" Darwinism with religion. Darwin could feel sure that his theory was firmly grounded and that, except in details, it would stand fast. His fame had grown so great that libraries had to make special catalogue entries for his theory. It is doubtful whether any

name was better known in Christendom than Charles
Darwin.

The history of Darwin's particular theory, Natural
Selection, has been a peculiar one. It has always antagonized philosophical minds, for philosophy demands
some metaphysical explanation of the force that "selects." Philosophers and theologians and logicians
have never been content with a theory that rests on mere
"chance" variations which are selected by purely "mechanical" processes. Hence there has always been in
human intellects a reservoir of dislike for Natural Selection. The flood of distrust has been ready to pour out
and drown the theory.

When Weismann's "germ-plasm" theory became
prominent about 1890, it opened the dikes of opinion
against Natural Selection. But Weismann explicitly declared his complete faith in Darwin's hypothesis.

A little later de Vries's "mutations" were supposed
to have blotted it out, but de Vries has declared unequivocally that he believes in Natural Selection.

Of late it has been supposed that Natural Selection
is pretty much swept away by genetics—the study of
heredity. The supposition has a good deal of warrant
because of the strong indictments made by such scholars
as the late William Bateson. It is now regular custom
in textbooks of biological subjects to say, "Natural Selection may be a factor in evolution, but," etc. I will
quote one example of this modern fashion, from Parker's
What Evolution Is (1926), page 119. Professor Parker's
name is an old and honored one in America; he has been
a Harvard professor of zoology since 1906. I italicize
three of his words.

This conviction has so impressed itself upon the
minds of *most* modern evolutionists that they have one
by one come to the conclusion that natural selection,

which in Weismann's time was declared to be all-sufficient in evolution, may after all be of *little* real significance. Opinions of this kind have been *frankly* expressed by such eminent authorities as Bateson in England and Morgan in America, and they reflect the view of the majority of biologists the world over.

It is true that Bateson was frank. Morgan was so far from frank that Prof. S. J. Holmes has cited him as one who is making Natural Selection more firmly established. The following words of Prof. T. H. Morgan on pages 146 and 194 of his *Critique* (1919) do not seem frankly opposed to Natural Selection: "This is the process Darwin called natural selection. Stated in these general terms there is nothing in the theory to which anyone is likely to take exception. . . . Evolution has taken place by the incorporation into the race of those mutations that are beneficial to the life and reproduction of the organism."

One of those evolutionists not included in Parker's "most" is J. Graham Kerr, who has been Regius Professor of zoology in Glasgow since 1902. I quote from pages 129, 132, and 272 of his *Evolution* (1926).

When we review carefully the knowledge of the day it is perhaps liable to cause surprise that we find only a single suggested explanation of evolutionary change in the animal kingdom that can establish its claim to be rigidly scientific, in making use of no factors that transcend actual observation and experience—namely, the hypothesis of natural selection.

Such is in bare outline the hypothesis of natural selection. That it is a true theory is undoubted.

As to the method by which variation is controlled and guided along definite paths so as to bring about evolutionary progress I regard the Darwinian hypothesis of natural selection, with certain modifications in detail, as still holding the field. . . . I adhere to the position of

Darwin that the potency of natural selection is in actual fact enormous; I hold that the attempts that have been made to minimize its importance are to a great extent fallacious, invalidated in some cases by their authors' want of experience and skill as field naturalists, and in others by the making of unwarrantable assumptions. . . . The natural selection theory has been greatly fortified since Darwin's day by the recognition of Mendelian inheritance.

My own reading indicates strongly that Professor Kerr is right and that "most" evolutionists agree with him. In the Appendix (page 441) I quote a number of them, not one of whom drops any hint that he belongs to a minority. Here I will cite only one, Edwin S. Goodrich, Linacre Professor of zoology at Oxford—a man who is not generally supposed to hold a minority opinion about Natural Selection. On page 108 of *Living Organisms* (1924) he says:

The Darwinian theory still stands unassailable as the one and only rational scientific explanation of evolution by "natural" forces, whose action can be observed, tested, and measured.

Darwin's Natural Selection has thus far withstood every succeeding flood of objection.

CHAPTER XIII

THE BOOKS AFTER THE ORIGIN: 1860-1881

1. Revisions of the Origin

PART of Darwin's work from 1860 to 1872 was revising the *Origin* for successive editions. Some small changes were made in the second edition, which appeared in January, 1860, and other changes for the third edition of April, 1861. In the spring of 1866 he put in ten weeks of hard work at a fourth edition, making alterations to meet the most persistent criticisms. Early in 1869 there was a fifth edition, and early in 1872 the sixth and last. His aim in these revisions was to make his meaning clearer, so as to keep critics from misunderstanding him. There were three principal efforts of this sort.

1. He increased and strengthened the explanations of the meaning of "chance"—that this word does not deny exact cause, but is a confession that the cause is unknown. This is the common and proper scientific use. He inserted many additional references to "law," "unknown laws," "unknown causes."

2. He labored to make it clear that "natural selection" was only a figure of speech, like "attraction" of gravitation or "affinity" of chemical substances. He tried to show that he was not personifying nature, that "selection" was merely a convenient name for the result of the actions of natural laws on organisms.

3. He tried to show that the cause of variation was

quite unknown and that his theory was independent of the cause—just as Huxley said it was.

This would be a technical question that should have no discussion in a biography if it was not now the most talked-about part of Darwin's theory. It is very commonly said nowadays that Darwin, late in life, accepted Lamarck's view of the nature of inheritance, that the view is now known to be wrong, and that therefore Darwin's theory has a big hole in it. In recent books about evolution there is an almost unanimous declaration to this effect: "Darwin accepted Lamarck's theory of the inheritance of acquired characters." It is therefore almost unanimously supposed by teachers of biology that Darwin's theory is, to that extent, antiquated.

But Darwin did not "accept" such inheritance in any sense that made a difference with his theory of natural selection. It is untrue to say that he "based his theory on" or "relied on" the inheritance of acquired characters. His acceptance was no stronger than the admissions still found in some recent texts. Darwin's observation and reasoning on this point are still curiously modern. If you care to take a biographer's word for it, you may omit the next section. If you care about the evidence, you will not find it very bulky or technical. The subject is a good example of Darwin's ability to penetrate to the heart of a matter and to keep his mind straight in spite of all the gusty opinions that beat upon it. The inheritance of acquired characters was the most constantly perplexing subject in Darwin's life. His treatment of it shows his generalship at its best.

2. Darwin Never Became Lamarckian

Until after 1880 it was taken for granted by every student of nature that bodily changes, made during a creature's lifetime, might be inherited by its offspring.

Such a famous student of cells as Virchow, such an anatomist as Huxley, such a philosopher as Herbert Spencer—all agreed that changes caused by climate or food or education might be inherited. Lamarck had assumed this as an axiom, and no scholar before 1880 would have denied his theory because of this assumption. Lamarck's theory was ridiculed by Huxley and Lyell because of a very different assumption.

Darwin could not suppose that the entire learned world was mistaken about the inheritance of acquired characters. He treated this universal belief with the respect that any rational man would have felt. He *conceded* that it was true. He never enjoyed it, never found it convenient in his theory, certainly never based any reasoning on it. He *conceded* that it was true and *allowed* for it.

The expression that he most commonly used for the inheritance of acquired characters was "the effect of conditions." Throughout his life the most baffling question he debated with himself was this: "Do the conditions of life cause variations that are inherited?" Lyell's sagacity had hardly raised the question; and it is not likely that Darwin raised it before 1837. In his Sketch of 1844 there is acknowledgment that heritable changes may be induced by conditions of life, but already the emphasis is on those other cases in which conditions will not account for changes.

Whether these peculiarities thus acquired during individual lives have been inherited I do not know. . . . The changes thus appearing during the lives of individual animals and plants are extremely rare compared with those which are congenital or which appear soon after birth. Slight differences thus arising are infinitely numerous.

Twelve years later he wrote to Hooker: "I see from

your remarks that you do not understand my notions about modification; I attribute very little to the direct action of climate, etc."

I will now give a series of quotations, from 1856 to 1881, in which Darwin reiterates his independence of the direct action of conditions.

Nov. 23, 1856, to Hooker. At present my conclusion is that external conditions do *extremely* little. [The italics are Darwin's.]

April, 1857, to Hooker. My general belief is quite to agree with what you say about the little direct influence of climate.

May, 1857, to Wallace. I most entirely agree with you on the little effects of "climatal conditions," which one sees referred to *ad nauseam* in all books: I suppose some very little effect must be attributed to such influences, but I fully believe that they are very slight.

September, 1857, to Gray. To talk of climate or Lamarckian habit producing such adaptations to other organic beings is futile.

September, 1859, to Lyell. Not that I think climate nearly so important as most naturalists seem to think. In my opinion no error is more mischievous than this.

October, 1859, to Lyell. It has taken me so many years to disabuse my mind of the too great importance of climate.

March, 1862, to Hooker. I have for years and years been fighting with myself not to attribute too much to natural selection—to attribute something to direct action of conditions; and perhaps I have too much conquered my tendency to lay hardly any stress on conditions of life. . . . I wish I had done what you suggest—started on the fundamental principle of variation being an innate principle.

August, 1868, to Lewes. I cannot admit that nails, claws, and hoofs would have been formed by the direct action of the conditions of life.

May, 1875, to Weismann. When I wrote the *Origin* I could not find any facts which proved the direct action

I hardly know why I am a little sorry, but my present work is leading me to believe rather more in the direct action of physical conditions. I presume I regret it because it lessens the glory of natural selection, and is so confoundedly doubtful. Perhaps I shall change again when I get all my facts under one point of view.

From this time on there are a number of confessions and admissions that perhaps in the *Origin* he has attributed too little effect to conditions. The most striking of these is dated October 13, 1876; he wrote to Moritz Wagner:

In my opinion the greatest error which I have committed has been not allowing sufficient weight to the direct action of the environment, i. e., food, climate, etc., independently of natural selection. . . . When I wrote the *Origin,* and for some years afterwards, I could find little good evidence of the direct action of the environment; now there is a large body of evidence, and your case of the Saturnia is one of the most remarkable of which I have heard.

Even if Darwin had at this time attained a new conviction about the effect of conditions, this could not have influenced a theory that had been put into final form in the last edition of the *Origin,* 1872. And there is no sign in this last edition of any shift of conviction.

A collation of the first and the sixth edition shows that Darwin altered statements about variation in two ways: (1) At several points he put in new concessions of this sort: "Of course variations *may* be caused by altered conditions." He wanted to make clear that he was not obstinately denying this possibility. (2) In several places he inserted passages to explain that there are two factors in the action of conditions of life; in each of these passages he increases the emphasis on the internal nature of the organism.

I will describe one of these cases. At the opening of

Chapter V in the first edition there was a paragraph that set forth "how susceptible the reproductive system is to changes in the conditions of life"; the emphasis was on the power of the conditions to cause variation. But in the sixth edition we read: "In all cases there are two factors, the nature of the organism, *which is much the most important of the two,* and the nature of the condi·· tions." The final form of the *Origin* is more in accord with Darwin's profound conviction about variation than the first form was.

How comes it, then, that so many writers misinform us about Darwin's treatment of variation? The explanation is simple. They all trusted—at first or second hand—a strange passage in Henry Fairfield Osborn's *From the Greeks to Darwin,* pages 240-243 (Macmillan, 1894). It is strange because the only evidence it gives for Darwin's change of mind is three letters,* of 1876-1878, which were written to foreigners with whom Darwin had no personal acquaintance. He was as polite to them as he once was to the Argentine ranchero with whom he discussed ladies' combs—and for the same reason: he thought politeness would do no harm and would please his correspondents.

A severe paleontologist and executive like Dr. Osborn might never guess at the finesse of Darwin's defer·· ential suavity in letters and books. Darwin called his method "truckling" and "subservience." I offer four exhibits in evidence.

February, 1866, to Lyell. I <u>cannot</u> make out what Hooker does believe. . . . I clearly saw Hooker's difficulty. . . . It was a mere piece of truckling on my part when I suggested that longitudinal belts of the world were cooled one after the other.

---

*The passages that Osborn quotes are given in Section 6 of the Appendix.

September, 1860, to Lyell. I put in the possibility of the Galapagos having been continuously joined to America out of mere subservience to the many who believe in Forbes's doctrine, and did not see the danger of the admission. . . . Certain facts . . . convinced me more than in any other case of other islands that the Galapagos had never been continuously united with the mainland: it was mere base subservience, and terror of Hooker and Co.

March, 1863, to Hooker. I have long regretted that I truckled to public opinion, and used the Pentateuchal term of *creation*, by which I really meant "appeared" by some wholly unknown process. It is mere rubbish thinking at present of the origin of life; one might as well think of the origin of matter.

As you read the next passage guess how literally you ought to take the polite words that Osborn quotes from Darwin's letters to Wagner and Semper. Darwin had previously said to his German translator Carus, "I fear that our views will meet a good deal of opposition in Germany."

November, 1880, to Dyer. Many of the Germans are very contemptuous about making out the use of organs; but they may sneer the souls out of their bodies, and I for one shall think it the most interesting part of natural history.

If you still need more concrete evidence, contrast the two following quotations. The first is what Darwin wrote to Dana about the coral-reef theory in December, 1849; the second is what Darwin wrote at the same time to Lyell *about* Dana.

I have not for some years been so much pleased as I have just been by reading your most able discussion on coral-reefs. . . . I consider that now the subsidence theory is established.

Dana is dreadfully hypothetical in many parts, and often as "d——d cocksure" as Macaulay. . . . His map is colored on some quite unintelligible principle, and he deduces subsidence from the vaguest grounds. . . . I utterly disbelieve his statements that most of the atolls have been lately raised a foot or two. He does not condescend to notice my explanation for such appearances. He misrepresents me also when he states that I deduce, without restriction, elevation from all fringing-reefs, and even from islands without any reefs! . . . Dana puts me in a passion several times by disputing my conclusions without condescending to allude to my reasons.

When you have such a background against which to read Osborn's excerpts from letters to "sneering Germans," you can see what pitiful shards of evidence he prints. It is too bad that in his youth he patched together three such fragments, omitted all reference to the big unbroken truth, and thus represented Darwin's thought as a "gradual recession from his exclusion of the Buffon-St. Hilaire factor." How Darwin would have enjoyed reading about himself as the sort of patch-work thought-monger who could "recede from an exclusion of a factor." The Darwin that I know was the man in whose scientific method no fault could be detected by Huxley, who thought more truly than Lyell and Gray and Herbert Spencer, who brought the whole intellectual world to a new way of conceiving life.

If the passage in *From the Greeks to Darwin* were simply a young man's aberration, it would not be worth our time here. But Osborn repeated his idea in stronger terms fifteen years later. In the American volume of centenary essays on Darwin he said: "It is *well known* that Darwin . . . finally adopted the Lamarckian principle." This statement, sometimes taken at second-hand from Schwalbe, is gravely rehearsed and relied upon by learned men who are building arguments in theology and biological philosophy. It is an absurd untruth. Even if it could be supported by ingenious dialectic based on the late letters of Darwin, it has no basis in all the row of books that Darwin made after 1860. In them there is not a glint of the wavering weaving of metaphysical threads that Osborn implies.

I must speak of Osborn's charge several times in this chapter because it has been cited by innumerable writers as the authority for their statement about Darwin's change of view. For a third of a century they have repeated after him, as if hypnotized by such a high priest of science, "It is well known that Darwin changed his mind." Because of this heedless repetition of untruth I am obliged to seem controversial when my wish is to describe Darwin's books. I will spend as little time as possible on the Osborn myth.

Turn your back on it for a time and go abroad with Darwin into the fields to look at some flowers.

3. The Fertilization of Orchids

Darwin's chief business for eight years after 1860 was to prepare for publication his vast assemblage of notes on variation, which he had intended should be an integral part of the *Origin*. The subjects were manifold. He was continually acquiring new information and conducting new experiments to test what other men reported. One of the investigations was into the way the flowers of orchids are fertilized. The findings were so numerous and novel and important that he had to make a separate book about them, which was published in 1862.

The gist of what Darwin learned is this: all the elaborate structures of flowers are devices for persuading insects to carry pollen from one flower to fertilize another flower. The discovery was not entirely original with Darwin; he gives generous acknowledgment to predecessors. But his orchid book was the first demonstration of the completeness of the truth. It showed botanists what flowers are. It opened the way to understanding the most dramatic fact in botany—that *every* colored flower is an adaptation for making insects carry pollen. The orchid book was the first revelation of the idea that flowers and insects have become modified in the most extraordinary ways to complement each other and live by each other's adaptations.

The importance of the book as a proof of evolution was not understood by most readers at the time of its publication. When Darwin received Asa Gray's report on it he replied:

Of all the carpenters for knocking the right nail on the head you are the very best; no one else has perceived that my chief interest in my orchid book has been that it was a "flank movement" on the enemy.

Each one of the botanical books that followed *Orchids* was another attack on the critics—so unobtrusively made that no counter-attack was thought necessary. The strategy of these flank movements was admirable. Within twenty years the enemy was surrounded by such powerful botanical proofs that he had to capitulate.

I will give some quotations which show how orchids became an important document in the study of variations that are selected by the conditions of life and modified into unimaginable adaptations.

28. In no other plant, or indeed in hardly any animal, can adaptations of one part to another, and of the whole to other organized beings widely remote in the scale of nature, be named more perfect than those presented by this Orchis.

92. A poet might imagine that whilst the pollinia
are borne from flower to flower through the air, adhering to a moth's body, they voluntarily and eagerly place
themselves, in each case, in that exact position in which
alone they can hope to gain their wish and perpetuate
their race.

146. In order to witness what I felt sure would take
place, I watched a group of plants on two or three occasions for an hour. . . . At last I saw both these insect-
species crawl into younger flowers and suddenly retreat
with a pair of bright yellow pollinia sticking to their
foreheads. . . . The insect was not so large as one of
the pollinia, and after causing the explosion it had not
force to remove them, and was thus punished for attempting a work beyond its strength, and perished
miserably.

197. In several flowers sent me by Mr. Bateman I
found the nectaries eleven and a half inches long. What
can be the use, it may be asked, of a nectary of such dis-
proportional length? . . . In Madagascar there must
be moths with probosces capable of extension to a length
of between ten and eleven inches!

202. Thus it would appear that there has been a race
in gaining length between the nectary and the proboscis
of certain moths; but the nectary has triumphed, for it
flourishes and abounds in the forests of Madagascar, and
still troubles each moth to insert its proboscis as far as
possible in order to drain the last drop of nectar.

306. Can we, in truth, feel satisfied by saying that
each orchid was created, exactly as we now see it, on a
certain "ideal type"; that the Omnipotent Creator, having fixed on one plan for the whole order, did not please
to depart from this plan; that He therefore made the
same organ to perform diverse functions—often of
trifling importance compared with their function—converted other organs into mere purposeless rudiments,
and arranged all as if they had to stand separate, and
then made them cohere? Is it not a more simple and
intelligible view that all orchids owe what they have in
common to descent from a monocotyledonous plant
. . . and that the now wonderfully changed structure

of the flower is due to a long course of slow modification?

351. The more I study nature, the more I become impressed with ever-increasing force with the conclusion that the contrivances and beautiful adaptations slowly acquired through each part occasionally varying in a slight degree but in many ways, with the preservation or natural selection of those variations which are beneficial to the organism under the complex and ever-varying conditions of life, transcend in an incomparable degree the contrivances and adaptations which the most fertile imagination of the most imaginative man could suggest with unlimited time at his disposal.

That one simple conclusion is the burden of everything Darwin wrote after 1860. You will not find in his books any theory-pasting nightmare such as Osborn describes: "Fourteen years later [1876] Darwin had positively included Buffon's factor"; "in 1878 he fully included Wagner's theory as one cause of origin of species." You will find only slight references to Darwin's own theorizing about the direct effect of environment or of use and disuse. Darwin forgets these troubles when he is really at work with orchids or pigeons or zebras. "Direct action of conditions" has only two brief mentions in the orchid book (pages 352 and 354):

Such details could only be vaguely accounted for by the direct action of the conditions of life, or the mysterious laws of correlation of growth.

. . . if the species were exposed to new conditions of life, *and the structure of the several parts varied ever so little,* such small details of structure might be modified by natural selection.

The central idea of Darwin's theory is as simple and as unmistakable as that. There is no theological thunder and lightning in it, no metaphysical earthquakes, no hurricanes of Lamarckism or Buffonian factors—oh, no. Darwin had one plain, workmanlike conception—that, as a matter of observation of all plants and animals in all circumstances, *the structures of the several parts vary.* That is a fact that no good observer ever denied. As to the cause of the fact, Darwin repeated for forty years that his ignorance was profound. The whole host of modern geneticists and cytologists is still in utter ignorance as to the *cause* of variations. Darwin started with the fact that there *are* variations. Next he observed that the struggle for existence among the orchids of Kent is very severe. From this he inferred that every unfortunate variation in a blossom would be unlikely to survive in heredity, and that every advantageous variation would be more likely to survive and be perpetuated in the race. The conditions of life were "selecting" certain variations. In the course of many generations those variations would diverge more and more from the ancestral forms: at first there would be a mere individual difference, then a sub-variety, then a well-marked variety, then a doubtful species, then a well-defined species, then a new genus.

Darwin never believed in such a process simply because it was logical. He wondered whether there were in nature any facts that would not fit such a hypothesis —and never found any. He wondered whether anybody would invent a better hypothesis—and nobody ever did. That is Darwinism.

4. *The Variation of Animals and Plants under Domestication*

This two-volume work, of nine hundred and sixty-eight pages, is a storehouse of data for the *Origin*. It was intended as an exhibit of the thousands of well-attested cases of the way animals and plants vary, and of the way breeders select the variations for their artificial purposes. To scientific readers of the *Origin* it had appeared that Darwin was speculating; he now offered the array of facts from which he had argued. The book was published in January, 1868.

It is by no means a proof of evolution. Darwin was never able to arrive at a proof. He could only point to probabilities and say, "Do you know any facts that make my idea improbable? Have you any other theory to propose?"

The probability pointed out in *Animals and Plants* is that the variations seen by artificial selectors are the same as variations that occur in a state of nature. No breeder can by any device produce the sort of variation he wants in a new stalk of wheat or a young rabbit; he can do nothing but be on the lookout for the variations that appear in young animals and plants. A gardener may observe cultivated flowers and wild flowers; an ornithologist may observe woodpeckers and domestic fowls. No difference can be seen between the variations in nature and the variations under domestication. In fact no line can be drawn between domesticated and wild animals. It appears to be the fact that in all animals and plants there is perpetual variation, and that man may select variations continuously until he produces well-marked new races.

Why may it not be, then, that the conditions of life in the struggle for existence act in a selective way? The two sorts of selection are utterly different: man acts for a purpose, to satisfy his own desire, not to benefit the organism; nature acts without any purpose—the hard conditions of life simply extinguish all forms that are not well enough adapted. Yet the likelihood that nature does select in this way is very strong. The process is natural selection.

To wander through the pages of *Animals and Plants*

is like being in a museum with an enthusiastic guide who makes you feel how "truly wonderful" variation is. Here is the silk-moth which is believed to have been domesticated in China as long ago as 2700 B. C. Disuse has apparently checked the growth of wings, "but the most important element no doubt has been the close attention to every promising variation." That is always the lesson at every show-case of this museum. Something must be conceded, of course, to use and disuse, to the way in which an environment may stimulate reproductive organs, to the possible effect of changed food or climate; but the great fact is always that variation springs, *from unknown causes,* out of the eggs and appears in the world as a novelty. Then artificial or natural selection may act on it.

Here is "a famous case described by Mr. White." An abnormal branch of a thumb was amputated; to Mr. White's astonishment it grew again and reproduced a nail. When a London surgeon made a deeper amputation the thumb grew out again. But when the report of this marvel was submitted to Sir J. Paget, he did not feel satisfied that Mr. White had made a reliable record. "This being so," Darwin concludes, "it is necessary for me to withdraw the view which I formerly advanced."

"Several distinguished botanists believe that long-continued propagation by cuttings, bulbs, etc., causes plants to become seedless"— that is, that the disuse of the seed-making function has become hereditary. But Mr. Darwin, because the evidence is insufficient, will not pronounce an opinion.

All the lavish profusion of data in the volumes has been sifted with the same canny carefulness. No such compilation of the facts of variation has been made since. It is lamentable to see, when we look in modern books for descriptions of variation, how we encounter once more our old friends of the pages of *Animals and Plants*. It is so much easier—and very much safer—to copy out of Darwin. But the authors don't always find it necessary to give credit to such an archaic source.

Chapter XXVII is the "Provisional Hypothesis of Pangenesis." This is the most ingenious, the most unsuccessful, and the most misunderstood of Darwin's efforts.

Darwin's aim was to make a mental picture of some conceivable way in which acquired characters could be inherited. He always seems dubious about such inheritance; he found the evidence for it slight. But the whole world said that there was such inheritance. Well, then, how could it conceivably take place? Darwin imagined that there might be in every part of the body of an animal a sort of germ of the part, exceedingly small, no bigger in proportion than a pollen-grain is to a plant. He imagined that these germs might be affected by the conditions of life, might be conveyed to the genitals of animals, might be aggregated there into an egg or sperm, and so cause offspring to inherit characters acquired late in life by parents. These migrating germs he named "gemmules."

His theory did account for every sort of inheritance; it deserved a hearing. The trouble with it was that its gemmules were almost beyond imagining and that there was no proof of their existence. Nothing like them has ever been discovered. Therefore an unimaginative biologist of to-day is excusable if he laughs at Darwin's guess.

Darwin, though he broached his theory in all seriousness, was quite aware that it was pure speculation. In many of the letters of 1867 and 1868 he poked fun at himself for hoping that he had thought out something worth while, yet he repeatedly expressed a hope that his strange theory would be useful some day.

October, 1867, to Gray. The chapter on what I call Pangenesis will be called a mad dream, and I shall be pretty well satisfied if you think it a dream worth publishing.

November, 1867, to Hooker. I shall be intensely anxious to hear what you think about Pangenesis; though I can see how fearfully imperfect, even in mere conjectural conclusions, it is.

February, 1868, to Hooker. I fear Pangenesis is stillborn. Bates says he has read it twice and is not sure that he understands it. H. Spencer says the view is quite different from his (and this is a great relief to me, as I feared to be accused of plagiarism, but utterly failed to be sure what he meant, so thought it safest to give my view as almost the same as his), and he says he is not sure he understands it. Am I not a poor devil?

February, 1868, to Wallace. You cannot well imagine how much I have been pleased by what you say about Pangenesis. None of my friends will speak out.

March, 1868, to Carus. Sir C. Lyell says to everyone, "You may not believe in Pangenesis, but if you once understand it you will never get it out of your mind."

There is a sense in which the world never did get Pangenesis out of its mind. How brilliant the theory was in one phase, how close it came to divining what modern cytology has painfully discovered, may be seen in three quotations from modern students of heredity— the very men who know best how wide of the facts Pangenesis was in one way.

Eduard Strasburger. Darwin showed a correct grasp of the problem in the enunciation of his Pangenesis hypothesis. . . . We can affirm that his idea that invisible gemmules are the carriers of hereditary characters and that they multiply by division has been re-

moved from the position of a provisional hypothesis to
that of a well-founded theory.

E. B. Poulton. It was in order to account for "the
inherited effects of use and disuse, etc." that Darwin
thought out his marvelous hypothesis of Pangenesis.
. . . Should it hereafter be proved that acquired characters are transmitted, I cannot but think that the interpretation will be on the lines of Charles Darwin's
hypothesis of Pangenesis.

E. B. Wilson. Darwin's ingenious attempt to picture such a process [i. e., of germ-cells as storehouses of
bodily impressions] was a legitimate speculation, worked
out with a power and insight that should stir enthusiasm
in even the most skeptical of critics. More than this, it
still remains, as I think, the only intelligible hypothesis
of the transmission of acquired characters.

When we read the judgments of such men we can feel
that Darwin's prophecy to Hooker was fulfilled: "You
will think me very self-sufficient when I declare that I
feel *sure* if Pangenesis is now stillborn it will, thank
God, at some future time reappear, begotten by some
other father, and christened by some other name."
The name "genes," which students of heredity now use,
is the second syllable of the name of Darwin's hypothesis.

5. *The Descent of Man*

In the *Origin* there is only the briefest reference to
the evolution of man. Darwin had planned to say nothing about this disagreeable subject, for he did not wish
to rouse more theological fury against himself than necessary. But, feeling that the omission would be coward-
ly or dishonest, he inserted a statement that man was
apparently in the same case as all the other animals.
After eight years of criticism had satisfied him that his
general theory was correct he planned a book to fill the
great gap in the *Origin*.

Perhaps you are now wondering when you are to

get away from the *Origin* to some other sort of book. Darwin never got away. All his writing was designed to supplement and buttress the argument of his first book on the evolution theory. *The Descent of Man* appeared in 1871, and a second edition in 1874.

In the preface to the second edition he mentions "the fiery ordeal through which the book has passed." The only reply he makes to the critics is in reference to the subject of which you are now weary—variation. It seems that the critics had been most heated about "chance" variations. Darwin replies:

Even in the first edition of *The Origin of Species* I distinctly stated that great weight must be attributed to the inherited effects of use and disuse, with respect both to the body and mind. I also attributed some amount of modification to the direct and prolonged action of changed conditions of life.

Yes, he had stated that weight *must* be attributed. That was, and had continued to be, the form of emphasis he employed. When he warms up in any chapter to a glowing account of his own observation or inference or conclusion, he is always speaking of how the variations, *whose cause is quite unknown,* are selected by the conditions of life. In these places his words are afire with interest and conviction. But whatever he says about inherited use and disuse or inherited results of conditions is cold, impersonal, perfunctory, slipped in as a concession that *must* be made.

There was a strong motive for saying every so often that "great weight must be attributed." In the very first letter that Huxley wrote to Darwin about the *Origin* he made this comment: "It is not clear to me why, if continual physical conditions are of so little moment as you suppose, variation should occur at all."

Hooker several times accused Darwin of making a hobby of natural selection: the connection between this hobby and the direct action of conditions was illuminated in the letter to Hooker that I quoted on page 337. Darwin was led to believe rather more in the direct action of conditions; he hardly knew why this made him sorry, but supposed it was because "it lessens the glory of natural selection." Every time he admitted the direct action of conditions he pleased the critics, showing them that he was less of a monomaniac about natural selection. Lyell had accused him of deifying natural selection. Philosophers like Spencer and Lewes thought that conditions and habitual use should be emphasized. The whole learned world remonstrated with him for making so much of the selection of chance variations, and granting so little to the effects of conditions and use. Darwin did not wish to oppose the universal opinion. He took pains to admit frequently that "of course my natural selection is not the only factor in evolution."

But such statements are in the nature of an admission; they give the impression that the author is a little sorry, that his heart is not in what he is saying. He never reports with enthusiasm any observation of his own which seems to show inheritance of use. If he talks of natural selection of chance variations in the rostellum of *Catasetum*, he grows lyrical with an excitement that electrifies the reader: but all he can say of direct action of conditions is that "it would only vaguely account for the details." I can not find in all his works one enthusiastic sentence about the Buffonian or the Lamarckian factor.

So my sympathy is with the critics whom Darwin addressed in his preface to the second edition of the *Descent* in 1874. The critics, to be sure, were wrong by a legalistic standard; but they had felt the underlying truth. Darwin was a little sorry whenever he "stated" one of his concessions; the living current of his argument was all about the natural selection of spontaneous variations.

How should you expect an author to proceed after reprimanding the critics for not noticing the "great weight of inherited use and disuse" that he had "stated"? If his heart is really in this cause, he ought now, in 1874, to show us some real zeal for it. And he seems to be making an effort of that sort in the first hundred pages.

35. Natural selection would probably have been greatly aided by the inherited effects of the increased or diminished use of the different parts of the body.

53. It is very difficult to decide how far these correlated modifications are the result of natural selection, and how far of the inherited effects of the increased use of certain parts.

60. As we now have evidence that mutilations occasionally produce an inherited effect, it is not very improbable that, etc.

61. I now admit . . . that in the earlier editions of my *Origin of Species* I perhaps attributed too much to the action of natural selection. . . . But I am convinced, from the light gained during even the last few years, that very many structures which now appear to us useless will hereafter be proved to be useful, and will therefore come within the range of natural selection.

Suppose that you were one of the critics, ardent for Lamarckism; should you feel that Mr. Darwin showed any change of heart? You notice that he does not pretend that his opinion has changed since the last edition of the *Origin* in 1872; he still refers to that as his standard of belief. Why must he say "*probably* have greatly aided"? If there has been "great" aid, it should be indisputable. Why is it still so "difficult to decide"?

The evidence for the inheritance of mutilations was an experiment by Brown-Sequard; why doesn't Mr. Darwin give a case of his own observation? If he is going to make an admission that amounts to anything, why qualify it with "perhaps" and "but I am convinced"?

In the next twenty-eight pages the proof of an altered view is of the same meager and unwilling sort.

68. Some actions . . . are inherited, but the greater number.

81. I have received several accounts.

89. The vocal organs would have been perfected through the principle of the inherited effects of use. But——

90. Handwriting is certainly inherited.

94. And habits are inherited.

Yet if you look up the reference for the statement about handwriting you will find that emphasis is not on the inheritance of training, but on the "curious combination of structure, character, and training."

As you approach the end of the last chapter on man you will find Mr. Darwin acting as if he had finished with his disagreeable concessions and was free to enjoy himself with the thrills of his old and profound conviction.

Of all the differences between the races of man, the color of the skin is the most conspicuous and one of the best marked. It was formerly thought that differences of this kind could be accounted for by long exposure to different climates; but Pallas first showed that this is not tenable, and he has since been followed by almost all anthropologists.

If, however, we look to the races of man as distributed over the world, we must infer that their characteristic differences can *not* be accounted for by the direct action of different conditions of life. . . . Nor can the differences between the races of man be accounted for by the inherited effects of the increased or decreased use of parts, except to a quite insignificant degree.

When you write your next criticism of Mr. Darwin you will have to say that you can not detect any real change in his feeling about the factors of Buffon and Lamarck.

Only two hundred and eight pages of the book are devoted to the evolution of man. Then follow four hundred and thirty pages on the theory of "Sexual Selection." This essay expounds an idea which is highly probable—namely: animals are likely to choose a mate that is attractive because of beauty or strength; hence there is a constant tendency to select certain characteristics and reject others; therefore the pairing of sexes is always a process of weeding out certain traits or forms and propagating others. It is hard to see how this theory could be untrue for human mating; surely the deformed or queer or colorless or weak are less likely to have their characteristics preserved in heredity. It is easy to imagine that there is a similar sort of selection among lower animals. Hence the theory sets forth a strong likelihood. But proof is difficult, perhaps impossible; and no real advance of knowledge has been made since Darwin's time.

6. *The Expression of the Emotions in Man and Animals*

Whenever* Darwin made a book he was putting together materials that he had been collecting since 1837. In 1868 he asked Huxley to contribute to the great store of examples of how people express their emotions.

I rejoice that your children are all pretty well. Give

---

*Except for *Insectivorous Plants*.

Mrs. Huxley the enclosed queries, and ask her to look out when one of her children is struggling and just going to burst out crying. A dear young lady near here plagued a very young child, for my sake, till it cried, and saw the eyebrows for a second or two beautifully oblique, just before the torrent of tears began.

Thus we see the depths to which Darwin sank in his greed for facts: though he was himself too tender-hearted to make a child suffer, he incited a dear young lady to do the brutal deed.

He gathered the observations of many persons upon the way children and savages and idiots and intellectual people and actors express emotions. He noted how animals express their emotions, and compared animals and men in this regard. In 1872 he published his thirty-year compilation as an extension of the *Descent*. This book of three hundred and seventy-two pages is devoted to one phase of one part of the great problem of how species originate. Its finding is that all human emotions are expressed by muscular actions of kinds that are essentially similar to the actions in animals, and that might have been evolved by natural selection.

I trust that as we approach the fateful year of 1876, when Darwin "positively included Buffon's factor," you are all keyed up to see the factors appearing in the books. In the *Expressions* I have checked seventeen places where the elements of heredity are mentioned: seven of these are inconclusive; four of them put strongly the inheritance of chance variations; six of them accept positively the Lamarckian factor of use or habit. Evidently the course by which the Buffon factor arrived was devious.

It is interesting to note that the final reference to inheritance (page 359) speaks of "variation and natural selection."

7. *Insectivorous Plants*

This volume, published in 1875, ought to show a strong tendency toward the Buffonian factor, for the direct action of the environment is much stronger upon plants than upon animals. But I have failed to find so much as a reference to the direct action of conditions. And of course there could not be any reference to Lamarckian use and disuse, since plants are not known to form habits of "use."

Darwin describes how he happened to write the book.

During the summer of 1860 I was surprised by finding how large a number of insects were caught by the leaves of the common sun-dew (*Drosera rotundifolia*) on a heath in Sussex. I had heard that insects were thus caught, but knew nothing further on the subject. . . . It was soon evident that *Drosera* was excellently adapted for the special purpose of catching insects, so that the subject seemed well worthy of investigation.

Darwin concluded, after years of the most painstaking and clever experiment, that all the elaborate trapping devices of sun-dew and pitcher-plants, all their complicated digestive juices, all their physiological adjustments for appropriating animal food, had come about by a series of slight and gradual changes through ages of varying adaptation. Whereas in the ordinary course of nature animals live on plants, certain plants had learned how to prey upon animals.

So Darwin's original motive and final result were precisely the same as they had been for every previous book. He had found another revelation of the power of organisms to become adapted by modifications of their structures. Chance variations, if they are beneficial, will tend to be inherited, will be accumulated, and will finally produce new adaptations—that is, new varieties or spe-

cies. A species originates by the gradual modification
due to natural selection.

In the preparation of *Insectivorous Plants* Darwin
was so absorbed with selection of chance variations that
he forgot to make concessions to the critics.

8. *Three More Botanical Books: 1876-1880*

Until 1881 Darwin did not publish anything about
animals. He found so much excitement in plants, so
much extraordinary evidence for the natural selection
of chance variations, that he limited himself to this
pleasurable line of work. So there is no possibility of
knowing what the Lamarckian factor of use and disuse
was doing in his mind. If it was present, he kept it there.
He printed nothing about it.

And as for the Buffon factor of direct action of conditions, there is hardly a trace in the next three botanical
books. In what did Darwin "fully include" Wagner's
theory of isolation after 1875? Did he include it in
his brain? in his correspondence with Germans? in
some secret papers to be released after his death? in a
cipher message that could be decoded?

An absurd question comes suddenly to my mind. Osborn uses the following ambiguous phrases on page 242:

the sixth edition of *The Origin of Species* (1880)

The Descent of Man (1881)

Can it be that some of the rigorous scientific quoters of
this passage thought that the dates showed when the
books were last revised? If they did, they would suppose that the Wagner theory was included in those two
most significant of Darwin's works. This is incredible.
Yet such an error would at least be possible for a sane
mind. To conceive that Darwin "fully included a theory

in nothing at all" is not an action possible for a sane mind.

There is another possible way—though even more absurd—in which Osborn may have been misunderstood. Perhaps he used "Lamarckian principle" to refer only to use and disuse, and perhaps the writers who cite him have wrongly extended his phrase to cover acquired characters. But after 1876 Darwin made hardly any mention of use and disuse; for his books were all about plants until 1881, and Lamarck does not apply use and disuse to plants. Nor did Darwin discuss use and disuse in his last book, on earthworms. So, if Osborn meant by "Lamarckian factor" use and disuse, he was talking about something which Darwin does not discuss.

Anyhow, no such refinement could make any difference in Osborn's argument. For there is only one issue, large and plain: Did Darwin alter his theory in *any* marked way after 1860? That is Osborn's charge, trusted by many biologists. It has no foundation.

Note that I am not relying simply on my interpretation of the books made after 1868, but on Darwin's honesty and directness of purpose. If he had positively or fully included in any concrete book any substantial change of view that made any difference in his reasoning, I should suppose he would at least call attention to the new arrival that had taken up its abode amidst his conceptions of evolution. He nowhere points out any such novelty. When I read the books five years ago I had no suspicion of anything new in his theory after 1859. When I now turn the pages again, I can not detect a change.

The best retort to the charge that Darwin altered his theory is a sentence that Weismann wrote in 1909: "Darwin was not fully convinced of the inheritance of acquired characters." *(Darwin and Modern Science,*

Cambridge University Press, page 22.) You will search Weismann's essays in vain for any statement that Darwin altered his theory after 1859. By what magical insight could a modern critic find it?

Osborn's strange interpretation of a few sentences in letters has been a boomerang. It just suited the purpose of such anti-evolution writers as Louis T. More and Father O'Toole. They have used it as an aid in proving that Darwin's reputation is damaged and that his theory is dead. They have hurled it back at its author, and it has been their best weapon.

Cross and Self-Fertilization (1876) gives a view of a great vista in the development of life. It shows, as proved by elaborate experiments, that most flowers produce stronger offspring if they are fertilized from another plant (i. e., crossed) than if they are self-fertilized. Hence, Darwin surmised, all colored or scented flowers have been evolved by gradually adapting themselves to allure and reward insects for carrying pollen. The book is, therefore, an extension of the idea in *Orchids*.

Darwin saw down the corridors of the geologic ages a vista of plant-development. There must have been a time when winged insects did not exist, and at that time cross-fertilization could be effected only by transport through water or air. If any ancient plant, after insects were evolved, happened to vary in such a way that one of its excretions happened to be inviting to an insect that happened to find this new food, and if some pollen from this variant plant stuck to the insect, was carried by it to another plant of the same species, and there fertilized an ovum—then the offspring of this seed would be likely to prosper, to be inviting to insects, to get itself cross-fertilized more often, and so have an advantage in the struggle for existence. Every variation toward producing more of the nectar, or toward making itself more alluring in color or odor, would be an advantage to the plant and would be added to the accumulating heritage. A series of new apparatus would evolve. And those insects which happened to have variations of proboscis or feet that made nectar-gathering easier would be aided in the struggle for existence. Their descendants would increase the beneficial variations and finally evolve new adaptations.

Sounds very fanciful, doesn't it? If any one had never heard of evolution and if he encountered such a paragraph as you have just read, he ought to regard it with complete skepticism. It would pass all the belief of a careful thinker. The achievement of Darwin's life was to make such an incredible idea seem possible, then probable, and finally inescapable. Any botanist or geologist who was skeptical about this conception would nowadays be a curiosity in a convention of scientists.

Botanists do not believe in evolution because of any Lamarckian or Buffonian factors. They believe because Darwin consistently followed out his profound conviction that the part played by environment is only to select variations. It may be—Darwin frequently states it with conviction—that a new environment stimulates reproductive organs to produce variations; but it is those organs which produce; the environment can not engender them. The environment can only select.

The Different Forms of Flowers on Plants of the Same Species appeared in 1877, dedicated to Asa Gray, "as a small tribute of respect and affection." The introduction says that the subject ought to have been treated by a professed botanist, and the general reader who attempts the book may feel that it is comprehensible only by a botanist. It is technical and treats a most complicated subject.

There are several passages that admit the possible

effect of environment in initiating changes; a college debater could cull several quotations that sound Buffonian. But if we are merely curious to see what Darwin's reasoning is, we shall find the old familiar steps: variations occur; they are preserved if they are beneficial.

It is probable that the first step towards a species becoming heterostyled is great variability in the length of the pistil and stamen. . . . It might well happen that our supposed species did not vary in function in the right manner. . . . If it had thus varied, it would never have been rendered heterostyled. . . . This change would be so highly beneficial to the species that there is no difficulty in believing that it could be effected through natural selection.

The Power of Movement in Plants (1880) describes the "circumnutation," the nodding round and round, of the tips of young stems, of tendrils, and of rootlets. How should you have enjoyed charting the aimless spirals and zigzags made in the course of a day by the first leaves that sprout from an orange seed? If you had been a Darwin, you would have found the pulpy, new-born things as interesting as babies, and almost as active. Not that their swinging and groping through the air is entertaining in itself, but that you are seeing one of the essential forces in the evolution of plants. You get a view of the sensitiveness in the tips of a plant, a variable, vital, all but intelligent force, which may be modified into all sorts of adaptations of stems and roots and leaves and tendrils. I quote from the last two pages of the book.

Finally, it is impossible not to be struck with the resemblance between the foregoing movements of plants and many of the actions performed unconsciously by the lower animals. . . . The habit* of moving at certain

---

*Darwin does not mean a "habit" formed by an individual during

periods is inherited both by plants and animals. . . . We believe that there is no structure in plants more wonderful, as far as its functions are concerned, than the tip of a radicle. If the tip be lightly pressed or burnt or cut, it transmits an influence to the upper adjoining part, causing it to bend away from the affected side; and, what is more surprising, the tip can distinguish between a slightly harder and softer object, by which it is simultaneously pressed on opposite sides. . . . In almost every case we can clearly perceive the final purpose or advantage of the several movements. Two, or perhaps more, of the exciting causes often act simultaneously on the tip, and one conquers the other, no doubt in accordance with its importance for the life of the plant. . . . It is hardly an exaggeration to say that the tip of the radicle thus endowed, and having the power of directing the movements of the adjoining parts, acts like the brain of one of the lower animals.

Thus at the end of Darwin's last book on evolution he has reached the mark he first proposed to himself when planning the campaign: "Show that plants are like animals."

The idea of a rootlet having a brain amused Hooker, of course, but it also astounded him. It opened before him a new prospect of the unity of all life. Hooker and Gray, the world's foremost botanists, were the ones who were quickest to perceive the novelty and immeasurable significance of Darwin's investigation of the movements and flower-forms and fertilization of plants. Darwin revealed to botanists a new conception of their profession, the evolutionary conception, which has become the foundation and framework of their science. The basic truths now taught to every college class were established by Darwin.

Contrast with such exploring of concrete wonders

---

its life; for he does not record any such astounding discovery as this would have been. He means "usual behavior of the species."

the process of "fully including" a Wagnerian factor in a mental abstraction. Darwin's mind was not a lumber-room where such tattered scenery of hypotheses was set up and taken down. It was a shop where facts were investigated. Its apparatus was just the same in 1860 as in 1881. The more you reflect on "It is well known that Darwin changed," the more astonishing the phrase will appear to you. Huxley and Hooker and Lyell had urged in very different ways that Darwin should change; yet not one of them detected any change. How marvelous that these men and Weismann overlooked an alteration in Darwin's thinking which is "well known" to a long line of those who copy myths out of books. The alteration can not be known by any rational person who takes time to review the evidence. It can not even be imagined by any one who notices the contents of Darwin's books.

9. The Formation of Vegetable Mould

It was not possible for Darwin's mind to busy itself with assorting cobwebs of evolutionary "factors" spun by metaphysical brains. He would not have known how to "recede from" such a factor or to "include another fully" in some catacomb of pure reason. His instinct was for acrobatic beetles and the coral in the high Andes. His life was one continuous effort to see what was going on in nature.

I have a passion to grow the seeds. . . . For love of heaven favor my madness and have some seeds scraped off and sent me. . . . I am like a gambler and love a wild experiment.

You will find a few sentences with a sort of definition of intelligence of worms. . . . I tried to observe what passed in my own mind when I did the work of a worm. If I come across a professed metaphysician, I will ask him to give me a more technical definition.

Darwin had been interested in earthworms all his mature life. Six months before he died he published a book which shows how worms are the gardeners for all the living beauty of landscapes, and how they have helped to form mountains. Did you ever think about the intellect or the gizzards or the vast importance of worms?

All the species which swallow earth are furnished with gizzards; and these are lined with so thick a chitinous membrane that Perrier speaks of it as "une véritable armature." . . .

In many parts of England a weight of more than ten tons of dry earth annually passes through their bodies and is brought to the surface on each acre of land; so that the whole superficial bed of vegetable mould passes through their bodies in the course of every few years. . . .

When we behold a wide, turf-covered expanse, we should remember that its smoothness, on which so much of its beauty depends, is mainly due to all the inequalities having been slowly leveled by worms. It is a marvelous reflection that the whole of the superficial mould over any such expanse has passed, and will again pass every few years, through the bodies of worms. The plough is one of the most ancient and most valuable of man's inventions; but long before he existed the land was in fact regularly ploughed, and still continues to be thus ploughed, by earthworms. It may be doubted whether there are many other animals which have played so important a part in the history of the world as have these lowly-organized creatures.

No reader of Darwin's works can mention his last book without a smile at the oddity of the subject, an affection for the enthusiasm that could make it entertaining, and a reverence for the man who could reveal such an extraordinary truth by observing the humblest creature. The wide expanse of beauty, the marvelous reflection, the lowly creatures—these are a fit epilogue to the life work of Darwin. He taught the world how lowly facts can irradiate the marvelous expanse of the beauty of life.

It will be expected that a biographer should give some concluding summary of what Darwin's books have meant for the human race. I could choose quotations that sound the pæans of the greatness of his achievements— and I should enjoy putting them here. They are true. "Modern science dates from the publication of the *Origin*," for example, or "No work has had so profound an effect on human thought."

If I were called upon to express what his life has meant, I should answer, "He destroyed the raging faith of the human brain that it can attain truth by logic." It is this faith which inspires us to interpret nature as if it were answerable to human reason, as if it must be clothed in "design" or "purpose" or "rectigradation." Darwin is slowly teaching the world that nature is utterly beyond our thinking and that we are absurd if we drape it in our mental tatters. We are rational only when we try to observe nature in Darwin's way.

But I feel as if the stern old humorist were standing by my desk and were not quite happy about my simile. A better summary of his work is given in a sentence that he wrote in 1842, in the scribbled first sketch of his theory. It suggests how Newton rescued the human mind from its welter of superstition about personality in inorganic nature. Newton showed that all matter is subject to regular laws. But organic nature still remained beyond law, a field for a riot of superstition. Darwin, in his study, concluding his first sketch of an evolution theory, set down his hope of the good it might accomplish—that it might make the facts of living matter intelligible.   And he made a parable for his hope:

We no longer look on an animal as a savage does at a ship.

We no longer look on an animal as a savage does at

CHAPTER XIV

DARWIN'S LIFE AFTER 1850

1. *The Home Life at Downe*

SIR FRANCIS DARWIN prepared the *Life and Letters*
of his father in 1887. He gained the affection of all
readers by making a chapter called "Reminiscences of
My Father's Everyday Life," in which he described the
daily routine of work and walks and jokes and affection
and backgammon and snuff and pets. Fortunate is the
biographer whose subject is so downright and lovable
that it takes on an added beauty when its homely details
are made public.

It seems wrong to cut out a few bits from such a
felicitous picture and paste them into my chapter. If
you have not the will to read Sir Francis's pages, you
have no right to see parts of it. But if you have not
time or opportunity to read his Chapter III, you can
gain some idea of it from the following excerpts. Rather
than print so much single-spaced matter, I will pirate the
quotations without that courtesy. All that follows in this
section is directly quoted.

He walked with a swinging action, using a stick
heavily shod with iron, which he struck loudly against
the ground, producing as he went round the "Sand-
walk" at Downe, a rhythmical click. . . . When interested in his work he moved about quickly and easily
enough, and often in the middle of dictating he went

eagerly into the hall to get a pinch of snuff, leaving the study door open, and calling out the last words of his sentence as he went. Indoors he sometimes used an oak stick like a little alpenstock, and this was a sign that he felt giddiness.

He could dissect well under the simple microscope, but I think it was by dint of his great patience and carefulness. It was characteristic of him that he thought many little bits of skilful dissection something almost superhuman.

He was so unhappy at having uselessly killed a crossbeak that he did not mention it for years, and then explained that he should never have thrown at it if he had not felt sure that his old skill had gone from him.

He had his chair in the study and in the drawing-room raised so as to be much higher than ordinary chairs; this was done because sitting on a low or even an ordinary chair caused him some discomfort. We used to laugh at him for making his tall drawing-room chair still higher by putting footstools on it, and then neutralizing the result by resting his feet on another chair.

His face was ruddy in color, and this perhaps made people think him less of an invalid than he was. . . . His eyes were bluish gray under deep overhanging brows, with thick, bushy, projecting eyebrows. His high forehead was much wrinkled, but otherwise his face was not much marked or lined. His expression showed no signs of the continual discomfort he suffered.

When he was excited with pleasant talk his whole manner was wonderfully bright and animated, and his face shared to the full in the general animation. His laugh was a free and sounding peal, like that of a man who gives himself sympathetically and with enjoyment to the person and the thing which have amused him. He often used some sort of gesture with his laugh, lifting up his hands or bringing one down with a slap.

He wore dark clothes, of a loose and easy fit. Of late years he gave up the tall hat even in London, and wore a soft black one in winter, and a big straw hat in summer. . . . Two peculiarities of his indoor dress were that he almost always wore a shawl over his shoulders, and that he had great loose cloth boots lined with fur which he could slip on over his indoor shoes. . . . Often a mental cause would make him too hot, so that he would take off his coat if anything went wrong in the course of his work.

He rose early, chiefly because he could not lie in bed, and I think he would have liked to get up earlier than he did.

After breakfasting alone about 7:45 he went to work at once, considering the 1½ hour between 8 and 9:30 one of his best working times. At 9:30 he came into the drawing-room for his letters—rejoicing if the post was a light one and being sometimes much worried if it was not. He would then hear any family letters read aloud as he lay on the sofa.

The reading aloud, which also included part of a novel, lasted till about half-past ten, when he went back to work till twelve or a quarter past. By this time he considered his day's work over, and would often say, in a satisfied voice, *"I've* done a good day's work." He then went out of doors whether it was wet or fine. Polly, his white terrier, went with him in fair weather.

She was a sharp-witted, affectionate dog; when her master was going away on a journey, she always discovered the fact by the signs of packing going on in the study, and became low-spirited accordingly. She began, too, to be excited by seeing the study prepared for his return home. She was a cunning little creature, and

used to tremble or put on an air of misery when my
father passed, while she was waiting for dinner, just
as if she knew that he would say (as he did often say)
that "she was famishing." My father used to make her
catch biscuits off her nose, and had an affectionate and
mock-solemn way of explaining to her beforehand that
she must "be a very good girl." She had a mark on
her back where she had been burnt, and where the hair
had re-grown red instead of white, my father used to
commend her for this tuft of hair as being in accordance
with his theory of pangenesis; her father had been a
red bull-terrier, thus the red hair appearing after the
burn showed the presence of latent red gemmules. He
was delightfully tender to Polly, and never showed any
impatience at the attentions she required.

My father's midday walk generally began by a call
at the greenhouse, where he looked at any germinating
seeds or experimental plants which required a casual
examination, but he hardly ever did any serious observing at this time. Then he went on for his constitutional
—either round the "Sand-walk" or outside his own
grounds in the immediate neighborhood of the house.

In earlier times he took a certain number of turns
every day, and used to count them by means of a heap
of flints, one of which he kicked out on the path each time
he passed.

Sometimes when alone he stood still or walked
stealthily to observe birds or beasts. It was on one of
these occasions that some young squirrels ran up his
back and legs, while their mother barked at them in an
agony from the tree. He always found birds' nests even
up to the last years of his life, and we, as children, considered that he had a special genius in this direction. In
his quiet prowls he came across the less common birds,
but I fancy he used to conceal it from me, as a little boy,

because he observed the agony of mind which I endured at not having seen the siskin or goldfinch, or whatever it might have been.

He was fond of quoting the saying of one of his little boys, who, having found a grass that his father had not seen before, had laid it by his own plate during dinner, remarking, "I are an extraordinary grass-finder!"

I used to like to hear him admire the beauty of a flower; it was a kind of gratitude to the flower itself, and a personal love for its delicate form and color. I seem to remember him gently touching a flower he delighted in; it was the simple admiration that a child might have.

He could not help personifying natural things. This feeling came out in abuse as well as in praise—e. g., of some seedlings: "The little beggars are doing just what I don't want them to." He would speak in a half-provoked, half-admiring way of the ingenuity of a Mimosa leaf in screwing itself out of a basin of water in which he had tried to fix it.

He used to tell how in South America he killed twenty-three snipe in twenty-four shots. In telling the story he was careful to add that he thought they were not quite so wild as English snipe.

Luncheon at Downe came after his midday walk; and here I may say a word or two about his meals generally. He had a boy-like love of sweets, unluckily for himself, since he was constantly forbidden to take them. He was not particularly successful in keeping the "vows," as he called them, which he made against eating sweets, and never considered them binding unless he made them aloud.

He drank very little wine, but enjoyed, and was revived by, the little he did drink. He had a horror of drinking, and constantly warned his boys that anyone might be led into drinking too much. I remember, in my innocence as a small boy, asking him if he had been ever tipsy; and he answered very gravely that he was ashamed to say he had once drunk too much at Cambridge. I was much impressed, so that I know now the place where the question was asked.

After his lunch he read the newspaper, lying on the sofa in the drawing-room. I think the paper was the only non-scientific matter which he read to himself. Everything else—novels, travels, history—was read aloud to him.

After he had read his paper came his time for writing letters. These as well as the MS of his books, were written by him as he sat in the huge horse-hair chair by the fire, his paper supported on a board resting on the arms of the chair.

He received many letters from foolish, unscrupulous people, and all of these received replies. He used to say that if he did not answer them he had it on his conscience afterwards.

Mr. Hacon, his solicitor, spoke especially of his letters as being such as a man seldom receives in the way of business—"Everything I did was right, and everything was profusely thanked for."

He habitually formed so humble an estimate of the value of all his works that he was generally surprised at the interest which they excited.

My father was wonderfully liberal and generous to all his children in the matter of money, and I have special cause to remember his kindness when I think of the way in which he paid some Cambridge debts of mine—making it almost seem a virtue in me to have told him of them. In his later years he had the kind and generous plan of dividing his surplus at the year's end among his children.

His anxiety to save came in a great measure from

his fears that his children would not have health enough to earn their own livings, a foreboding which fairly haunted him for many years. And I have a dim recollection of his saying, "Thank God, you'll have bread and cheese," when I was so young that I was rather inclined to take it literally.

When letters were finished, about three in the afternoon, he rested in his bedroom, lying on the sofa and smoking a cigarette, and listening to a novel or other book not scientific. He only smoked when resting, whereas snuff was a stimulant, and was taken during working hours. He took snuff for many years of his life, having learnt the habit at Edinburgh as a student. He had a nice silver snuff-box given him by Mrs. Wedgwood of Maer, which he valued much—but he rarely carried it, because it tempted him to take too many pinches.

Smoking he only took to permanently of late years.

The reading aloud often sent him to sleep, and he used to regret losing parts of a novel, for my mother went steadily on lest the cessation of the sound might wake him.

From about half-past four to half-past five he worked; then he came to the drawing-room, and was idle till it was time (about six) to go up for another rest with novel-reading and a cigarette.

Latterly he gave up late dinner, and had a simple tea at half-past seven (while we had dinner), with an egg or a small piece of meat. After dinner he never stayed in the room, and used to apologize by saying he was an old woman, who must be allowed to leave with the ladies. This was one of the many signs and results of his constant weakness and ill-health. Half an hour more or less conversation would make to him the difference of a sleepless night, and of the loss perhaps of half the next day's work.

After dinner he played backgammon with my mother, two games being played every night; for many years a score was kept, and in this score he took the greatest interest. He became extremely animated over these games, bitterly lamenting his bad luck and exploding with exaggerated mock-anger at my mother's good fortune.

After backgammon he read some scientific book to himself.

In the evening he would often lie on the sofa and listen to my mother playing the piano. He had not a good ear, yet in spite of this he had a true love of fine music. He used to lament that his enjoyment of music had become dulled with age, yet within my recollection his love of a good tune was strong. . . . He was sensitive to differences in style, and enjoyed the late Mrs. Vernon Lushington's playing intensely; and in June, 1881, when Hans Richter paid a visit at Downe, he was roused to strong enthusiasm by his magnificent performances on the piano.*

His nights were generally bad, and he often lay awake or sat up in bed for hours, suffering much discomfort. He was troubled at night by the activity of his thoughts, and would become exhausted by his mind working at some problem which he would willingly have dismissed. At night, too, anything which had vexed or troubled him in the day would haunt him, and I think it was then that he suffered if he had not answered some troublesome person's letter.

He was extremely fond of novels, and I remember well the way in which he would anticipate the pleasure of having a novel read to him, as he lay down, or lighted

---

*This is an interesting comment on the standard notion that science killed Darwin's sensibility to beauty. The notion arose from Darwin's statement in the *Autobiography*: "Now for many years I can not endure to read a line of poetry. . . . I have almost lost my taste for pictures or music." See the Note at the end of this section, page 382.

his cigarette. He took a vivid interest both in plot and characters, and would on no account know beforehand how a story finished: he considered looking at the end of a novel as a feminine vice.

I do not think that his literary tastes and opinions were on a level with the rest of his mind. He himself considered that in matters of literary taste he was quite outside the pale, and often spoke of what those within it liked or disliked as if they formed a class to which he had no claim to belong.

This way of looking at himself as an ignoramus in all matters of art was strengthened by the absence of pretense, which was part of his character.

When he was looking at the Turners in Mr. Ruskin's bedroom he did not confess, as he did afterwards, that he could make out absolutely nothing of what Mr. Ruskin saw in them. But this little pretense was not for his own sake, but for the sake of courtesy to his host.

He used to call German the "Verdammte," pronounced as if in English. He was especially indignant with Germans, because he was convinced that they could write simply if they chose.

I have often heard him say that he got a kind of satisfaction in reading articles which (according to himself) he could not understand. I wish I could reproduce the manner in which he would laugh at himself for it.

It was a sure sign that he was not well when he was idle at any times other than his regular resting hours; for, as long as he remained moderately well, there was no break in the regularity of his life. Week-days and Sundays passed by alike, each with their stated intervals of work and rest. It is almost impossible, except for those who watched his daily life, to realize how essential to his well-being was the regular routine that I have sketched: and with what pain and difficulty anything beyond it was attempted. Any public appearance, even of the most modest kind, was an effort to him. In 1871 he went to the little village church for the wedding of his eldest daughter, but he could hardly bear the fatigue of being present through the short service.

He was generally persuaded by my mother to take these short holidays when it became clear from the frequency of "bad days," or from the swimming of his head, that he was being overworked. He went unwillingly, and tried to drive hard bargains, stipulating, for instance, that he should come home in five days instead of six.

Even a fairly long journey, such as that to Coniston, tired him wonderfully little, considering how much an invalid he was; and he certainly enjoyed it in an almost boyish way, and to a curious extent.

It was characteristic of him that, although he was so anxious to observe accurately the expression of a crying child, his sympathy with the grief spoiled his observation.

We, his children, all took especial pleasure in the games he played at with us, but I do not think he romped much with us; I suppose his health prevented any rough play. He used sometimes to tell us stories which were considered especially delightful, partly on account of their rarity.

I do not believe he ever spoke an angry word to any of his children in his life; but I am certain that it never entered our heads to disobey him. I well remember one occasion when my father reproved me for a piece of carelessness; and I can still recall the feeling of depression which came over me, and the care which he took to disperse it by speaking to me soon afterwards with especial kindness. He kept up his delightful, affectionate manner towards us all his life.

It is a proof of the terms on which we were, and also of how much he was valued as a playfellow, that one of his sons when about four years old tried to bribe him with sixpence to come and play in working hours. We all knew the sacredness of working-time, but that any-one should resist sixpence seemed an impossibility.

We used to dread going in for sticking-plaster, because he disliked to see that we had cut ourselves, both for our sakes and on account of his acute sensitiveness to the sight of blood.

On his return from a fortnight's water cure I could hardly bear to have him in the room, the expression of tender sympathy and emotion in his face was too agitating, coming fresh upon me after his little absence.

He cared for all our pursuits and interests, and lived our lives with us in a way that very few fathers do. But I am certain that none of us felt that this intimacy interfered the least with our respect or obedience. Whatever he said was absolute truth and law to us.

He always spoke to servants with politeness, using the expression "would you be so good," in asking for anything. He was hardly ever angry with his servants; it shows how seldom this occurred that when, as a small boy, I overheard a servant being scolded, and my father speaking angrily, it impressed me as an appalling circumstance, and I remember running up stairs out of a general sense of awe. . . . He used to ask doubtfully whether he might have a horse and cart to send to Keston for Drosera.

It was pleasant to see the way in which he shook hands with a guest who was being welcomed for the first time; his hand used to shoot out in a way that gave one the feeling that it was hastening to meet the guest's hand. With old friends his hand came down with a hearty swing into the other hand in a way I always had a satisfaction in seeing. His goodbye was chiefly characterized by the pleasant way in which he thanked his guests, as he stood at the door, for having come to see him.

It was this absence of pose, and the natural and simple way in which he began talking to his guests, so as to get them on their own lines, which made him so charmingly a host to a stranger. His happy choice of matter for talk seemed to flow out of his sympathetic nature, and humble, vivid interest in other people's work. To some, I think, he caused actual pain by his modesty.

He used to say of himself that he was not quick enough to hold an argument with anyone, and I think this was true.

When he gave his evidence before the Royal Commission on vivisection he came out with his words about cruelty, "It deserves detestation and abhorrence." When he felt strongly about any similar question, he could hardly trust himself to speak, as he then easily became angry, a thing which he disliked excessively.

He was particularly charming when "chaffing" anyone, and in high spirits over it. His manner at such times was light-hearted and boyish, and his refinement of nature came out most strongly.

My father enjoyed Mr. Huxley's humor exceedingly, and would often say, "What splendid fun Huxley is!"

His relationship to the village people was a pleasant one; he treated them, one and all, with courtesy, when he came in contact with them, and took an interest in all relating to their welfare. Some time after he came to live at Downe he helped to found a Friendly Club, and served as treasurer for thirty years. He took much trouble about the club, keeping its accounts with minute and scrupulous exactness, and taking pleasure in its prosperous condition. Every Whit-Monday the club used to march round with band and banner, and paraded on the lawn in front of the house. There he met them, and explained to them their financial position in a little speech seasoned with a few well-worn jokes.

Mr. Brodie Innes, vicar of Downe, has been so good as to give me his recollections: "In all parish matters he was an active assistant; in matters connected with the schools, charities, and other business, his liberal contribution was ever ready, and in the differences which at times occurred in that, as in other parishes, I was always sure of his support."

I must say something of his manner of working: one characteristic of it was his respect for time; he never forgot how precious it was. He never wasted a few spare minutes from thinking that it was not worth while to set to work. . . . The same eager desire not to lose time was seen in his quick movements when at work. . . . All these processes were performed with a kind of restrained eagerness.

If anyone had looked at his tools, etc., lying on the table, he would have been struck by an air of simpleness, make-shift, and oddness. . . . For instance, instead of having a box made of a desired shape, and stained black inside, he would hunt up something like what he wanted and get it darkened inside with shoe-blacking; he did not care to have glass covers made for the tumblers in which he germinated seeds, but used broken bits of irregular shape.

I think he personified each seed as a small demon trying to elude him by getting into the wrong heap, or jumping away altogether; and this gave to the work the excitement of a game.

Perseverance seems hardly to express his almost fierce desire to force the truth to reveal itself.

My sister, Mrs. Litchfield, writes about helping to correct proofs: "He was always ready to be convinced that any suggested alteration was an improvement, and full of gratitude for the trouble taken. I do not think that he ever used to forget to tell me what improvement he thought I had made, and he used almost to excuse himself if he did not agree with any corrections."

He often laughed or grumbled at himself for the difficulty which he found in writing English, saying, for instance, that if a bad arrangement of a sentence was possible, he should be sure to adopt it. He once got much amusement and satisfaction out of the difficulty which one of the family found in writing a short circular. He had the pleasure of correcting and laughing at obscurities, involved sentences, and other defects, and thus took his revenge for all the criticism he had himself to bear with.

In the *Origin*, p. 440, there is a description of a larval cirripede, "with six pairs of beautifully constructed natatory legs, a pair of magnificent compound eyes, and extremely complex antennæ." We used to laugh at him for this sentence, which we compared to an advertisement.

The tone of such a book as the *Origin* is charming, and almost pathetic; it is the tone of a man who, convinced of the truth of his own views, hardly expects to convince others; it is just the reverse of the style of a fanatic, who wants to force people to believe. The reader is never scorned for any amount of doubt which he may be imagined to feel, and his skepticism is treated with patient respect. A skeptical reader, or perhaps even an unreasonable reader, seems to have been generally present to his thoughts.

In cases where, as in the case of ——'s experiments on Drosera, he thought lightly of the author, he speaks of him in such a way that no one would suspect it. In other cases he treats the confused writings of ignorant persons as though the fault lay with himself for not appreciating or understanding them.

In spite of having so strong a respectful feeling towards what he read, he had the keenest of instincts as to whether a man was trustworthy or not. He seemed to form a very definite opinion as to the accuracy of the men whose books he read.

He bore his illness with such uncomplaining patience that even his children can hardly realize the extent of his habitual suffering. In their case the difficulty is heightened by the fact that, from the days of their earliest recollections, they saw him in constant ill-health—and saw him, in spite of it, full of pleasure in what pleased them. Thus, in later life, their perception of what he endured had to be disentangled from the impression produced in childhood by constant genial kindness under conditions of unrecognized difficulty. No one, indeed, except my mother knows the full amount of suffering he endured, or the full amount of his wonderful patience. For all the latter years of his life she never left him for a night; and her days were so planned that all his resting hours might be shared with her. . . . It is a principal feature of his life that for nearly forty years he never knew one day of the health of ordinary men, and thus his life was one long struggle against the weariness and strain of sickness.

A Note on Science as a Destroyer of Esthetic Powers

I wish I knew how many doleful sermons against science have been preached from the text of Darwin's supposed loss of esthetic powers. I wish I knew how much truth would remain in them if three assumptions were removed:

1. The assumption that the study of science was the cause of the loss.
2. The assumption that Darwin did not exaggerate his loss and that his accusation of himself is to be taken at face value.
3. The assumption that Darwin's case is typical.

As to the second assumption, no argument could avail with a person who still makes it after reading this book.

As to the first assumption, Darwin did not accuse science of causing his loss. He accused the quality of his own mind: "A man with a mind more highly organized or better constituted than mine would not, I suppose, have thus suffered."

Grant, for the sake of argument, that Darwin's estimate of his own mind was wrong; the third assumption remains unaccounted for. What other cases are known of scientists losing esthetic powers *because of* the deadening effect of science? Huxley and Hooker were quite as thoroughly devoted to science as Darwin was, yet there is no record of their higher sensibilities being damaged by science. How many cases similar to Darwin's could be found in history? I have never heard of even one. Unless there are many, a sermon about the deadening effect of science is untruthful.

2. Darwin as a Mere Human Being after 1851

This section is a mosaic of odds and ends taken from Volume II of *Emma Darwin: a Century of Family Letters,* compiled and annotated by Darwin's daughter Henrietta (Mrs. R. B. Litchfield). Many of the letters from which I quote were written by Mrs. Darwin. It should be understood that these were intimate and hasty notes, full of abbreviations and queer collocations of ideas—just the sort of thing that we all send to close relatives and friends. There is a sort of violence in printing such extracts, for which I may well be blamed. My excuse is that the Darwin family were more entertaining that I could be.

The references to the children can be understood from the following list of the birth-dates and names of the seven who grew to maturity. All seven survived their father.

> William Erasmus, 1839
> Henrietta Emma, 1843
> George Howard, 1845
> Elizabeth, 1847
> Francis, 1848
> Leonard, 1850
> Horace, 1851

Feb. 24, 1852. Charles Darwin to his son William at Rugby.

My dear old Willy,

Your letter was a very good one, and told us all that we liked to hear: it was well expressed and you must have taken some pains to write it. . . . I go my morning walk and often think of you, and Georgy draws every day many Horse-guards, and Lenny is as fat as ever.

Henrietta Darwin's note in the summer of 1853. We were now six children at home. The picture comes back to me of the furniture pushed on one side, and a troop of little children galloping round the room, whilst my mother played what was called the "galloping tune," composed by herself, and very well suited for its purpose. . . . She was courageous, even rash, in what she let her children do. My brother William was taught to ride without stirrups and got some bad falls in consequence.

1856, Charles Darwin to his son at Rugby.
My dear old Willy,

I am very glad indeed to hear that you are in the sixth; and I do not care how difficult you find the work: am I not a kind father? I am even almost as glad to hear of the Debating Society, for it will stir you up to read. Do send me as soon as you can the subjects; I will do my very best to give you hints; and Mamma will try also. . . . Mamma desires that you will read the chapters in Chapel very well; and the dear old Mammy must be obeyed.

1857, Charles Darwin to his son at Rugby.
My dear old Willy or William,

You want a jobation about your handwriting— dreadfully bad and not a stop from beginning to end! After severe labor in deciphering we *rather think* that your outlay was £1. 12. 0. and accordingly I send that, but I hope it is too little to punish you for such a scrawl. I am glad that you were tipped, but that makes no difference in my repaying your outlay. By the way have you no paper, so that you cross your letter, or do you think your handwriting is too clear? You want pitching into severely.

1857, note by Henrietta Darwin. This year I broke down in health. The entries in my mother's diary show what years of anxiety she suffered, first with one child and then another. Sometimes it is my health which is thus chronicled day by day, sometimes one of the boys. Both parents were unwearied in their efforts to soothe and amuse whichever of us was ill; my father played backgammon with me regularly every day, and my mother would read aloud to me. . . .

But in spite of all the troubles connected with our ill-health those first fifteen years at Downe must have been full of happiness. I see a constant come and go of the relations chronicled in her diary, and a certain amount of sociability with our neighbors—also visits from my father's scientific friends.

I am sorry to say that as growing-up children we were sometimes impatient of her kindness to the unprosperous. I remember how constant she was in giving invitations to a certain family, who were generally tabooed on account of a disagreeable father.

Every now and then there is an entry in her little diary of a concert or a play, but I should think not more than a dozen times in all the years whilst we were children.

One day a new boy misunderstood the orders, and as my father and mother reached the Sand-walk they found a great heap of wild ivy torn up by its roots and the abhorred dog's mercury flourishing alone. My father could not help laughing at her dismay and the whole misadventure, but the tragedy went too deep, and he used to say that it was the only time she was ever cross with him.

May, 1858, Charles Darwin to his son William at Rugby. I have just received your nice note and the hexagon, for which very many thanks, but I hope and think I shall not have to use it as I had intended, which was delicately to hint to one of the greatest mathematicians that he had made a blunder in his geometry, and sure enough there came a letter yesterday wholly altering what he had previously told me.

1858, Charles Darwin to his son William at Cambridge. Go and have at once a good and deliberate look at my old rooms and if you then prefer them make the change, though it is a confounded bore that money should have been wasted over papering, etc. . . . I know well, far too well, what temptations there are at Cambridge to idleness; so I am sure these ought to be avoided. . . . So much for preachment, but it is a good and old established custom that he who pays may preach; and as I shall have to pay if you move (as I rather advise), so I have had my preach. . . .

The backs of the Colleges (N. B. not Colle*d*ges as some people spell it) are indeed beautiful.

1859, Charles Darwin to his wife. A scheme just came into my head, viz. that when I am back that you should come here for a fortnight's hydropathy. Do you not think it might do you real good? I could get on perfectly with the children. You might bring Etty with you. Think of this my own dearest wife. I wish you knew how I value you; and what an inexpressible blessing it is to have one whom one can always trust, one always the same, always ready to give comfort, sympathy and the best advice. God bless you, my dear, you are too good for me.

1859, note by Henrietta Darwin. My mother helped my father with correcting the proof-sheets of the *Origin*. . . . There was much excitement over the letters which he received on its publication, but I remember my mother would not show me Professor Sedgwick's horrified reprobation of it.

In our childhood and youth my mother was not only sincerely religious—this she always was in the true sense of the word—but definite in her beliefs. She went regularly to church and took the Sacrament. She read the Bible with us and taught us a simple Unitarian Creed, though we were baptized and confirmed in the Church of England. In her youth religion must have largely filled her life, and there is evidence in the papers she left that it distressed her, in her early married life, to know that my father did not share her faith. She wrote two letters to him on the subject. He speaks in his autobiography of "her beautiful letter to me, safely preserved, shortly after our marriage." In this she wrote:

The state of mind that I wish to preserve with respect to you is to feel that while you are acting conscientiously and sincerely wishing and trying to learn the truth, you cannot be wrong; but there are some reasons that force themselves upon me, and prevent my being always able to give myself this comfort. I daresay you have often thought of them before, but I will write down what has been in my head, knowing that my own dearest will indulge me. Your mind and time are full of the most interesting subjects and thoughts of the most absorbing kind, viz. following up your own discoveries, but which makes it very difficult for you to avoid casting out as interruptions other sorts of thoughts which have no relation to what you are pursuing, or to be able to give your whole attention to both sides of the question. . . .

I do not wish for any answer to all this—it is a satisfaction to me to write it, and when I talk to you about it I cannot say exactly what I wish to say, and I know you will have patience with your own dear wife. Don't think that it is not my affair and that it does not much signify to me. Everything that concerns you concerns me, and I should be most unhappy if I thought we did not belong to each other for ever. I am rather afraid my own dear N. will think I have forgotten my promise not to bother him, but I am sure he loves me, and I cannot tell him how happy he makes me, and how dearly I love him and thank him for all his affection, which makes the happiness of my life more and more every day.

And in her second letter:

I find the only relief to my own mind is to take suffering as from God's hand, and to try to believe that all suffering and illness is meant to help us to exalt our minds and to look forward with hope to a future state. When I see your patience, deep compassion for others, self-command, and above all gratitude for the smallest thing done to help you, I cannot help longing that these precious feelings should be offered to Heaven for the sake of your daily happiness. . . . It is feeling and not reasoning that drives one to prayer. I feel presumptuous in writing this to you.

I remember her once telling me that she had often felt she could only bear her anxiety by saying a prayer for help. As years went on her beliefs must have greatly changed, but she kept a sorrowful wish to believe more, and I know that it was an abiding sadness to her that her faith was less vivid than it had been in her youth.

July 30, 1860, Charles Darwin to his son William at Cambridge. Poor Etty will long be an invalid, but we are now too happy even at that poor prospect. Your letter has amused us all extremely, and was read with roars of laughter. Etty has not yet heard it; but you cannot think what a pleasure your letters are to her; they amuse and cheer her so nicely. I shall copy your account of dialogue before the Bishop and send it to Hooker and Huxley.

August 28, 1860, Mrs. Darwin to Lady Lyell. We have sent Frank to school, and as yet he has been quite happy there.* George is in the first class, and a person of some authority there, so he is a great protection. But I think boys are better than they used to be, and he is sure to be liked by the masters from his industry and zeal. Charles is too much given to anxiety, as you know, and his various experiments this summer have been a great blessing to him, as he can always interest himself about them. At present he is treating Drosera just like a living creature, and I suppose he hopes to end in proving it to be an animal.

---

*The four younger sons were all sent to a school at Clapham.

Feb. 1863, note by Henrietta Darwin. In February, 1863, we went to see Fechter and Kate Terry in the *Duke's Motto.* My mother's old taste for the play remained as strong as ever, and she admired Kate Terry with enthusiasm.

Nov. 13, 1863, Mrs. Darwin to her son Leonard at Clapham. (Note by H. D.: The following letter is written in a tiny hand on a little sheet of paper 3½ by 2¼ inches.) My dear Lenny, You cannot write as small as this *I* know. It is done with your crow-quill. Your last letter was not interesting, but very well spelt, which I care more about. We have a new horse on trial, very spirited and pleasant and nice-looking, but I am afraid too cheap. Papa is much better than when Frank was here. We have some stamps for you: one Horace says is new Am. 5 cent. Yours, my dear old man, E. D.

[Some educational leaders of to-day would be horrified at Mrs. Darwin's preference of good spelling to interest; they would not understand that good spelling may show a good conscience.]

April 28, 1866, Mrs. Darwin to an aunt, from London. Our last days here have been so pleasant and successful that I must write you a scrap. The greatest event was that Charles went last night to the Soirée at the Royal Society, where assemble all the scientific men in London. He saw every one of his old friends, and had such a cordial reception from them all as made it very pleasant. He was obliged to name himself to almost all of them, as his beard alters him so much. The President presented him to the Prince of Wales. There were only three presented, and he was the first. The Prince looked a nice good-natured youth, and very gentlemanlike. He said something Charles could not hear, so he made the profoundest bow he could and went on. . . . My event was nearly as wonderful, going to see *Hamlet* with

Fechter. The acting was beautiful, but I should prefer anything to Shakespeare, I am ashamed to say.

Spring of 1867, note by H. D. In the spring of 1867 my mother offered to take charge of the seven children of Mr. and Mrs. Huxley for a fortnight. Mrs. Huxley wrote to me of my mother:

Towards your mother I always had a sort of nestling feeling. More than any woman I ever knew, she *comforted*. . . . I first wrote that I was too weak and ill to be out of my home, that I could not get downstairs till 1 o'clock. Her reply was that that was the usual state of the family at Downe, and I should just be following suit. . . . My heart is very full, and tears dim my eyes as I write of her.

1867, Mrs. Darwin to her aunt. Charles's book is done and he is enjoying leisure, tho' he is a very bad hand at that. I wish he could smoke a pipe or ruminate like a cow.

Jan. 24, 1868, Charles Darwin to his son George on the occasion of his being second wrangler.
My dear old fellow,

I am so pleased. I congratulate you with all my heart and soul. I always said from your early days that such energy, perseverance, and talent as yours would be sure to succeed; but I never expected such brilliant success as this. You have made my hand tremble so I can hardly write.

Jan., 1868, Mrs. Darwin to her daughter Henrietta. We had a pleasant interlude yesterday in the appearance of Leo and Horace from school. George's success made a tremendous stir at Clapham. Wrigley [the headmaster] had never been seen in such a state. He gave out the fact from the platform as if he was going to cry, and gave a half-holiday and sent them all to the Crystal

Palace. Leo however staid at home at his work. . . .
When the boys [i. e., at home, at Downe House] heard
about G. in the 1st class room they had a regular
saturnalia, and played at football for some time to the
great danger of the windows and pictures.

April 2, 1868, Mrs. Darwin to her sister. Mr. Farrer
offered Fanny to sing to Charles, but he could not contrive it those last days; indeed I think his fondness for
singing is pretty well merged into Natural Selection, etc.

1868, note by H. D. In 1868 we took one of Mrs. Cameron's little houses at Freshwater, Isle of Wight. Tennyson came several times to call on my parents, but he did
not greatly charm either my father or my mother. They
also saw Longfellow and his brother-in-law Tom Appleton, full of the wonders of table-turning, spirits and
ghosts. Mr. Appleton described to us how he has impressed Tennyson with his spirit stories, telling them to
him after dinner, by the light of a lanthorn in the
orchard.

July 26, 1868, Charles Darwin to his son Horace. We
do not know Leonard's address, and I must write to
someone, else I shall burst with pleasure at Leonard's
success. [He had come out second in the entrance examination for Woolwich.] We saw the news yesterday,
and no doubt you will have seen it. Is it not splendid?

August, 1868, Mrs. Darwin to her aunt. Mrs. Cameron very good-naturedly took me and Bessy to call on
Mrs. Tennyson. It was pouring rain, and the more it
rained the slower we walked, so when we got there we
left our dripping cloaks in the hall.

Mr. Tennyson brought in a bottle of light wine and
gave us each a glass to correct the wet. Mrs. Tennyson
is an invalid, and very pleasing and gracious. After
sitting a reasonable time Tennyson came out with us and
shewed us all about, and one likes him, and his absurd

talk is a sort of flirtation with Mrs. Cameron. The only Tennysonian speech was when he was talking of his new house; I asked where it was, and he answered half in joke "Shan't tell you where," also telling that the *Illustrated News* wanted to send an artist to take him laying the first stone. Charles spent a very pleasant hour with him the day before. We ended in a transport of affection with Mrs. Cameron, Eras. calling over the stairs to her, "You have left eight persons deeply in love with you." I think she was fondest of Horace.

1868, note by H. D. This autumn was one of unusual sociability. There were pleasant parties of friends and relations staying in the house; and we also had much intercourse with Charles Norton, of Cambridge, Mass., and his family, who were staying for some time at Keston Rectory, a neighboring parish to Downe. A warm friendship sprang up between the two families, and this intimacy led to my brother William's marriage many years later to Mrs. Norton's sister, Sara Sedgwick.

About this time we ceased to call our father and mother "Papa" and "Mamma." "F" from now onwards in my mother's letters means "your father," although she sometimes still speaks of him as "Papa." My father, who was very conservative (though he was a Liberal in politics), said when we spoke about the change, "I would as soon be called Dog."

In January, 1870, I went to Cannes. . . . Whilst I was abroad the proof-sheets of *The Descent of Man* were sent out to me to read. My mother wrote to me of one of the chapters: "I think it will be very interesting, but that I shall dislike it very much as again putting God further off."

March, 1870, Mrs. Darwin to her daughter Henrietta. F. is wonderfully set up by London, but so absorbed about work and all sorts of things that I shall force him off somewhere before very long. F. Galton's experiments about rabbits to prove Pangenesis are failing, which is a dreadful disappointment to them both. F. Galton said he was quite sick with anxiety till the rabbits' *accouchements* were over, and now one naughty creature ate up her infants and the other has perfectly commonplace ones. He wishes this experiment to be kept quite secret as he means to go on, and he thinks he shall be laughed at, so don't mention.

Dec., 1870, note by H. D. In the years when we were growing up, I believe my mother was often puzzled as to what rules to make about keeping Sunday. . . . It was a question in her own mind whether she might rightly embroider, knit, or play patience.

March, 1871, Erasmus Darwin to Henrietta Darwin. I think the way Wallace carries on controversy is perfectly beautiful, and in future histories of science the Wallace-Darwin episode will form one of the few bright points among rival claimants.

Sept. 4, 1871, Charles Darwin to his daughter Henrietta, on her wedding tour, now Mrs. Litchfield. I have had my day and a happy life, notwithstanding my stomach; and this I owe almost entirely to our dear old mother, who, as you know well, is as good as twice refined gold. Keep her as an example before your eyes, and then Litchfield will in future years worship and not only love you, as I worship our dear old mother.

Dec. 5, 1871, Charles Darwin to his son Horace. We are so rejoiced, for we have just had a card from that good George in Cambridge saying that you are all right and safe through the accursed Little Go. I am so glad, and now you can follow the bent of your talents and work as hard at mathematics and science as your health will permit.

Jan. 21, 1873. Mrs. Darwin to her aunt. We have

just been reading a very grand sermon of Moncure Conway's on Darwinism. I sometimes feel it very odd that anyone belonging to me should be making such a noise in the world.

Feb., 1873, note by H. D. Mr. Huxley needed a long rest. Mr. Lyell suggested to my mother that a very few of his intimate friends might privately join in making a gift to him to get away. Two thousand one hundred pounds were at once subscribed, and my father was deputed to write the letter accompanying the gift. "He sent off the awful letter to Mr. Huxley yesterday, and I hope we may hear tomorrow. It will be awful," my mother wrote. It was not, however, awful at all. Mr. Huxley took the gift in the spirit in which it was offered.

Autumn, 1873, Mrs. Darwin to her daughter Henrietta. F. is much absorbed in Desmodium gyrans and went to see it asleep last night. It was dead asleep, all but its little ears, which were having most lively games, such as he never saw in the daytime.

Jan., 1874, note by H. D. Spiritualism was making a great stir at this time. During a visit of my father and mother to Erasmus Darwin a *séance* was arranged with Mr. Williams, a paid medium, to conduct it. We were a largish party, sitting round a dining-table, including Mr. and Mrs. G. H. Lewes (George Eliot).

This summer there was a second marriage in the family. My third brother, Francis, married Amy, daughter of Mr. Ruck. Frank had been educated as a doctor, but did not wish to practise, and took up botany. He was the only one of my father's children with a strong taste for natural history. He now became my father's secretary, and he and his wife came to live at Downe.

Leonard, now in the Royal Engineers, went to New Zealand to observe the transit of Venus.

Nov. 8, 1875, Mrs. Darwin to her son Leonard. F. went to the Vivisection Commission at two. Lord Cardwell came to the door to receive him and he was treated like a Duke. . . . It was over in ten minutes, Lord C. coming to the door and thanking him.

1876, Charles Darwin to his son Francis. If your case of Teazle holds good it is a wonderful discovery. . . . I would work at this subject, if I were you, to the point of death. . . . For heaven's sake report progress on your work.

July 13, 1876, Charles Darwin to his son George. One line to say how I, and indeed all of us, rejoice that Adams thinks well of your work, and that if all goes well will present your papers to Royal Soc.

Horace goes on Monday to lecture on his dynam. at Birmingham. Frank is getting on very well with Dipsacus and has now made experiments which convince me that the matter which comes out of the glands is real live protoplasm about which I was beginning to feel horrid doubts. Leonard goes to build forts.

Oh Lord, what a set of sons I have, all doing wonders.

[William became a banker in Southampton and was one of its prominent and most useful citizens. George became a professor of astronomy at Cambridge. Francis was president of the British Association in 1908 and was knighted in 1913. Leonard became a major, an M. P., president of two learned societies, and a writer on bimetallism and eugenics. Horace devoted himself to the making of precision instruments at Cambridge, and became so useful to science in this way that he was knighted.]

Note by H. D. In the autumn of 1876 my brother Francis lost his wife and came with his new-born baby, Bernard, to live in the old home. The shock and the loss

had a very deep effect on my mother and I think made
her permanently more fearful and anxious. The baby
was a great delight to both my parents, and my mother
took up the old nursery cares as if she were still a young
woman.

June, 1877, Mrs. Darwin to her daughter. F. was
made very happy by finding two very old stones at the
bottom of the field, and he has now got a man at work
digging for the worms. I must go and take him an
umbrella. . . .

We are really going to Stonehenge tomorrow. . . .
I am afraid it will half kill F.—two hours' rail and a
twenty-four mile drive—but he is bent on going, chiefly
for the worms, but also he has always wished to see
it. . . .

We started yesterday at 6:45. We had telegraphed
on Monday to George to meet us at Salisbury and there
he was at the station with our open carriage and pair,
looking very bright and smiling, and I think he enjoyed
it more than any of us, though he had seen it twice
before. . . .

They did not find much good about the worms, who
seem to be very idle out there.

Sept. 29, 1877, Charles Darwin to Sara Sedgwick. I
must tell you how deeply I rejoice over my son's good
fortune. You will believe me when I say that for very
many years I have not seen any woman whom I have
liked and esteemed so much as you. I hope and firmly
believe that you will be very happy together. . . .
Judging from my own experience life would be a most
dreary blank without a dear wife to love with all one's
soul.

Nov. 17, 1877, Mrs. Darwin to her son William, describing the conferring of an LL. D. upon her husband
at Cambridge. It was a great disappointment your not

coming yesterday to witness the honors to F., and so I will tell you all about it.

Bessy and I and the two youngest brothers went first to the Senate House and got in by a side door, and a most striking sight it was. The gallery crammed to overflowing with undergraduates, and the floor crammed too with undergraduates climbing on the statues and standing up in the windows. There seemed to be periodical cheering in answer to jokes which sounded deafening; but when F. came in, in his red cloak, ushered in by some authorities, it was perfectly deafening for some minutes. I thought he would be overcome, but he was quite stout and smiling and sat for a considerable time waiting for the Vice-Chancellor. The time was filled up with shouts and jokes, and groans for an unpopular Proctor, Mr. ——, which were quite awful, and he looked up at them with a stern, angry face, which was very bad policy. We had been watching some cords stretched across from one gallery to another wondering what was to happen, but were not surprised to see a monkey dangling down which caused shouts and jokes about our ancestors, etc. A Proctor was foolish enough to go up to capture it and at last it disappeared I don't know how. Then came a sort of ring tied with ribbons which we conjectured to be the "Missing Link." At last the Vice-Chancellor appeared, more bowing and hand-shaking, and then F. was marched down the aisle behind two men with silver maces, and the unfortunate Public Orator came and stood by him and got thro' his very tedious harangue as he could, constantly interrupted by the most unmannerly shouts and jeers; and when he had continued what seemed an enormous time, someone called out in a cheerful tone "Thank you kindly." At last he got to the end with admirable nerve and temper, and then they all marched back to the Vice-

Chancellor in scarlet and white fur, and F. joined his hands and did not kneel but the Vice-Chancellor put his hands outside and said a few Latin words, and then it was over, and everybody came up and shook hands. . . .

I felt very grand walking about with my LL. D. in his silk gown.

Oct. 29, 1878, Charles Darwin to his son George. All of us are delighted, for considering what a man Sir William Thomson is, it is most grand that you should have staggered him so quickly, and that he should speak of your "discovery etc." and about the moon's period. I also chuckle greatly about the internal heat. How this will please the geologists and evolutionists. That does sound awkward about the heat being bottled up in the middle of the earth. . . .

Hurrah for the bowels of the earth and their viscosity and for the moon and for the Heavenly bodies and for my son George (F. R. S. very soon).

Dec. 12, 1878, Charles Darwin to his son William. I have a curious bit of news to tell you. A few days ago Mr. Anthony Rich, of Heene, Worthing, wrote to me that he with his sister was the last of his family, and that he had always thought under such circumstances "those should be remembered, whose abilities etc., etc., had been devoted etc., etc., for the benefit of mankind"; with more to the same effect and to my great honor. Therefore he had bequeathed to me nearly all his property after his and his sister's death. The property . . . brings in annually rather above £1,100.

March, 1879, W. E. Darwin to his mother. Our drive with Carlyle was interesting, but it was difficult to catch all he said. . . . He also talked of the frightful difficulty of rewriting the 1st vol. when the manuscript had been burnt. . . . He also said that he thought at one time that he should have gone mad with all the horror and mystery of the world and his own difficulties, if he had not come across Goethe. . . . As we came away he asked after my father, and said with a grin, "but the origin of species is nothing to me."

August, 1879, note by H. D. My father and mother spent the month of August at Coniston. My father enjoyed the journey there with the freshness of a boy. . . . One expedition was made to Grasmere. My father was in a state of enthusiastic delight, jumping up from his seat in the carriage to see better at every striking moment. . . . Ruskin spoke of the new and baleful kind of cloud which had appeared in the heavens, and his distressed look showed that his brain was becoming clouded.

In the autumn of 1879 my youngest brother Horace became engaged to Ida, only daughter of Lord Farrer, and they were married on January 3rd, 1880. This marriage added a great happiness to my mother's life, as Ida became another daughter to her.

Jan. 17, 1880, Charles Darwin to his children. I have just found on my table your present of the magnificent fur coat. . . . The coat, however, will never warm my body so much as your dear affection has warmed my heart. My good dear children, Your affectionate Father.

N. B. I should not be myself if I did not protest that you have all been shamefully extravagant to spend so much money over your old father, however deeply you may have pleased him.

Summer, 1880, Mrs. Darwin to her son Leonard. F. has no proof sheets and has taken to training earthworms but does not make much progress, as they can neither see nor hear. They are, however, amusing and spend hours in seizing hold of the edge of a cabbage leaf and trying in vain to pull it into their holes.

Dec., 1880, Mrs. Darwin to her daughter, about

the effort to secure a pension for Wallace. F. is so full of Wallace's affair he has no time for his own, and has concocted provisional letters to Gladstone and the Duke of Argyll.

The last I am sure he will send—the first is not quite certain. He is influenced by Huxley feeling so sure that Gladstone would like to oblige him.

Feb. 27, 1881, Charles Darwin to his son George in Madeira. Thanks for looking out for worm-casings. It is hopeless where the soil is dry. . . . I have just returned from a very long call on the Duke of Argyll. He was very agreeable and we discussed many subjects, and he was not at all cocky. He was awfully friendly and said he should come some day to Downe, and hoped I would come to Inverary.

June 2, 1881, note by H. D. I think that this second visit to the Lake country was nearly as full of enjoyment as the first. It was an especial happiness to my mother for the rest of her life to remember her little strolls with my father by the side of the lake. I have a clear picture in my mind of the two often setting off alone together for a certain favorite walk by the edge of some fine rocks going sheer down into the lake.

Erasmus Darwin died on August 26th, after four days' illness. . . . He was buried at Downe.

Oct. 1881, Mrs. Darwin to her daughter-in-law Sara. F. and I often reflect how well off we are in daughters-in-law and how easily our sons might have married very nice wives that would not have suited us old folks, and above all that would not really have adopted us so affectionately as you have done. I never think without a pang of the third that is gone.

Nov. 23, 1881, Mrs. Darwin to her daughter. F. is at last getting some reward for these months at the microscope, in finding out something quite new about the structure of roots. However, it makes him work all the harder now.

Note by H. D. My father's health had given much cause for uneasiness in the autumn of 1881, but in the beginning of 1882 he was for a time somewhat better. At the end of January his health relapsed. All February and March he did not dare to walk far from the house for fear of the heart pain seizing him. He had, however, happy times, sitting with my mother in the orchard, with the crocus eyes wide open and the birds singing in the spring sunshine.

On March 13th my mother entered in her diary "looked out of window," as if that was a step; then came a rally of a fortnight. On the 17th April she wrote, "Good day, a little work, out in orchard twice." On the 18th, "Fatal attack at 12."

I arrived on the morning of the 19th and found him being supported by mother and by my brother Frank. She went away for a little rest, whilst we stayed with him. During that time he said to us, "You are the best of dear nurses." But my mother and my sister soon had to be sent for, and he peacefully died at half-past three on the 19th April.

It was the wish of the family that Darwin should be buried at Downe, but a number of members of the House of Commons had requested that he be buried in Westminster Abbey, the Dean had approved, and Sir John Lubbock advised that "from a national point of view it is clearly right that he should be buried in the Abbey." The family assented.

Ten illustrious men were his pall-bearers: Hooker, Huxley, Wallace, Lubbock, Canon Farrar, Spottiswoode (president of the Royal Society), James Russell Lowell, the Earl of Derby, and the Dukes of Devonshire and

Argyll. The procession of representatives of countries, universities, and learned societies moved to the east end of the north aisle of the nave, where the coffin was lowered near the remains of Lyell. Two slabs in the pavement commemorate the friends who had fought so well, though so differently, for the liberation of the human mind.

Mrs. Darwin lived until October 2, 1896. Her winters were spent at Cambridge, where two of her sons lived. In the summers she gathered a troop of grandchildren about her at Downe House.

Shortly before her spring migration in 1886 to her beloved Downe she wrote to her daughter about some wild flowers brought to her by her children and grandchildren:

The oxlips were quite lovely in masses in the wood, and with such variety that they seemed of quite different species. How F. would have liked to see such variation going on.

THE END

Argyll. The procession of representatives of countries, universities, and learned societies moved to the east end of the north aisle of the nave, where the coffin was lowered near the remains of Lyell. Two slabs in the pavement commemorate the friends who had fought so well, though so differently, for the liberation of the human mind.

Mrs. Darwin lived until October 2, 1896. Her winters were spent at Cambridge, where two of her sons lived. In the summers she gathered a troop of grandchildren about her at Downe House.

Shortly before her spring migration in 1896 to her beloved Downe she wrote to her daughter about some wild flowers brought to her by her children and grandchildren:

The oxlips were quite lovely in masses in the wood, and with such variety that they seemed of quite different species. How F. would have liked to see such variation going on.

THE END

APPENDIX

APPENDIX

I HAVE used the so-called "second edition" of the *Histoire Naturelle*, of which thirty-six volumes appeared during Buffon's life, published from 1750 to 1788. The quotations are from the first series of volumes, fifteen in number, 1750-67. Volume I discusses the methods of studying nature; Volume II treats of "generation"; Volume III gives the "Natural History" of man; then follow three volumes about domestic animals; the last nine tell of wild animals. Each animal is treated in a double way: first there is a "Histoire Naturelle" by Buffon, a spirited and discursive essay on the general characteristics; then a "Description" by Daubenton, giving technical specifications of weights, dimensions and classification.

We can guess (though no such scheme is announced) that Buffon designed to put man in the forefront of his treatise as the chief *animal*, and to follow with the horse and the ass; for the discussion of mules (hybridism) is brought to bear on the whole mysterious question of what a "species" is, of species as being perhaps mere "degenerations" by hybridism, and of man as a mere species of animal.

The first three volumes were issued in 1750. The tone of them is entirely frank and unhampered; the judgments are sound and unmistakable. For example, when he is taking up different theories of the history of the earth he devotes three pages to Burnet's *Sacred Theory,* which had been a notable work, influential and much applauded, on the history revealed by the Bible. Buffon sums up unambiguously: "It is a well-written romance, and a book which we can read for amusement, but which we cannot consult to gain information." M. Buffon shows no interest in the revelation that the Bible makes of the history of the earth.

Through twenty-five pages he proposes his theory of the origin of the earth. He is not a whit confused as to what he is about; he is offering a hypothesis, which he thinks is plausible, which is not proved at all, but which seems worth thinking about:

May we not imagine with some sort of probability that a comet, hitting upon the surface of the sun, had displaced that star and had separated from it some small parts, to which it had imparted a driving movement in the same direction and by the same clash, so that the planets had formerly belonged to the body of the sun and that they had been detached by a driving force common to them all, which they preserve to the present time? That appears at least as likely as the opinion of M. Leibnitz. . . . The matter which composes the planets did not rush out of that star in globes full-formed . . . but in the form of a torrent.

That description could have been used by Chamberlin to describe his conception of the origin of the earth in his Planetesimal Hypothesis.

Buffon is the direct and uncompromising scientist when he discourses on reproduction in Volume II: "If one asks *why* animals and plants reproduce themselves, we recognize that this question is insoluble; but if one asks *how,* this is a question of fact." He shows no interest in the theological disputation about design in nature.

He rejects the metaphysical theory of reproduction that all future organisms were contained, potentially, in the first creature; and he equally rejects the theological doctrine that there is a new and special creation at every birth. His point of view and his mode of treatment are entirely scientific.

But all is mystifyingly different in Volume IV, which appeared three years later. Something seems to have changed his mode of attack upon questions in natural history. We can guess with perfect safety at the cause of the change. For Volume IV opens with a letter from the Deputies and the Syndic of the Faculty of Theology of the Sorbonne. It appears that M. Buffon has politely assured the Faculty that he will gladly satisfy them about any parts of his *Histoire* that are found blameworthy, and that they accordingly submit to him fourteen propositions which seem to them objectionable. Numbers 2 and 4 are the hypothesis of the way the planets were formed; number 9 is the statement that "mathematical evidence and physical certitude are therefore the only two respects in which we ought to view truth." His reply is also printed—a long and polite sentence in which he thanks them for "giving me the opportunity to explain in a way that shall leave no uncertainty about the correctness of my intentions." He prints his explanations of the statements, and also the letter from the Faculty in which they express their "extreme joy" at the "very Christian spirit" he has shown, which they think "cannot be praised too much."

So a very strong theological compulsion was on him when he prepared Volume IV. It was no longer wise to appeal only to physical certitude or to disregard the truths revealed in the Bible. When, therefore, he has completed the four-hundred-page account of the horse and is prepared to reason about the nature of all organic life by a comparison of the horse and the ass, he must follow out two purposes: (1) to say what he thinks, (2) not to offend the Faculty. Read the following passage and see if you can detect any irony or the point at which he passes abruptly from purpose 1 to purpose 2:

In observing the ass, even with careful scrutiny and in very close detail, it appears to be nothing but a degenerate horse. . . . What seems to favor this idea is that horses vary much more than asses in the color of their hair. . . . Do the horse and the ass, then, come originally from the same stock? Are they, as the classifiers say, of the same *family*? Or are they not, and have they always been separate animals?

This question—of which physiologists well understand the wide application, the difficulty, the consequences, and which we have believed ought to be treated in this section, because it comes up for the first time—touches more closely upon the reproduction of living beings than any other, and requires for clearing it up that we consider Nature under a new point of view. If, amidst the immense variety offered us by the animated beings which people the universe, we should choose an animal, or even the body of a man, to serve as a basis of our investigations, and should bring to it, by way of comparison, the other organic beings, we should find that, though all these beings exist separately and that they all vary by infinitely fine gradations, there exists at the same time an original and general design which we can follow distantly and of which the gradations are much less abrupt than those of the shapes and of other obvious correspondences. . . . There is an extraordinary resemblance, which necessarily suggests to us the idea of an original design, according to which everything seems to have been planned. [He shows how, when a detailed comparison is made, the skeleton of man and horse have a strikingly similar general plan.] The foot of a horse, so different in appearance from the hand of a man, is nevertheless made up of the same bones, and we have at the end of each of our fingers the same little bone, like a horseshoe, that terminates the foot of this animal. . . .

From this point of view not only the ass and the horse, but even man, the ape, the quadrupeds, and all animals can be considered as forming simply the same *family*. . . . If these *families* actually exist, they could not have been formed except by the mixture, the successive variation, and the degeneration of the original species; and if we once admit that there are *families* among the plants and among the animals, that the ass belongs to the *family* of the horse, and that it does not differ from the horse except because it has degenerated, we could equally well say that the ape belongs to the *family* of man, that it is a degenerate man, that the man and the ape have had a common origin like the horse and the ass, that every *family*, of animals as well as of plants, has had only one stem, and even that all animals have come from a single animal, which, with the passage of time, has produced, by improving and degenerating, all the races of other animals.

The naturalists who set up *families* so lightly among animals and plants seem not to have understood the full extent of the consequences, which would reduce the direct output of creation to as small a number as we wished: for if it was once proved that we could reasonably set up these *families*, if it was granted that among animals, or even among plants, there was one single species which had been produced by the degeneration of another species, if it was true that the ass is nothing but a degenerate horse, there would no longer be bounds to the power of Nature, and we should not be wrong in assuming that from a single being she had drawn in the course of time all other organized beings.

But no. It is certain, from revelation, that all animals have had an equal share in the grace of creation, and that the original pair of each species and of all species issued full-formed from the hands of the Creator, and we must believe that they were the same then, very nearly, as they are now represented to us by their descendants. (Tome IV, pages 377-383.)

After this sermon about creation he proceeds with his proper business of characterizing the ass—thus: "The horse whinnies, the ass brays, which it does by making a loud cry, very long, very disagreeable, and harsh because of discordant sounds alternating from shrill to deep and from deep to shrill; ordinarily the ass does not make this noise except when it is impelled by love or desire for food; the she-ass has a voice more pure and more piercing; an ass that has been gelded brays only in a low voice, and, although he appears to make the same effort and the same movements of the throat, his cry cannot be heard so far."

The irony of speaking so frequently and piously, in italics, about families is this: no naturalist had ever thought of denying that there are *families* of animals. Buffon puts the case against naturalists in a comically exaggerated way, and he emphasizes the exaggeration by using italics every time he refers to *family*. Any naturalist who read the book would see broad sarcasm in the reference to "naturalists who set up families so lightly"; for Buffon himself assumes them lightly and frequently throughout his volumes. Any one who was familiar with the first three volumes would be struck as by an unseemly antic when he perceived Buffon casting his eyes up to heaven and protesting that "it is certain from revelation." Burnet's *Sacred Theory* is absolutely certain from revelation; yet Buffon had dismissed it as a romance.

The other references to an evolution theory are interjected without warning, capriciously, enigmatically, at wide intervals, through seven thousand pages; they form only a fraction of one per cent of the entire work; they so contradict themselves that no one could ever be sure about what Buffon really thought. For example, just after his ironical (or solemn) argument against the mutability of species, based on divine revelation, he makes an equally strong argument against mutability that is based (at least it appears to be based) on scientific conviction. Who can follow this man? Samuel Butler, after a prolonged and sympathetic study of the fifteen volumes, pronounced in favor of the theory of sarcasm to avoid trouble with the theologians; yet he confesses at the end of his discussion: "I therefore leave Buffon with the hope that I have seen him more justly than some others have done, but with the certainty that the points I have caught and understood are few in comparison with those I have missed." Poulton judges that Butler's judgment is quite wrong.

But any one who spends a few hours with Buffon at those points where he talks about classification and homologies will certainly gather an impression of this sort: "My Lord! it *does* look as if all life was a continuous series, with man, as an animal part of it, at the top of it." If he is a fundamentalist, he will squirm and dislike what he reads. So Buffon's influence must, on the whole, have been against the theory of special creation. Make your own guess at his influence when you have read the following passage from Volume XIV, pages 27-30, where he is nominally discussing the classification of apes:

It is generally admitted that man, the quadruped, the whale, the bird, the reptile, the insect, the tree, the plant take food, grow, and reproduce by the same law. The form of all that breathes is nearly the same; in dissecting the ape we could compare its anatomy with man's. . . . And this anatomical plan is always the same, always followed from man to ape, from ape to quadrupeds, from quadrupeds to whales, from whales to birds, to fishes, to reptiles. . . . And when we wish to extend it and pass from what lives to what vegetates, we see this plan, which had not varied from the beginning except by delicate gradations, alter gradually from reptiles to insects, from insects to worms, from worms to zoophytes, from zoophytes to plants. . . .

And the very ones whose form seems to us most perfect—that is, most closely approaching our own—the apes, appear together and require attentive eyes to distinguish one from another, because it is less to form than to size that the distinction of an isolated species is attached; and man himself, though a unique species, infinitely different from all those species of animals, having only a mediocre height, is less isolated and has more neighbors than the large animals. We shall see in the account of the orangoutang that if we paid no attention to anything but the shape, we could equally well regard this animal as the first of the apes or the last of the men, because, with the exception of the soul, he lacks nothing at all that we have, and because he differs less from man in body than he differs from the other animals to which we have given the same name of "ape."

SECTION 2: ERASMUS DARWIN

THE American edition of the poems that I have used is in three volumes: I. *The Economy of Vegetation*, II. *The Loves of the Plants*, III. *The Temple of Nature*. The first two of these poems were later called Parts I and II of *The Botanic Garden*.

A passage that illustrates how careful Erasmus Darwin was to verify information, and how credulous he would seem to a grandson at Edinburgh in 1825, is the following about the upas tree, from *Loves of the Plants*, Canto IV. All the details are translated from a Dutch author who was supposed to be honest and authoritative.

> Fierce in dread silence on the blasted heath
> Fell Upas sits, the Hydra-Tree of death.
> Lo; from one root, the envenom'd soil below,
> A thousand vegetative serpents grow;
> In shining rays the scaly monster spreads
> O'er ten square leagues his far-diverging heads;
> Or in one trunk entwists his tangled form,
> Looks o'er the clouds, and hisses in the storm.
> Steep'd in fell poison, as his sharp teeth part,
> A thousand tongues in quick vibration dart;
> Snatch the proud Eagle towering o'er the heath,
> Or pounce the Lion, as he stalks beneath;
> Or strew, as marshall'd hosts contend in vain,
> With human skeletons the whiten'd plain.

Examples of the evolutionary teaching in the poems are the following from *The Temple of Nature*:

From Canto I, which is describing the successive forms of life "born beneath the shoreless waves":

> First forms minute, unseen by spheric glass,
> Move on the mud, or pierce the watery mass;
> These, as successive generations bloom,
> New powers acquire, and larger limbs assume;

Whence countless groups of vegetation spring,
And breathing realms of fin, and feet, and wing.

He declares that the Oak, the Whale, the Lion, Eagle, man
[why is he not honored with a capital *m?*], who "styles himself
the image of his God,"

Arose from rudiments of form and sense,
An embryon point, or microscopic ens!

He poetizes the law of recapitulation—that is, that every person passes through, in his embryo life, the stages of animal existence:

Half-reasoning Beavers long-unbreathing dart
Through Erie's waves with perforated heart.
                    *   *   *
Thus in the womb the nascent infant laves
Its natant form in the circumfluent waves;
With perforated heart unbreathing swims,
Awakes and stretches all its recent limbs.

He thus describes the Struggle for Existence in Canto IV of
The Economy of Vegetation:

Herb, shrub, and tree with strong emotions rise
For light and air, and battle in the skies.

And in the fourth Canto of *The Temple of Nature* there are
two gory passages on the same subject:

All these, increasing by successive birth,
Would each o'erpeople ocean, air, and earth.
So human progenies, if unrestrained,
          *   *   *   *   *
                         would spread
Erelong, and deluge their terraqueous bed;
But war, and pestilence, disease, and dearth
Sweep the superfluous myriads from the earth.

Air, earth, and ocean, to astonish'd day
One scene of blood, one mighty tomb display!
From Hunger's arm the shafts of Death are hurl'd,
And one great Slaughter-house the warring world!

The following excerpts from the notes to the poems contain most that is significant for a student of the history of the evolution theory. The notes cover an endless array of topics. They speak of "the immortal Franklin," refer frequently to the chemical researches of Priestley, discuss meteors, four times cite Linnæus's opinion that "all plants may have come from not more than sixty original kinds," argue in favor of spontaneous generation, and refer without disapproval to the theory of Buffon and Helvetius "that mankind arose from one family of monkeys on the banks of the Mediterranean." An evolution theory is not mentioned often, and nowhere at length.

Economy of Vegetation, note 39. Anthers and stigmas are therefore separate beings, endued with the passion of reproduction.

From notes to *Loves of the Plants,* Canto I:

Line 65. Other animals have marks of having in a long process of time undergone changes in some parts of their bodies, which may have been effected to accommodate them to new ways of procuring their food. [He has spoken of the "rudiments of stamens" and illustrated by speaking of "two little knobs" on flies "which appear to be rudiments of hinder wings."]
Line 373. The colours of insects and many smaller animals contribute to conceal them from the larger ones which prey upon them. Caterpillars which feed on leaves are generally green; butterflies which frequent flowers are coloured like them; small birds . . . and hence are less visible to the hawk. Hence there is apparent design in the colours of animals.
Line 415. The air-bladders of fish are nicely adapted to their intended purpose.
Line 435. The funguses make a kind of isthmus connecting the two mighty kingdoms of animal and of vegetable matter.
From Canto III, line 285. The method of making tulips break into colours is by transplanting them into a meagre or sandy soil, after they have previously enjoyed a richer soil.

From *The Temple of Nature*:

Preface. The aim of the poem is simply to amuse by bringing distinctly to the imagination the beautiful and sublime images of the operations of nature in the order, as the Author believes, in which the progressive course of time presented them.
Canto I, line 295. Nor is this unanalogous to what still occurs.

All quadrupeds and mankind in their embryon state are aquatic animals, and thus may be said to resemble gnats and frogs. . . . Those microscopic animalcules situated on dry land may gradually acquire new powers to preserve their existence; and by innumerable successive reproductions for some thousands, or perhaps millions of ages, may at length have produced many of the vegetable and animal inhabitants which now people the earth. . . . Linnæus asserts that the boundaries of these orders of Amphibia can scarcely be ascertained.

Additional Note VIII. During the decomposition of organic bodies . . . new microscopic animals are produced; and these possess the wonderful power of reproduction. . . . but with frequent additional improvements; which the preceding parent might in some measure have acquired by his habits of life or accidental situation. [For more quotations that illustrate this Lamarckian view of inheriting acquired characters see the passages from *Zoonomia* below. A very apposite one is this from the Additional Notes to *The Economy of Vegetation:* Some acquiring wings, others fins, and others claws, from their ceaseless efforts to procure their food, or to secure themselves from injury.''.]

Canto II, line 118. The manner in which the similarity of the progeny to the parent, and the sex of it, are produced by the powers of the imagination, is treated in *Zoonomia*.

Canto II, line 122. Perhaps all the productions of nature are in their progress to greater perfection; an idea . . . consonant to the dignity of the Creator of all things.

It is noteworthy that nowhere in the poems or the notes or the *Zoonomia* does Erasmus Darwin refer to the frequent and strong assertions made by Linnæus and Buffon about the fixity of species; he never mentions that there is in the world a faith in the fixity of species; he does not debate the question, but simply puts forward the speculation that appealed to him about the mutability of species.

Examples of most of the important shreds of evolutionary theory in the *Zoonomia* are furnished in the following excerpts, several of which are strikingly similar to ideas developed in detail by Charles Darwin.

The general tenor of the work is thus announced: "The great CREATOR of all things has infinitely diversified the works of his hands, but has at the same time stamped a certain similitude on the features of nature, that demonstrate to us, that *the whole is one family of one parent*. . . . A theory founded upon nature, that should bind together the scattered facts of medical knowledge, and converge into one point of view the laws of organic life would thus on many accounts contribute to the interest of society. . . . A great part of this work has lain by the writer above twenty years.

Figures before the following quotations refer to the pages of Volume I.

73. That the vegetable world possesses some degree of voluntary powers appears from their necessity to sleep. . . . Voluntary power seems to be exerted in the circular movement of the tendrils of vines.

76. I think we may truly conclude that plants are furnished with a common sensorium belonging to each bud, and that they must occasionally repeat those perceptions either in their dreams or waking hours, and consequently possess ideas of so many of the properties of the external world and of their own existence.

362. [It is remarkable that Erasmus Darwin rejects this theory of Buffon's, though it is the heart of Charles Darwin's "Pangenesis."] Mr. Buffon has, with great ingenuity, imagined the existence of certain organic particles, which are supposed to be partly alive, and partly mechanic springs. . . . These organic particles he supposes to exist in the spermatic fluids of both sexes, and that they are derived thither from every part of the body, and must therefore resemble, as he supposes, the parts from whence they are derived. These organic particles he believes to be in constant activity, till they become mixed in the womb, and then they instantly join and produce an embryon, or foetus, similar to the two parents.

Many objections might be adduced to this fanciful theory; I shall mention only two: First, that it is analogous to no known animal laws; and, secondly, that, as these fluids, replete with organic particles, derived both from the male and female organs, are supposed to be similar, there is no reason why the mother should not produce a female embryon without the assistance of the male, and realize the lucina sine concubitu.

369. Mr. Buffon mentions a breed of dogs without tails, which are common at Rome and at Naples, which he supposes to have been produced by a custom, long established, of cutting their tails close off.

133. One circumstance I shall relate which fell under my own eye, and shewed the power of reason in a wasp, as it is exercised among men. [When a breeze prevented the wasp from carrying the carcass of a fly, it lighted and clipped off the wings.] Go, proud reasoner, and call the worm thy sister!

[The following beginnings of paragraphs, pages 130-132, are of interest because they are so like Charles Darwin's way of massing a set of illustrations drawn from many and varied sources.] There are some kinds of insects that migrate like the birds before mentioned. . . . The accurate Mr. Adanson, near the river Gambia, in Africa, was witness to the migration of these insects. . . . In this country the gnats are sometimes seen to migrate in clouds, like the musketoes of warmer climates. . . . I am well informed that the bees that were carried into Barbadoes ceased to lay up any honey after the first year, as they found it not useful to them. . . . As the death of our hives of bees appears to be owing to their being kept so warm as to require food when their stock is exhausted, a very observing gentleman, at my request, put two hives for many weeks into a dry cellar. . . . There is another observation on bees well ascertained. . . . According to the late observations of Mr. Hunter, it appears that the bees-wax is not made from the dust of the anthers of flowers. . . . The dormouse consumes but little of its food during the rigor of the season.

297. On further considering the action of contagious matter, since the former part of this work was sent to the press, . . . I prevailed on my friend Mr. Power, surgeon at Bosworth, to try whether the small-pox could be inoculated by using the blood of a variolous patient, instead of the matter from the pustules; as I thought such an experiment might throw some light, at least, on this interesting subject. . . . Many more experiments and observations are required before this important question can be satisfactorily answered.

342. Contrary to the opinion of Buffon and Needham above cited.

The following quotations are from the 39th section, "Generation."

353. Owing to the imperfection of language the offspring is termed a *new* animal, but is in truth a branch or elongation of the parent; since a part of the embryon-animal is, or was, a part of the parent. . . . At the earliest period of its existence the embryon, as secreted from the blood of the male, would seem to consist of a living filament, with certain capabilities of irritation, sensation, volition, and association. [This "filament" is his standard metaphor for the original, simple organism with which all life began.]

356. The process of generation is still involved in impenetrable obscurity; conjecture may nevertheless be formed concerning some of its circumstances. . . . In objection to this

theory of generation it may be said, if the animalcula in semine, as seen by the microscope, be all of them rudiments of homunculi, when but one of them can find a nidus, what a waste nature has made of her productions? . . . But such a profusion of them corresponds with the general efforts of nature to provide for the continuance of her species of animals. .. . . . Every individual fish produces innumerable spawn.

357. That the embryon is secreted or produced by the male, and not by the conjunction of fluids from both male and female, appears from the analogy of vegetable seeds.

358. This analogy is as forcible, in so obscure a subject, as it is curious; and may, in large buds, as of the horse chestnut, be almost seen by the naked eye. . . . This paternal offspring of vegetables, I mean their buds and bulbs, is attended with a very curious circumstance; and that is that they exactly resemble their parents, as is observable in grafting fruit-trees, and propagating flower-roots; whereas the seminal offspring of plants, being supplied with nutriment by the mother, is liable to perpetual variation. Thus, also, in the vegetable class dioicia, where the male flowers are produced on one tree and the female ones on another, the buds of the male trees uniformly produce either mule flowers or other buds similar to themselves. and the buds of the female trees produce either female flowers or other buds similar to themselves; whereas the seeds of these trees produce either male or female plants. From this analogy of the production of vegetable buds without a mother, I contend, that the mother does not contribute to the formation of the living ens in animal generation, but is necessary only for supplying its nutriment and oxygenation.

There is another vegetable fact published by M. Koelreuter, which he calls "a complete metamorphosis of one natural species into another," which shews, that in seeds as well as in buds, the embryon proceeds from the male parent, though the form of the subsequent mature plant is in part dependent on the female.

359. Those who have attended to the habits of the polypus, which is found in the stagnant water of our ditches in July, affirm that the young ones branch out from the sides of the parent, like the buds of trees, and after a time separate themselves from them. This is analogous to the manner in which the buds of trees appear to be produced, that these polypi may be considered as all male animals, producing embryons, which require no mother to supply them with a nidus.

360. From all these analogies I conclude that the embryon is produced solely by the male, and the female supplies it with a proper nidus. . . . Many ingenious philosophers have found so great difficulty in conceiving the manner of re-production, that they have supposed all the numerous progeny to have existed in

miniature in the animal originally created; and that these infinitely minute forms are only evolved or distended as the embryon
increases in the womb. This idea ascribes a greater tenuity to
organized matter than we can readily admit; as these included
embryons are supposed each of them to consist of the various and
complicate parts of animal bodies, they must possess a much
greater degree of minuteness than that which was ascribed to the
devils that tempted St. Anthony, of whom 20,000 were said to
have been able to dance a saraband on the point of the finest
needle without incommoding each other.

Others have supposed that all the parts of the embryon are
formed in the male, previous to its being deposited in the egg or
uterus; and that it is then only to have its parts evolved or distended; but this is only to get rid of one difficulty by proposing
another equally incomprehensible.

366.   The form, solidity, and colour of the particles of nutriment laid up for the reception of the first living filament, as well
as their peculiar kind of stimulus, may contribute to produce a
difference in the form, solidity, and colour of the foetus, so as to
resemble the mother, as it advances in life. . . . This explains
why hereditary diseases may be derived either from the male or
female parent, as well as the peculiar form of either of their
bodies.

368.   Secondly, when we think over the great changes introduced into various animals by artificial or accidental cultivation,
as in horses, which we have exercised for the different purposes
of strength or swiftness, in carrying burthens, or in running
races; or in dogs, which have been cultivated for strength and
courage, as bull-dogs; or for acuteness of his sense of smell, as
the hound and spaniel; or for the swiftness of his foot, as the
greyhound; or for his swimming in the water, or for drawing
snow sledges, as the rough-haired dogs of the north; or lastly, as
a play-dog for children, as the lap-dog; with the changes of the
form of the cattle, which have been domesticated from the greatest antiquity, as camels and sheep, which have undergone so total
a transformation, that we are now ignorant from what species of
wild animals they had their origin. Add to these the great
changes of shape and colour which we daily see produced in
smaller animals from our domestication of them, as rabbits or
pidgeons; or from the differences of climates and even of seasons;
thus the sheep of warm climates are covered with hair instead of
wool; and the hares and partridges of the latitudes which are
long buried in snow, become white during the winter; add to
these the various changes produced in the forms of mankind, by
their early modes of exertion; or by the diseases, occasioned by
their many generations. Those who labour at the anvil, the oar,

or the loom, as well as those who carry sedan-chairs, or who have been educated to dance upon the rope, are distinguishable by the shape of their limbs; and the diseases occasioned by intoxication deform the countenance with leprous eruptions, or the body with tumid viscera, or the joints with knots and distortions. . . .

Fifthly, from their first rudiment to the termination of their lives, all animals undergo perpetual transformations, which are, in part, produced by their own exertions, in consequence of their desires and aversions . . . and many of these acquired forms or propensities are transmitted to their posterity. [This idea of "desires" and "transmitted to posterity" are pure Lamarckism; it is hard to believe that Lamarck invented for himself this theory, which is the heart of his *Philosophie Zoologique* and which Darwin published fifteen years before the *Philosophie*. The theory is repeated in the next two quotations.]

The three great objects of desire, which have changed the forms of many animals by their exertions to gratify them, are those of lust, hunger, and security. . . . The final cause of this contest amongst the males seems to be that the strongest and most active animal should propagate the species, which should thence become improved. . . . The trunk of the elephant, . . . strong jaws or talons . . . rough tongue and palate of cattle . . . harder beaks . . . longer beaks [all these, he says, have been "acquired"]. All which seem to have been gradually produced during many generations, by the perpetual endeavour of the creatures to supply the want of food, and to have been delivered to their posterity, with constant improvement of them for the purpose required.

372. Swiftness of wing has been acquired by hawks and swallows, to pursue their prey; and a proboscis, of admirable structure, has been acquired by the bee, the moth, and the humming-bird, for the purpose of plundering the nectaries of flowers. All which seem to have been formed by the original living filament, excited into action by the necessities of the creatures which possess them, and on which their existence depends. . . . Would it be too bold to imagine, that, in the great length of time since the earth began to exist, perhaps millions of ages before the commencement of the history of mankind,—would it be too bold to imagine, that all warm-blooded animals have arisen from one living filament, which THE GREAT FIRST CAUSE endued with animality, with the power of acquiring new parts . . . ; and thus possessing the faculty of continuing to improve by its own inherent activity, and of delivering down those improvements by generation, to its posterity, world without end!

Sixthly, the cold-blooded animals, as the fish tribes, which are furnished with but one ventricle of the heart . . . differ so much in their general structure from the warm-blooded animals, that it may not seem probable, at first view, that the same living filament could have given origin to this kingdom of animals, as to the former. Yet there are some creatures, which unite or partake of both these orders of animation, as the whales and seals; and more particularly the frog.

The numerous tribes of insects without wings. . . . And yet the changes which many of them undergo in their early state to that of their maturity are as different as one animal can be from another.

Vermes . . . The simplicity of their structure, however, can afford no argument against their having been produced from a living filament as above contended.

Last of all, the various tribes of vegetables are to be enumerated amongst the inferior orders of animals. Of these the anthers and stigmas . . . have been announced amongst the animal kingdom, and to these must be added the buds and bulbs. The former I suppose to be beholden to a single living filament for their seminal or amatorial procreation; and the latter to the same cause. . . .

Linnæus supposes, in the Introduction to his Natural Orders, that very few vegetables were at first created, and that their numbers were increased by their intermarriages.

376. Our domesticated animals lose their natural colours, and break into great variety, as horses, dogs, pigeons. The final cause of these colours is easily understood, as they serve some purposes of the animals; but the efficient cause would seem almost beyond conjecture.

377. [An example of his own "conjecture."] And thus, like the fable of the cameleon, all animals may possess a tendency to be coloured somewhat like the colours they most frequently inspect; and finally, that colours may be thus given to the egg-shell by the imagination of the female parent. . . . Nor is this more wonderful than that a single idea of imagination should, in an instant, colour the whole surface of the body of a bright scarlet, as in the blush of shame, though by a very different process. In this intricate subject, nothing but loose analogical conjectures can be had, which may, however, lead to future discoveries; but certain it is that both the change of the colour of animals to white in the winters of snowy countries, and the spots on birds' eggs, must have some efficient cause; since the uniformity of their production shews it cannot arise from a fortuitous concurrence of circumstances: and how is this efficient cause to be detected, or explained, but from its analogy to other animal facts?

379. This production of mules . . . cannot be ascribed to the imagination of the male animal, which cannot be supposed to

operate so uniformly; but to the form of the first nutritive particles, and to their peculiar stimulus exciting the living filament to select and combine them with itself.

There is a similar uniformity of effect in respect to the colour of the progeny produced between a white man and a black woman, which, if I am well informed, is always of the mulatto kind. . . . As this effect is uniform and consistent, and cannot therefore be ascribed to the imagination of either of the parents.

383. And it is hence probable, that if vegetables could only have been produced by buds and bulbs, and not by sexual generation, that there would not, at this time, have existed one thousandth part of their present number of species, which have probably been originally mule productions; nor could any kind of improvement or change have happened to them, except by the difference of soil or climate.

384. [This comment on "chance" is of interest, in view of the endless trouble that was caused for Charles Darwin by his use of the word in this exact and scientific sense.] I ask, in my turn, is the sex of the embryon produced by accident? Certainly, whatever is produced has a cause; but when this cause is too minute for our comprehension, the effect is said, in common language, to happen by chance, as in throwing a certain number on dice.

389. The living filament is a part of the father, and has therefore certain propensities, or appentencies which belong to him; which may have been gradually acquired during a million of generations, even from the infancy of the habitable earth; and which now possess such properties as would render, by the apposition of nutritious particles, the new foetus exactly similar to the father; as occurs in the buds and bulbs of vegetables, and in the polypus, and taenia or tape-worm. But as the first nutriment is supplied by the mother, and therefore resembles such nutritive particles as have been used for her own nutriment or growth, the progeny takes, in part, the likeness of the mother.

The second volume of *Zoonomia* is a classified list of diseases. There are four classes; each class is divided into ordines, each ordo into genera, each genus into species—four hundred and seventy-three of them. The following quotation from the preface is significant, (1) as showing that no boundaries could be fixed in classification between a species and a genus, (2) as showing that all classifiers, even the most ardent believers in the fixity of species, admitted that within a species there might be "varieties"— that is, types which differed in a regular way from the normal type of the species. "Many species in this system are termed genera in the systems of other writers; and the species of those writers are in consequence here termed varieties. . . . It would seem more analogous to botanical arrangement, which these nosologists profess to imitate, to call the distinct and confluent small-pox varieties than species. Because the species of plants in botanical systems propagate others similar to themselves; which does not uniformly occur in such vegetable productions as are termed varieties."

Section 3: Lamarck

THE brilliant imagination of Lamarck succeeded when it was confined to the objective facts that were before it; hence his well-deserved fame as a classifier. Hence, also, he has received full credit for perceiving the probability that there were never any "catastrophes" in geological history, that the earth is immensely old, and that all forms of life have developed by gradual change through the ages. These visions of probable truth deserve the highest praise. But what shall we say of Lamarck's mentality in any other field? I quote estimates of it from A. S. Packard's *Lamarck: His Life and Work*, 1901. Packard was a thorough devotee of Lamarck. He speaks of making a "pilgrimage" to Bazentin, and he honors Lamarck for having "a mind that was essentially philosophical." We must therefore honor the biographer for telling plainly how his hero's mind worked and for quoting other adverse opinions from "just and discriminating judges." I am glad to be relieved of this unpleasant task, which might have made me seem prejudiced. The quotations are from pages 83-88. The first two are Packard's words.

Full of over-confidence in the correctness of his views . . . Lamarck quixotically attempted to substitute his own views for those of Priestley and Lavoisier. [He quotes Lamarck's words about Lavoisier:] "It is not true, and it seems to me even absurd. . . . There are a thousand ways of refuting this error without the possibility of a reply. This hypothesis, the best of all those which had been imagined when Lavoisier conceived it, cannot now be longer held, since I have discovered what caloric really is."

The excuse for his rash and quixotic course in respect to his physico-chemical vagaries is that he had great mental activity. [This is surely a novel kind of excuse.] Lamarck was a synthetic philosopher. . . . When he came to publish his views, he found not a single supporter. His speculations were received with silence and not deemed worthy of discussion.

425

[From Cleland's *Britannica* article.]   The most prominent defect in Lamarck must be admitted to have been want of control in speculation.   The speculative tendency outran the legitimate deductions from observation, and led him into the production of volumes of worthless chemistry without experimental basis, as well as into spending much time in fruitless meteorological predictions.

[Barus]   Lamarck's genius, which seems to have been destitute of the instinct of an experimentalist . . . the broadly philosophic tendencies of Lamarck's mind . . . evolving a system of chemical physics out of himself.

[Bolton]   Lamarck made no experiments, but depended upon his imagination for his facts [i. e., in chemistry] ; he proposed a fanciful scheme of abstract principles that remind one of alchemy.

Packard also describes Lamarck's assumption that minerals undergo regular changes, of which he had no evidence; his assumption that the moon influences weather (though daily observation for a year would have made the assumption practically untenable) ; his assumption that all rocks and minerals originated from organic life; his assumption about instincts—"to illustrate his thoughts he does not give us any examples, nor did he apparently observe to any great extent the habits of animals"; his assumption about the essential difference between the brain of a man and the brain of an insect.   All of these were pure assumptions, without any attempt, and apparently without any desire, to verify them.

Modern zoology has almost unanimously concluded that Lamarck's reasonings about life are pure assumptions.   But a few men who have faith in pure reason are still attracted to some form of "neo-Lamarckism."   Even Packard, veteran entomologist though he was, thus comments on Lamarck's cogitations about how the giraffe got its long neck by continued stretchings that were inherited: "We submit that Lamarck's mode of evolution of the giraffe is quite as reasonable as the very hypothetical one advanced by Mr. Wallace; that is, that a variety occurred with a longer neck than usual."   Of course Lamarck's mode is quite as "reasonable"; it is even more in accord with human reason than Wallace's mode.   But reason, alas, seems to have nothing to do with the case. Biology can not discover any facts which support the Lamarckian assumption.

Packard made a valiant effort to prove that in 1901 the trend of biological opinion was toward Lamarck. He compiled a long muster-roll of scientists who were deserting Darwinism, and thus commented: "We have cited the foregoing conclusions and opinions of upwards of forty working biologists, many of whom were brought up, so to speak, in the Darwinian faith, to show that the pendulum of evolutionary thought is swinging away from the narrow and restricted conception of natural selection, pure and simple, as the sole or most important factor, and venturing in the direction of Lamarckism."

But the pendulum has refused to continue swinging since 1901. In 1927 it is moving steadily the other way. I doubt whether any first-rate biologist now lives who considers that evolution came about by the method of "will" and "appetence" and "needs" that Lamarck described. The world of biology seems to feel about Lamarck in 1927 just as Darwin did in 1825.

Lamarck's approach to the species puzzle is interesting as illustrating how every nineteenth-century naturalist, even the most unphilosophical one, grew uneasy in proportion as he acquired knowledge of *the vast number* of species. When Bates went to the Amazon or Huxley to Australia or Darwin to South America or Wallace to the East Indies, their eyes were opened to new conceptions of the endless prodigality of forms in nature. When Lamarck became familiar with the boundless numbers of kinds of plants, and later with the chaotic multitudes of the lower kinds of animals, his mind perceived that a species was not a reality of nature, for classifiers could not agree as to what it was; Lamarck began to see a species as a mere opinion held by a mind that possessed only partial knowledge. Packard quotes various bits of Lamarck's comments on "an infinity of organisms, a portion of creation still almost unknown."

Their enormous multiplicity, the diversity of their systems of organization, and the extreme fugacity show us the true course of nature and the means which she has used to give existence to all the living bodies.

Our catalogues of species, and the names of the productions

of nature of the most interest to us, are, so to speak, buried in these enormous lists.

The study of forms should not be an acquiring of a vast nomenclature, but studying nature herself—her course, her means, and the constant results that she knows how to attain.

Nothing of all this classification exists in nature; she knows neither classes, orders, genera, nor species.

The following quotations illustrate Lamarck's conceptions of evolution. The first one is Packard's translation of a passage in a "Discours" of 1896; the others I have made from *Philosophie Zoologique*, first edition, mostly from Chapter VII of Part 1, which begins on page 218 of Volume I. The numbers show the pages in Volume I.

All that nature has made individuals to acquire or lose by the sustained influence of circumstances where their race has existed for a long time she has preserved by heredity in the new individuals which have originated from them. These verities are firmly grounded, and can only be misunderstood by those who have never observed and followed nature in her operations. [The word that Packard translates by "heredity" is *génération*. I doubt the wisdom of suggesting so much modern knowledge by using "heredity," and have therefore, in the following passages, used "reproduction" for Lamarck's *génération*.]

7. As for the bodies that possess life, nature has made everything little by little and successively; it is no longer possible to doubt this.

10. The study of invertebrates ought to be of special interest to the naturalist: (1) because the species of these animals are more numerous than those of the vertebrates; (2) because, being more numerous, they are more varied; (3) because the variations of their structure are much larger, more decided, and more peculiar; (4) finally, because the order that nature follows in shaping successively the different organs of animals is very much more manifest in the mutations that these organs undergo among the invertebrates.

13. Those who have not devoted themselves to anything but the study of species find it very difficult to grasp the general relations between things, do not understand at all the true plan of nature, and perceive hardly any of its laws.

14. In the first Part . . . I am going to discuss the idea that we ought to form of what is called "a species" among living organisms.

218. We are not concerned here with abstract reasoning, but with the investigation of a positive fact, which is of wider application than we think, and to which we have failed to give the attention it deserves, no doubt because it is usually hard to detect. This fact consists in the influence which conditions exert upon the different organisms that are subjected to them.

221. Whatever the conditions may be, they do not produce *directly* in the form and in the structure of animals any alteration whatever. But great changes in the conditions cause, for the animals, great changes in their *needs*, and such changes in the needs necessarily cause changes in the actions. Now, if the new needs become fixed or permanent, the animals then acquire new *habits*, which are as permanent as the needs which have originated them. This is easy to prove, and does not even require any explanation to be understood.

The above explanation deserves emphasis. Ignorance of it has led to some undeserved jibing at Lamarck's notions of the way in which the environment induces alterations.

224. If conditions, remaining the same, make habitual and fixed the state of the under-nourished, injured, or sickly individuals, their inner structure is thus finally modified, and reproduction among these individuals preserves the acquired modification and at length gives rise to a race very distant from the one whose individuals are always in conditions favorable to their development.

234. It will be easy to see how the new needs could be satisfied and the new habits formed if we pay some heed to the two following laws of nature, which observation has always verified:

First Law. In every animal that has not gone beyond the limit of its development the more frequent and prolonged use of any organ gradually strengthens this organ, develops it, increases it, and gives it a power proportionate to the duration of this use; whereas the constant lack of use of such an organ very gradually enfeebles it, deteriorates it, increasingly lessens its powers, and at length causes it to disappear.

Second Law. Everything that nature has made individuals gain or lose by the influence of conditions to which the race has been very long exposed—and therefore by the influence of the prevailing use of such an organ, or by the regular lack of use of such a part—it preserves by reproduction in the new individuals that originate from them, provided the acquired changes are common to both sexes, or to those that have borne these new individuals.

238. As for the conditions that nature needs and that she uses every day for varying all that she keeps producing, we may say that they are, in a way, inexhaustible for her. The chief ones originate from climates . . . from the diversity of places . . . from habits . . . from means of self-preservation, manner of life, self-defense, reproduction, etc.

250. On the other hand, the bird whose way of life accustoms it to perch in trees and which is descended from individuals that have all formed this habit will of course have its feet more elongated, and shaped differently from those of the aquatic animals that I have mentioned. Its claws, in time, are elongated, made sharp, and curved into a hook for grasping the branches on which the animal rests so often.

In the same way we see that a shore-bird, which does not care to swim, but which has need of approaching the edge of the water to find its prey there, is constantly in danger of sinking into the mud. Now, this bird, wishing to act in such a way that its body shall not dip into the water, makes every effort to extend and lengthen its feet. The result of this is that the long-continued habit which this bird and all those of its race form, of continually extending and lengthening their feet, causes the individuals of this race to be raised as if on stilts, having gained, little by little, long, bare legs—that is, stripped of feathers up to the thighs, and often higher.

251. Suppose an animal, to satisfy its needs, makes repeated efforts to lengthen its tongue; the tongue will acquire a remarkable length (the ant-eater, the popinjay). Suppose an animal has need of seizing something with the same organ, then the tongue will divide and become forked. That of the humming-birds, which seize with their tongue, and that of lizards and serpents, which use their tongue for feeling and reconnoitering the objects in front of them, are proofs of what I assert.

256. The ruminating animals . . . cannot fight except by giving blows with the head, pointing the top of this part at each other. During their fits of anger, which are frequent, especially among the males, their inner feeling, by its efforts, drives the fluids more strongly toward this part of their head, and it there causes a secretion of horny matter in some animals and of bony matter mixed with horny matter in others, which gives rise to solid protuberances: thence the origin of horns and antlers, with which most of these animals have the head armed.

When we read these speculations about "fluids" that were never observed, about habits that "caused individuals to be raised," we concede that Lamarck originated the conceptions.

We wonder to what extent he was original in other ways. He seems to have felt, or to have wished his readers to feel, that he was entirely original in all ways; for he makes no acknowledgements to predecessors for his ideas. There were only two of them who can be thought to have furnished him with anything significant—Buffon and Erasmus Darwin. Samuel Butler speaks with polite severity of Lamarck's failure to mention Buffon: "I find in *Philosophie Zoologique* a little more claim to independence than is acceptable to one who is fresh from Buffon and Erasmus Darwin. . . . It is a little grating to read the words 'la mienne propre' and to recall no mention of Buffon. . . . The paragraphs on this subject [the struggle for existence] are taken with very little alteration from Buffon's work." The reproach is more mild than would have occurred to me. For it is certain that Lamarck must have been familiar with Buffon, and it would be a miracle if he had arrived at his notions of evolution independently of Buffon. He was a believer in the fixity of species until twelve years after Buffon's death.

How much did he owe to Erasmus Darwin? Packard has this strange reason for believing that he owed nothing: "If he had actually seen and read the *Zoonomia,* he would have been manly enough to have given credit for any novel ideas." What is this mystic quality of "manliness" that would have operated in the case of Erasmus Darwin, while it had not acted at all in the case of Buffon? There is small evidence that Lamarck was much indebted to Erasmus Darwin, but it is hard to believe that he did not borrow from *Zoonomia* the most essential part of his theory—namely, the function of an animal's desires and exertions.

Buffon was the fountain from which flowed the conception that all life may have developed into myriad forms from a common beginning. Erasmus Darwin borrowed this, acknowledged more indebtedness to Buffon than he seems to owe, and did his own thinking. Lamarck borrowed Buffon's great idea, borrowed also the idea that species change by adjusting to changed conditions, and expanded Darwin's conjecture about the operation of needs and desires in producing the change.

The only clue furnished to Charles Darwin by these three

precursors was artificial selection among domestic animals. That was Buffon's contribution; it was adopted with thanks by Erasmus Darwin; it was adopted without acknowledgement by Lamarck.

I AM only too conscious that controversy is usually tiresome and petty. I dislike to use space for the following pages of evidence as to Lyell's views on evolution. I should like to avoid arguing against Professor Judd's description of those views in his charming book, very useful to me, *The Coming of Evolution*. But Judd's verdict—so natural and affable and easy to credit— tends to destroy any true conception of what Darwin's mind was wrestling with between 1831 and 1859. Darwin, who owed everything to Lyell's geology, was opposed and baffled by Lyell's *biology*.

In this paragraph I will state concisely what is confused in Judd's estimate of Lyell as an evolutionist; then a reader may go as far as he likes in reading the evidence that is appended below. Lyell taught that natural law accounts for all which science can deal with, that the natural causes which we now see in operation about us are the causes that have always operated on the earth, that science never encounters any other causes or laws. So, in a kind of general and philosophical way, Lyell's teaching might be called "evolutionary." He taught that whatever now exists in nature was produced by, or developed out of, previous conditions, and by natural law. He taught Darwin to seek always for some natural law as an explanation of any phenomena. But one kind of evolution—the development of plants and animals—was very differently regarded by Lyell. He could not find any proof that species have evolved out of previous species; he wrote Volume II for the express purpose of proving that there had *not* been any progressive development in organic life. He was always the opponent that Darwin feared most, and most desired to convert.

The quotations on which Professor Judd relies to show that Lyell believed in evolution when he first made his *Principles* are as follows:

433

From a long letter to Sir J. F. W. Herschel, June 1, 1836:

When I first came to the notion . . . of a succession of extinction of species, and creation of new ones, going on perpetually now, and through an indefinite period of the past, and to continue for ages to come, all in accommodation to the changes which must continue in the inanimate and habitable earth, the idea struck me as the grandest which I had ever conceived, so far as regards the attributes of the Presiding Mind.

But the whole argument of Volume II of the *Principles* is to prove that "the creation of new species" was *not* evolution. When Professor Judd tells us that Lyell, in 1831, used the word *creation*, as Darwin often used it, to mean *evolved*, he denies everything that Lyell tried to teach in Volume II.

Judd says that Huxley learned, from reading Lyell's letters, that Lyell had been, "at a very early date, convinced that evolution was true of the organic as well as of the inorganic world." Judd refers to the Collected Essays, Volume V, page 101, for proof of this extraordinary statement. But Huxley's note on that page declares: "What I mean by 'evolutionism' is consistent and thoroughgoing uniformitarianism." Huxley, in this place, was not speaking of an evolution of one species out of another, but of the general principle that *natural law always operates uniformly*. Huxley could not possibly have learned that Lyell, in 1831, believed in any form of Darwinian evolution. For Huxley, according to Judd's own citation (page 139), declared that Lyell had been, up to 1859, "a pillar of the antitransmutationists"—that is, he had been a strong opponent of evolution. Darwin's greatest hope while he prepared *The Origin of Species* was to persuade Lyell to renounce his faith in creation and to accept evolution.

To the last edition of the *Origin* Darwin prefixed a most scrupulously compiled list of all the names he could find of the men who had published any evolutionary opinions, however slight and vague, before the first edition of the *Origin* appeared. He mustered twenty-six names. By a remarkable stretching of credit he even tucked in at the end Huxley and Hooker. But Lyell's name is not there. To declare that Lyell had "been convinced that organic evolution was true" would have been farcical.

It is hard to see how Judd is ingenuous when he says (page 64), speaking of Lyell's work on species in Volume II: "He was greatly influenced by the arguments in favor of evolution advanced by Lamarck." To be sure the volume teems with evidence that Lyell was influenced—against evolution. But the implication of Judd's paragraph is that Lyell was influenced *in favor of* evolution. And no sentence can be cited, except some ironical one, which contains a speck of such an influence.

Judd quotes what Darwin wrote to Lyell in 1845: "I have long wished to acknowledge more plainly how much I geologically owe you." Quite so. Darwin was always unstinted and unwearied in acknowledging how his mind had been transformed geologically by Lyell; but I know not where to find in Darwin's works any sentence that acknowledges how much he biologically or evolutionally owed to Lyell.

Judd very skilfully quotes Huxley (page 81), who testified: "I cannot but believe that Lyell, for others as for myself, was the chief agent in smoothing the road for Darwin. For consistent uniformitarianism postulates evolution as much in the organic as in the inorganic world. The origin of a new species by other than ordinary agencies would be a vastly greater 'catastrophe' than any of those which Lyell successfully eliminated from sober geological speculation." We must entirely agree with Huxley. In my Chapter IV, I tried to draw a picture of how inconceivable and miraculous a catastrophe was Lyell's postulate of a "calling into being" or a "creation" of a new species. If he believed in his own mind that the "creations" were effected by natural means, he nowhere affirms this; he could not indicate a shadow of evidence that any natural means existed; he left his reader to infer some catastrophic or miraculous means. That is precisely the marvel of Volume II—it is not *consistent* uniformitarianism. Elsewhere the consistent appeal throughout Lyell's three volumes is to the uniform operation of natural law; that is the lesson he taught to Huxley and to his age; that is the way in which he smoothed the road for Darwinism. But his teaching about the "creation" of species was an egregious inconsistency and was the greatest obstacle in the road to Darwinism.

Lyell had to hedge and wriggle when critics from both

camps—theologians and infidels—challenged his "creation" of new species at the present time. To Sedgwick he wrote (and Judd quotes part of the letter): "I have studiously avoided laying down the doctrine dogmatically as capable of proof. I have left it to be inferred, instead of enunciating it even as my opinion, that the place of lost species *is* filled up (as it *was* of old) from time to time by new species." This is wriggling. Of course Lyell had not stated his doctrine dogmatically. He kept it almost invisible, because he could not refer to any particle of a fact which would give any indication of how a species could be "created" by natural law. He wanted his readers to gather such an idea, but wanted to avoid the scientific odium of proposing it as a part of science. The burden of his whole doctrine of geology was "the adequacy of known causes"; but in this one case of species he deserted his doctrine and left his readers to infer a cause which he dared not name and which has forever remained utterly unknown.

He admitted, in a letter to Whewell, March 7, 1837 (from which Judd quotes), the kind of duplicity he had practised in Volume II. He was telling Whewell of the advice he had received from Herschel, an enthusiastic admirer who read the fourth edition of the *Principles* three times. Herschel had urged Lyell to say plainly that new species must be originated by some natural law, rather than by divine intervention. Lyell explained his predicament to the Rev. William Whewell, who was a Cambridge professor of mineralogy, a moral philosopher, and a redoubtable man in the scientific discussions of the period:

I allude to the changes from one set of animal and vegetable species to another. . . . You remember what Herschel said in his letter to me. If I had stated as plainly as he has done the possibility of the introduction or origination of fresh species being a *natural*, in contradistinction to a *miraculous* process, I should have raised a host of prejudices against me, which are unfortunately opposed at every step to any philosopher who attempts to address the public on these mysterious subjects.

It is therefore probable that Lyell believed his "creation" of species was brought about by some quite unknown operation of natural law. It is certain that Lyell chose, as a matter of policy, to conceal his belief and to let readers infer that a "creation" was a miraculous interposition of the hand of God. Judd considers that Lyell was justified in this policy, and I have no wish to argue the point. But when Judd asserts that Lyell's "creation by natural causes" is a process of deriving one species from another, I appeal to Lyell's extended argument in Volume II. Unless that entire book is an elaborate and purposeless mystification, Lyell was doing his mightiest to prove that one species can *not* be derived from another, that there is no such process as organic evolution.

The most striking, and at first sight convincing, quotation which Judd makes is from a very long postscript which Lyell dictated for the letter to Herschel of June 1, 1836. The second sentence shows that Lyell had hoped that readers like Herschel would infer the opposite of what he wanted theologians to infer.

In regard to the origination of new species, I am very glad to find that you think it probable that it may be carried on through the intervention of intermediate causes. I left this rather to be inferred, not thinking it worth while to offend a certain class of persons by embodying in words what would only be a speculation. But the German critics have attacked me vigorously, saying that by the impugning of the doctrine of spontaneous generation, and substituting nothing in its place, I have left them nothing but the direct and miraculous intervention of the First Cause, as often as a new species is introduced, and hence I have overthrown my own doctrine of revolutions, carried on by a regular system of secondary causes.

The German critics had inescapable logic on their side; I do not see how any number of amiable Judds could refute it. In Lyell's postscript there is not a tincture of evolution. Lyell is speaking only of natural causes of new species, of a succession of "natural creations of new species," precisely as he does in Volume II.

The following quotations from Volume II of Lyell's *Principles* show how utterly opposed he was to any theory of evolution. The figures refer to the pages of the first edition.

18-21. In the first place, the various groups into which plants and animals may be thrown seem almost invariably, to a beginner, to be so natural that he is usually convinced at first, as was Linnæus to the last, "that genera are as much founded in nature as the species which compose them." . . . When the student finds all lines of demarcation to be in most instances obliterated, he grows more and more skeptical as to the real existence of genera, and finally regards them as mere arbitrary and artificial signs. . . . Doubts are then engendered in his mind as to whether species may not also be equally unreal. . . . His opinions are now fairly unsettled, and every stay at which he has caught has given way one after another; he is in danger of falling into any new and visionary doctrine which may be presented to him; for he now regards every part of the animate creation as void of stability, and in a state of continual flux. In this mood he encounters the Geologist, who relates to him how there have been endless vicissitudes in the shape and structure of organic beings in former ages—how the approach to the present system of things has been gradual—that there has been a progressive development of organization subservient to the purposes of life, from the most simple to the most complex state—that the appearance of man is the last phenomenon in a long succession of events —and finally that a series of physical revolutions can be traced in the inorganic world, coeval and coextensive with those of organic nature.

These views seem immediately to confirm all his preconceived doubts as to the stability of the specific character, and he thinks he can discern an inseparable connexion between a series of changes in the inanimate world, and the capability of species to be indefinitely modified by the influence of external circumstances. Henceforth his speculations know no definite bounds; he gives the rein to conjecture, and fancies that the outward form, internal structure, instinctive faculties, nay, that reason itself, may have been gradually developed from some of the simplest states of existence—that all animals, that man himself, and the irrational beings, may have had one common origin; that all may be parts of one continuous and progressive scheme of development from the most imperfect to the more complex; in fine, he renounces his belief in the high genealogy of his species, and looks forward, as if in compensation, to the future perfectibility of man in his physical, intellectual, and moral attributes.

Let us now proceed to consider what is defective in evidence, and what fallacious in reasoning, in the grounds of these strange conclusions.

22. If Lamarck could introduce so much certainty and precision into the classification of several thousand species of recent and fossil shells, notwithstanding the extreme remoteness of the organization of these animals from the type of those vertebrated

species which are best known, and in the absence of so many of the living inhabitants of shells, we are led to form an exalted conception of the degree of exactness to which specific distinctions are capable of being carried, rather than to call in question their reality.

23. It is by no means improbable that the species of certain genera may differ less widely from each other than do the mere varieties of certain species. If such a fact could be established, it would by no means overthrow our confidence in the reality of species. It is almost necessary, indeed, to suppose that varieties will differ in some cases more decidedly than some species, if we admit that there is a graduated scale of being, and assume that the following laws prevail in the economy of the animate creation: first, that the organization of individuals is capable of being modified to a limited extent by the force of external causes; secondly, that these modifications are, to a certain extent, transmissible to their offspring; thirdly, that there are fixed limits beyond which the descendants from common parents can never deviate from a certain type; fourthly, that each species springs from one original stock, and can never be permanently confounded, by intermixing with the progeny of any other stock; fifthly, that each species shall endure for a considerable period of time. Now if we assume, for the present, these rules hypothetically, let us see what consequences may naturally be expected to result.

We must suppose that when the Author of Nature creates an animal or plant, all the possible circumstances in which its descendants are destined to live are foreseen, and that an organization is conferred upon it which will enable the species to perpetuate itself.

32. [Speaking of the great transformations caused in plants by domestication.] These, and a multitude of analogous facts, are undoubtedly among the wonders of nature, and attest more strongly, perhaps, the extent to which species may be modified than any examples derived from the animal kingdom. But in these cases we find that we soon reach certain limits, beyond which we are unable to cause the individuals, descending from the same stock, to vary; while, on the other hand, it is easy to show that these extraordinary varieties could seldom arise, and could never be perpetuated in a wild state for many generations, under any imaginable combination of accidents. They may be regarded as extreme cases brought about by human interference, and not as phenomena which indicate a capability of indefinite modification in a natural world.

60. We have already remarked that the theory of progressive development arose from an attempt to ingraft the doctrines of the

transmutationists upon one of the most popular generalizations in geology. But modern geological researches have almost destroyed every appearance of that gradation in the successive groups of animate beings, which was supposed to indicate the slow progress of the organic world from the more simple to the more compound structure. In the more modern formations we find clear indications that the highest orders of the terrestrial mammalia were fully represented during several successive epochs.

64. Close of Chapter IV. For the reasons, therefore, detailed in this and the two preceding chapters we draw the following inferences in regard to the reality of *species* in nature.

First, That there is a capacity in all species to accommodate themselves, to a certain extent, to a change of external circumstances, this extent varying greatly according to the species.

2dly. When the change of situation which they can endure is great, it is usually attended by some modifications of the form, colour, size, structure, or other particulars; but the mutations thus superinduced are governed by constant laws, and the capability of so varying forms part of the permanent specific character.

3dly. Some acquired peculiarities of form, structure, and instinct are transmissible to the offspring; but these consist of such qualities and attributes only as are intimately related to the natural wants and propensities of the species.

4thly. The entire variation from the original type, which any given kind of change can produce, may usually be effected in a brief period of time, after which no farther deviation can be obtained by continuing to alter the circumstances, though ever so gradually—indefinite divergence, either in the way of improvement or deterioration, being prevented, and the least possible excess beyond the defined limits being fatal to the existence of the individual.

5thly. The intermixture of distinct species is guarded against by the aversion of the individuals composing them to sexual union, or by the sterility of the mule offspring. It does not appear that true hybrid races have ever been perpetuated for several generations, even by the assistance of man; for the cases usually cited relate to the crossing of mules with individuals of pure species, and not to the intermixture of hybrid with hybrid.

6thly. From the above consideration it appears that species have a real existence in nature, and that each was endowed, at the time of its creation, with the attributes and organization by which it is now distinguished.

124. Without dwelling on the above and other refuted theories, let us inquire whether we can substitute some hypothesis as

simple as that of Linnæus. . . . The following may, perhaps, be reconcilable with known facts: Each species may have had its origin in a single pair, or individual, where an individual was sufficient, and species may have been created in succession at such times and in such places as to enable them to multiply and endure for an appointed period, and occupy an appointed space on the globe.

174. It is idle to dispute about the abstract possibility of the conversion of one species into another, when there are known causes so much more active in their nature, which must always intervene and prevent the actual accomplishment of such conversions.

179. Is it possible that new species can be called into being from time to time, and yet that so astonishing a phenomenon can escape the observation of naturalists?

Humboldt has characterized these subjects as among the mysteries which natural science cannot reach; and he observes that the investigation of the origin of beings does not belong to zoological or botanical geography. To geology, however, these topics do strictly appertain; and this science is only interested in inquiries into the state of animate creation as it now exists, with a view of pointing out its relations to antecedent periods when its condition was different.

Before offering any hypothesis towards the solution of so difficult a problem, let us consider what kind of evidence we ought to expect, in the present state of science, of the first appearance of new animals or plants, if we could imagine the successive creation of species to constitute, like their gradual extinction, a regular part of the economy of nature.

180. What kind of proofs, therefore, could we reasonably expect to find of the origin at a particular period of a new species?

Perhaps it may be said in reply that within the last two or three centuries some forest tree or new quadruped might have been observed to appear suddenly in those parts of England or France which had been most thoroughly investigated—that naturalists might have been able to show that no such being inhabited any other region of the globe, and that there was no tradition of anything similar having before been observed in the district where it had made its appearance.

182. If we divide the surface of the earth into twenty regions of equal area, one of these might comprehend a space of land and water about equal in dimensions to Europe, and might contain a twentieth part of the million of species which we will suppose to exist. In this region one species only would, according to the rate of mortality before assumed, perish in twenty years, or only five out of fifty thousand in the course of a cen-

tury. But as a considerable proportion of the whole would belong to the aquatic classes . . . only one species might be lost in about forty years among the terrestrial tribes. . . . It would require more than eight thousand years before it would come to the turn of the conspicuous quadrupeds to lose one of their number even in a region of the dimensions of Europe.

It is easy, therefore, to conceive that in a small portion of such an area . . . periods of much greater duration must elapse before it would be possible to authenticate the first appearance of one of the larger plants and animals. . . .

In the present deficiency of historical records, we have to trace up the subject to that point where geological monuments alone are capable of leading us on to the discovery of ulterior truths.

245. Those naturalists, therefore, who infer that the ancient flora of the globe was, at certain periods, less varied than now, merely because they have as yet discovered only a few hundred fossil species of a particular epoch, while they can enumerate more than fifty thousand living ones, are reasoning on a false basis, and their standard of comparison is not the same in the two cases.

The following quotations about Species are from Lyell's Letters. Beyond the first three the arrangement is chronological and shows the change in Lyell's opinion. The first three are probably somewhat jocose. If they really indicate any readiness to be persuaded, they reveal what is entirely concealed in all the rest of the correspondence.

March, 1827. I read Lamarck rather as I hear an advocate on the wrong side, to know what can be made of the case in good hands. I am glad he has been courageous enough and logical enough to admit that his argument, if pushed as far as it must go, if worth anything, would prove that men may have come from the Orang-Outang. But after all, what changes species may really undergo! How impossible will it be to distinguish and lay down a line, beyond which some of the so-called extinct species have never passed into recent ones.

April, 1856. After all, did we not come from an Ourang, seeing that man is of the Old World, and not from the American type of anthropomorphous mammalia? [He has been exclaiming about the follies of the classifiers of birds.]

July, 1856. So long as they feared that a species might turn out to be a separate and independent creation, they might feel checked; but once abandon this article of faith, and every man becomes his own infallible Pope. In truth it is quite immaterial to you* or me which creed proves true, for it is like the astronomical question still controverted, whether our sun and our whole system is on its way towards the constellation Hercules.

Oct. 1830. The Etna shells lived, on a moderate computation, 100,000 years ago, and after so many generations are quite unchanged in form. It must therefore have required a good time for Orang-Outangs to become men on Lamarckian principles.

Feb., 1831. I would as lief start [i. e., in trying to make out by fossils which rocks are oldest] with vertebrated animals and freshwater, as with a universal ocean and the simplest forms of animal life.

Jan., 1832. Murchison had pointed out that d'Halloy had based part of his new *Elements of Geology* on the Lamarckian transmutation system, more than a justification of my having expended so much powder and shot upon it.

May, 1837. Whewell, in his excellent treatise on the Inductive Sciences, appears to me to go *nearly* as far as to *contemplate* the *possibility* at least of the introduction of fresh species being governed by general laws. (This was to Herschel. Italics are mine.)

Jan., 1838 (to Sedgwick, objecting to what Sedgwick had said in a lecture about Lyell's theory of species). The reporter says: "Mr. Lyell's theory, that the creation of new species is going on at the present day, was also condemned as rash and unphilosophical."

No significant reference to species occurs in Lyell's letters during the next sixteen years.

Nov., 1854. When we were at Charles Darwin's we talked over this and other like matters, and Hooker astonished me by an account of an orchidaceous plant. . . . You probably know about this, which will figure in C. Darwin's book on "Species," with many other "ugly facts," as Hooker, clinging like me to the orthodox faith, calls these and other abnormal vagaries.

Feb., 1856. (He was speaking of the wingless beetles of Madeira.) Query, was it not foreseen that wings would only cause them to be blown out to sea and drowned?

April, 1856. When Huxley, Hooker, and Wollaston were at Darwin's last week, they (all four of them) ran a tilt against

---

*He is writing to Hooker, who was known at this time to be somewhat in sympathy with Darwin.

species farther I believe than they are deliberately prepared to go. I cannot easily see how they can go so far and not embrace the whole Lamarckian doctrine. (This is the letter which he closed with the query, "After all, did we not come from an Ourang?")

July, 1856, to Hooker. This kind of work will be very indispensable from some one of authority, seeing where we are drifting to; for whether Darwin persuades you and me to renounce our faith in species or not, I foresee that many will go over to the indefinite modifiability doctrine.

Aug., 1857. So long as it is admitted that man came last, and the idea of progress is cherished as the only way of uniting that fact with paleontological data, I suppose these views will find favor [i. e., views that plants have progressed in organization through the geological ages].

Oct., 1859, to Darwin after reading the *Origin*. I have long seen most clearly that if any concession is made, all that you claim in your concluding pages will follow.

It is this which has made me so long hesitate, always feeling that the case of Man and his Races, and of other animals, and that of plants, is one and the same, and that if a *vera causa* be admitted for one instant, of a purely unknown and imaginary one, such as the word "creation," all the consequences must follow.

Nov., 1859. Hooker is finishing the printing of an Essay on the "Flora of Australia," in which the great question of the mutability of species is treated of, and as he has for years been discussing this great problem with Charles Darwin, and goes nearly as far as he does, I long to read it before I have my say in the new edition of my *Manual*.

May, 1860. Agassiz honestly felt that if he had to allow that the Negro and European came from one stock, he should go more than half over to the transmutationists. This he candidly confessed in one of his reviews. . . . Darwin would otherwise have rejoiced in believing that the rise from the sponge to the cuttle-fish, and thence through fish, reptile, and bird to marsupial had occurred, and from that to the intelligence of the Gyrencephala, and from the Chimpanzee to the Bushman, and at length to naked Britons, all by a law of creation ending with the development into an Anglo-Saxon. This successive evolution of sensation, instinct, intelligence, reason, which is such a popular creed with those who shrink from transmutation, is the direct way which leads to Lamarckism—possibly the road of truth, but they who travel by it hardly, I think, see the natural consequences or the goal to which they are approximating.

Oct., 1860. If Darwin's theory is ever established, it will

be by the facts and arguments of the progressionists such as Agassiz, whose development doctrines go three parts of the way, though they don't seem to see it.

Nov., 1860. The Oxford Professor of Geology, J. Phillips, has fought Darwin by citing me in pages out of my *Principles*, but I must modify what I said in a new edition. Agassiz helped Darwin and the Lamarckians by going so far in his *Classification*, not hesitating to call in the creative power to make new species out of nothing.

March, 1863, to Hooker. Darwin has sent me a useful set of criticisms for the new edition I am busy in preparing. He seems much disappointed that I do not go farther with him, or do not speak out more. I can only say that I have spoken out to the full extent of my present convictions, and even beyond my state of *feeling* as to man's unbroken descent from the brutes. . . .

I don't care what people have been expecting as to the extent to which I may go with Darwin, but certainly I do not wish to be inconsistent with myself. Though, as I have been gradually changing my opinion, I do not want to insist on others going round at once. When I read again certain chapters of the *Principles*, I am always in danger of shaking some of my confidence in the new doctrine, but am brought back again on reconsidering such essays as Darwin's, Wallace's, and yours.

The ambiguity of Lyell's opinion after 1863 is traced in Chapter XII.

Section 5: Witnesses for Natural Selection

Each of the following scholars is at least as authoritative a witness as Professor Parker; not one of them knows that "most modern evolutionists" think what Professor Parker says they think.

E. B. Wilson (probably the best-known authority on cells in the world). To such minds [i. e., as his own mind] it will seem that the principle of natural selection, while it may not provide a master key to all the riddles of evolution, still looms up as one of the great contributions of modern science to our understanding of nature.

S. J. Holmes. The discoveries in the few years that have elapsed since the publication of Bateson's address [of 1914] have afforded positive evidence of its unsoundness. . . . The status of natural selection has become more firmly established than it was in the time of Darwin.

P. C. Mitchell (in 1900). The estimate in which natural selection is held has changed very little since Darwin and Wallace first expounded their theories.

C. C. Nutting. It seems to me that we are justified in maintaining that Mendelism and the mutation theory have neither weakened nor supplanted the Darwinian conception of the origin of species by means of natural selection.

L. L. Woodruff. Selection is not shorn of its importance either practical or theoretical. . . . Natural selection may afford an explanation of the adaptations of organisms to their environing conditions.

W. F. Ganong. The Darwinian conception of evolution by selection of such variations will probably prove correct in the end.

H. F. Osborn. Natural selection is continually operating at every stage of the transformation. Pure Darwinism has been refined and extended and powerfully advocated by Weismann and de Vries.

A. W. Grabau. The principle of natural selection has come to be of fundamental significance in all biological studies, and its discovery and announcement mark the beginning of a new epoch in the intellectual development of the human race.

Since it is commonly thought that Weismann, and later de Vries, "overthrew" Darwinism, I subjoin their opinions about natural selection.

A. Weismann. Natural selection is the only possible explanation applicable to whole classes of phenomena. . . . Natural selection alone enables us to understand the transmutation of organisms in adaptation to the conditions of their life.

H. de Vries. My work claims to be in full accord with the principles laid down by Darwin. . . . The great principle enunciated by Darwin reigns supreme.

SECTION 6: DARWIN DID NOT BECOME A LAMARCKIAN

Osborn's first quotation is from a letter of 1876 to Moritz Wagner:

When I wrote the *Origin,* and for some years afterwards, I could find little good evidence of the direct action of the environment; now there is a large body of evidence, and your case of the Saturnia is one of the most remarkable of which I have heard.

Darwin did not respect Wagner's reasoning. In 1872 he said to Weismann, "In the first part of your essay I thought that you wasted too much powder and shot on M. Wagner." In 1878 he said to Semper, "With respect to all adapted structures I cannot see how M. Wagner's view throws any light." Notice that Darwin's politeness bears this interpretation: "There is now a large body of evidence—assembled by Charles Darwin." Darwin's *Animals and Plants* was the first great storehouse of evidence, and still remains incomparable.

Osborn's second quotation is from a letter of 1877 to E. S. Morse: "I quite agree about the high value of Mr. Allen's works, as showing how much change may be expected apparently through the direct action of the conditions of life." Darwin had struggled for forty years with this *apparent* cause of change. If he had italicized "apparently," Mr. Morse would not have been flattered—nor Mr. Osborn led to attach so much importance to this courteous note.

Osborn's third reference is not quoted, but is described as "Letter to Semper in 1878." There are two letters to Semper in 1878, on the same page, dated only four days apart. I quote what might be pertinent in each:

When I published the sixth edition of the *Origin* I thought a good deal on the subject to which you refer, and the opinion therein expressed was my deliberate conviction. I went as far as I could, perhaps too far, in agreement with Wagner; since that time I have seen no reason to change my mind, but then I must add that my attention has been absorbed on other subjects. . . . I remember well, long ago, oscillating much; when I thought of the fauna and flora of the Galapagos Islands I was all for isolation, when I thought of South America I doubted much. Pray believe me, Yours very sincerely. . . . In North America, in going from north to south or from east to west, it is clear that the changed conditions of life have modified the organisms in the different regions. It is further clear that in isolated districts, however small, the inhabitants almost always get slightly modified, and how far this is due to the nature of the slightly different conditions to which they are exposed, and how far to mere interbreeding, in the manner explained by Weismann, I can form no opinion.

Somehow Osborn managed to extract from these records of oscillation and lack of opinion this conclusion: "In 1878 Darwin fully included Wagner's theory as one cause of origin of species, through the direct action of environment in the same country or through geographical isolation."

BIBLIOGRAPHY

BIBLIOGRAPHY

I. OF PRIME IMPORTANCE FOR THE LIFE

1. *The Life and Letters of Charles Darwin,* two volumes, edited by Sir Francis Darwin.
2. *More Letters of Charles Darwin,* two volumes, edited by Sir Francis Darwin.
3. *Emma Darwin: A Century of Family Letters,* two volumes, edited by Henrietta Emma Darwin (Mrs. R. B. Litchfield).
4. *Darwin's Journal of Researches,* second edition, 1845.
5. Captain Robert Fitz-Roy's *Narrative of the Surveying Voyages of His Majesty's Ships Adventure and Beagle,* Vol. II.

II. FOR SIDE-LIGHTS

(Each of the following is in two volumes)

1. *Life and Letters of Sir Joseph Dalton Hooker,* by Leonard Huxley.
2. *Life and Letters of Thomas Henry Huxley,* by Leonard Huxley.
3. *Life, Letters, and Journals of Sir Charles Lyell, Bart.,* by his sister-in-law, Mrs. Lyell.
4. *My Life,* by Alfred Russell Wallace.
5. *The Letters of Asa Gray,* edited by Mrs. Gray.

III. FOR DARWIN'S PREDECESSORS

1. *Buffon's Histoire Naturelle,* first 14 volumes, the so-called second edition, Paris, 1750-1767.
2. *Lamarck's Philosophie Zoologique,* first edition, 1809.

453

3. Erasmus Darwin's poems: *The Botanic Garden, The Temple of Nature.* His medical treatise: *Zoonomia; or the Laws of Organic Life.*

4. *The Life of Erasmus Darwin,* by Ernst Krause, with a Preliminary Notice by Charles Darwin.

5. *Lamarck: His Life and Work,* by A. S. Packard.

6. *Evolution Old and New,* by Samuel Butler.

7. *Vestiges of Creation,* by Robert Chambers (first American edition, from the first English edition, 1845).

IV. FOR THE HISTORY OF DARWIN'S THEORY

1. *Darwin and Modern Science,* the Cambridge Centenary essays, invaluable for estimates of Darwin in 1909.

2. *Fifty Years of Darwinism,* the American Centenary essays, good material to supplement the Cambridge volume.

3. *August Weismann's Address at the University of Freiburg for the Darwin Centenary* (printed in the Report of the Smithsonian Institution for 1909).

4. *The Foundations of the Origin of Species.* This volume contains the sketches of 1842 and 1844, with discussion by Sir Francis Darwin—Cambridge University Press, 1909.

5. *Lyell's Principles,* editions of 1831, 1847, and 1872, exhibit his non-evolutionary conception of species.

6. *The Coming of Evolution,* by John W. Judd. Its 160 pages are crammed full of first-hand information, charmingly presented.

7. *Darwiniana,* by Asa Gray (his *Atlantic* reviews and other articles).

8. *Darwiniana,* by T. H. Huxley (Vol. II of his collected works).

9. *Charles Darwin as Geologist,* by Sir Archibald Geikie—a glowing but quite judicious tribute.

10. *Darwin and After Darwin,* by G. J. Romanes.

11. *Introduction to Geology,* by Robert Bakewell, third American, from the fifth London edition (1839); contains an interesting Appendix by Silliman.

12. *Life of James Dwight Dana,* by D. C. Gilman.

13. *Articles and Addresses by J. D. Dana* (a bound collection in the Yale library).
14. *Life of Benjamin Silliman,* by G. P. Fisher.
15. *A Lecture to Teachers,* by Karl Pearson, March 21, 1923.
16. *Darwinism and Lamarckism,* by F. W. Hutton.

V. Biographies

1. Within ten years of Darwin's death three brief lives appeared, which attempted no more than to give an outline of facts, and which are of no interest now. They were by G. Allen, G. T. Bettany, and C. F. Holder. In 1896 E. B. Poulton's *Charles Darwin and the Theory of Natural Selection* was published. This is a small, workmanlike book which is still of use as showing the judgment of thirty years ago.
2. I can not learn of any other biography until 1926, when Gamaliel Bradford's *Darwin* appeared. This is a "psychograph" in which the author analyzes and evaluates the personality of Darwin without much reference to his work.
3. In January, 1927, Leonard Huxley's *Charles Darwin* appeared. It is a very brief but dependable sketch in 145 pages.
4. George A. Dorsey's *The Evolution of Charles Darwin,* issued in May, 1927, is more than twice as large as Huxley's book, tells four times as much, and is packed with many delightful quotations. Dr. Dorsey's attack on the subject is by way of behaviorism: "The problem is to ascertain what factors inevitably and necessarily preceded this or that form of his behavior."

VI. Books by Charles Darwin, A Chronological List

1839. *Journal and Remarks,* as Vol. III of Fitz-Roy's *Narrative of the Voyages.* Second ed., somewhat altered, as a separate publication, 1845. Third ed., called *A Naturalist's Voyage,* 1860.

1839-1841. Edited five Parts of the *Zoology of the Voyage,* which were monographs by six specialists.

1842. First pencil sketch of an evolution theory. The MS was supposed to have been destroyed and was not found till 1896.

1842-1846. *Geological Observations.* Part I was *Coral-Reefs,* 1842; Part II was *Volcanic Islands,* 1844; Part III was *Geological Observations on South America,* 1846. Parts II and III were republished as a second edition in one volume, 1876.

1844. *Complete sketch of theory of natural selection,* written but not published.

1851. First volume of *Cirripedia* and first volume of fossil cirripedes.

1854. Second volume of *Cirripedia* and second volume of fossil cirripedes.

1859. *On the Origin of Species by means of Natural Selection.* 2d ed. 1860, 3d ed. 1861, 4th ed. 1866, 5th ed. 1869, 6th and last ed. 1872.

1862. *On the Various Contrivances by which Orchids are Fertilized by Insects.* 2d ed. 1877.

1868. *The Variation of Animals and Plants under Domestication.* 2d ed. 1875.

1871. *The Descent of Man, and Selection in Relation to Sex.* 2d ed. 1874.

1872. *The Expression of the Emotions in Man and Animals.*

1875. *Insectivorous Plants.*

1876. *Autobiography* written; first published in *Life and Letters,* 1887.

1876. *Cross and Self-Fertilization.* 2d ed. 1878.

1877. *The Different Forms of Flowers on Plants of the Same Species.* 2d ed. 1880.

1880. *The Power of Movement in Plants.*

1881. *The Formation of Vegetable Mould through the Action of Worms.*

INDEX

INDEX